A COURSE IN MATHEMATICAL ANALYSIS
VOLUME III, PART ONE

A COURSE IN MATHEMATICAL ANALYSIS

VOLUME III, PART ONE

VARIATION OF SOLUTIONS

PARTIAL DIFFERENTIAL
EQUATIONS OF
THE SECOND ORDER

BY

ÉDOUARD GOURSAT

TRANSLATED BY

HOWARD G. BERGMANN

Associate Professor of Mathematics
The City University of New York

DOVER PUBLICATIONS, INC.
NEW YORK

Originally published in French under the title
Cours d'Analyse Mathématique, copyright © 1956
by Gauthier-Villars.

Published in Canada by General Publishing Com-
pany, Ltd., 30 Lesmill Road, Don Mills, Toronto,
Ontario.
Published in the United Kingdom by Constable
and Company, Ltd., 10 Orange Street, London
WC 2.

This Dover edition, first published in 1964, is an
unabridged English translation of the fifth edition
of Volume III, Part One of *Cours d'Analyse Mathématique*, as published by Gauthier-Villars in 1956.
This edition is published by special arrangement
with Gauthier-Villars.

International Standard Book Number: 0-486-61176-0

Library of Congress Catalog Card Number: 60-320

Manufactured in the United States of America
Dover Publications, Inc.
180 Varick Street
New York, N.Y. 10014

TRANSLATOR'S NOTE

The translator wishes to express his appreciation for the generous and most valuable assistance given him, especially in detecting errors in the French text, by Professors Bennington P. Gill and Jesse Douglas, colleagues at the City College. Since the number of typographical errors in the French edition was appallingly high, it is likely that a few have escaped his attention, and for these the translator accepts sole responsibility. Any errors detected by readers and brought to the attention of the editorial department of Dover Publications will be corrected in future printings.

H.G.B.

CONTENTS

CHAPTER V. LINEAR EQUATIONS OF ELLIPTIC
TYPE 170

CHAPTER I

VARIATION OF SOLUTIONS

The study of functions defined by a differential equation, in their entire domain of existence, is a problem whose complete solution, in the general case, exceeds the power of analysis at the present time. However, results of the greatest interest have been obtained by restricting the study to that of integrals infinitesimally close to a known integral. It was thus that, in his memorable works on the *problem of three bodies*,[1] H. Poincaré was able to prove the existence of an infinite number of periodic solutions and of solutions asymptotic to a periodic solution. The investigation of solutions infinitesimally close to a known solution led him to a system of linear differential equations which he calls *equations of variation*; the analogous system for partial differential equations had already been considered by G. Darboux[2] under the name of *auxiliary system*. The results of H. Poincaré have been made use of since then by M. Painlevé[3] and several other mathematicians in a problem of pure analysis, the construction of differential equations with fixed critical points.

In this chapter we shall prove the fundamental theorem of H. Poincaré, after studying the integrals of a system of differential equations, considered as functions of their initial values. This study has already been made (Volume II, Part 2, Section 27; hereafter referred to as II, 2, **27**) in the case where the second members are

---

[1] *Acta mathematica*, Vol. XIII, 1890; *Les méthodes nouvelles de la Mécanique céleste*, Vol. I and III.

[2] *Comptes rendus*, Vol. XCVI, March 19, 1883, p. 766; Note XI of Vol. IV of the *Leçons sur la théorie générale des surfaces*, pp. 505–516. In a paper in Vol. XXIII of the *Annales de l'École Normale* (3rd Series, 1906), I have extended the fundamental theorem of H. Poincaré to certain systems of partial differential equations.

[3] *Bulletin de la Société mathématique*, Vol. XXVIII, p. 201; *Acta mathematica*, Vol. XXV, 1902, pp. 1–85.

analytic functions. We take it up again in the general case, by means of Picard's method of successive approximations, which yields the result very simply, by requiring the maximum hypotheses.

I. EQUATIONS OF VARIATION

1. Comments on linear equations. We shall, first of all, make a few remarks concerning the applications of Picard's method to linear equations. Let us consider, to be specific, a system of two linear equations

$$(1) \qquad \frac{dy}{dx} = ay + bz + c, \qquad \frac{dz}{dx} = a_1y + b_1z + c_1,$$

a, b, c, a_1, b_1, c_1 being continuous functions of the real variable x in the interval $x_0 < x < x_1$. To apply Picard's method to the determination of integrals having the values y_0 and z_0 for $x = x_0$, we can take as first approximations to these integrals, instead of the initial values themselves, any two functions $u(x)$ and $v(x)$ whatever, continuous in the interval (x_0, x_1). This results in setting

$$y_1(x) = y_0 + \int_{x_0}^{x} [a \cdot u(t) + b \cdot v(t) + c]\, dt,$$

$$z_1(x) = z_0 + \int_{x_0}^{x} [a_1u(t) + b_1v(t) + c_1]\, dt,$$

x being replaced by t in a, b, c, a_1, b_1, c_1; and, for $n > 1$,

$$y_n(x) = y_0 + \int_{x_0}^{x} [a \cdot y_{n-1}(t) + b \cdot z_{n-1}(t) + c]\, dt,$$

$$z_n(x) = z_0 + \int_{x_0}^{x} [a_1y_{n-1}(t) + b_1z_{n-1}(t) + c_1]\, dt.$$

All these functions y_n, z_n are clearly continuous in the interval (x_0, x_1). This granted, let M be an upper bound of the absolute values of the coefficients a, b, a_1, b_1, in the interval (x_0, x_1), and H an upper bound of the absolute values of $y_1 - u$ and of $z_1 - v$ in the same interval. We see immediately that we have, at every point of the interval (x_0, x_1),

$$|y_2(x) - y_1(x)| < 2MH(x - x_0), \qquad |z_2(x) - z_1(x)| < 2MH(x - x_0),$$

and then we verify step by step that for any n

$$|y_n(x) - y_{n-1}(x)| < H \frac{2M(x - x_0)]^{n-1}}{(n - 1)!} ,$$

$$|z_n(x) - z_{n-1}(x)| < H \frac{[2M(x - x_0)]^{n-1}}{(n - 1)!} .$$

The argument is concluded as in the general case (II, 2, **28**); y_n and z_n tend uniformly toward the limits $y(x)$ and $z(x)$ which are the integrals of system (1), taking on the values y_0 and z_0 at $x = x_0$.

We say, to be brief, that a function $F(x)$ of the real variable x is a *dominant* of another function $f(x)$, in an interval (α, β), if $F(x)$ is positive and greater than the absolute value of $f(x)$ for every value of x in that interval. Let us replace in the system (1) the coefficients a, b, c, a_1, b_1, c_1 by the continuous functions A, B, C, A_1, B_1, C_1 which are respectively dominants of the first set in the interval (x_0, x_1), and let us propose to obtain the integrals of the new system

$$(2) \qquad \frac{dY}{dx} = AY + BZ + C, \qquad \frac{dZ}{dx} = A_1Y + B_1Z + C_1$$

which, for $x = x_0$, take on the positive values Y_0 and Z_0, respectively greater than $|y_0|$ and $|z_0|$. If we take as first approximations the functions $U(x)$ and $V(x)$, respectively dominants of $u(x)$ and $v(x)$, we see easily step by step that all the successive approximations $Y_n(x)$, $Z_n(x)$ of the integrals of the new system are positive in the interval (x_0, x_1), and dominants for the approximations of same order $y_n(x)$ and $z_n(x)$ of the integrals of the first system. The integrals $Y(x)$ and $Z(x)$ of system (2), which take on the values Y_0 and Z_0 for $x = x_0$, are consequently dominants in every interval (x_0, x_1) for the first integrals $y(x)$ and $z(x)$ of system (1). By taking positive constants for A, B, C, A_1, B_1, C_1 we obtain an auxiliary system with constant coefficients, and it would be easy to deduce from it bounds for the absolute values of the integrals of system (1) in the interval (x_0, x_1). Let us remark also that these properties are extended without difficulty to a complex domain, when a, b, c, a_1, b_1, c_1 are holomorphic functions of x in this domain.

A final remark, which can be extended to a system of any number whatever of linear equations, is the following. Let $y' = ay + b$ be a linear equation where the coefficients a and b are continuous functions, the first *positive*, in an interval (x_0, x_1), with $x_1 > x_0$, and let

$Y(x)$ be the integral of this equation which is equal to y_0 for $x = x_0$. If we take for the first approximation a function $u(x) \le Y(x)$ at every point of the interval, *all the other approximations* y_n *will also be less than or at most equal to* $Y(x)$. This property is an immediate consequence of the recurrence relation

$$Y(x) - y_n(x) = \int_x^x a(t) \left[Y(t) - y_{n-1}(t) \right] dt,$$

and of the hypothesis on the first approximation.

2. Application to a semi-linear system. Let us consider a particular system of the following form:

$$(3) \qquad \begin{cases} \dfrac{dy}{dx} = f(x, y), \\[2mm] \dfrac{dz}{dx} = \phi(x, y)z + \psi(x, y), \end{cases}$$

where $f(x, y)$, $\phi(x, y)$, $\psi(x, y)$ are three continuous functions of the variables x and y, when x and y remain in the intervals $(x_0, x_0 + a)$, $(y_0 - b, y_0 + b)$, a and b being two positive numbers; we assume further that the function $f(x, y)$ satisfies the Lipschitz condition in this domain, with respect to y. In order to obtain the integrals of system (3) which take on, respectively, the values y_0 and z_0 for $x = x_0$, it is natural to proceed as follows. We first of all seek the integral of the first equation, which is equal to y_0 for $x = x_0$, by the Picard method, for example. Let $Y(x)$ be this integral which is continuous in an interval $(x_0, x_0 + h)$, h being a positive number $\le a$. Then replacing y by $Y(x)$ in $\phi(x, y)$ and $\psi(x, y)$, we shall obtain by two quadratures the integral $Z(x)$ of the second equation which takes on the value z_0 for $x = x_0$.

But we could also apply the method of successive approximations to system (3) entirely by taking y_0 as the first approximation to y, and any constant K whatever as a first approximation to z, which leads to setting

$$y_1 = y_0 + \int_{x_0}^x f(t, y_0)\, dt, \qquad z_1 = z_0 + \int_{x_0}^x [\phi(t, y_0)K + \psi(t, y_0)]\, dt$$

and, in general,

$$y_n(x) = y_0 + \int_{x_0}^{x} f[t, y_{n-1}(t)] \, dt,$$

$$z_n(x) = z_0 + \int_{x_0}^{x} \{\phi[t, y_{n-1}(t)]z_{n-1}(t) + \psi[t, y_{n-1}(t)]\} \, dt.$$

When n increases without bound, y_n tends uniformly toward $Y(x)$ in the interval $(x_0, x_0 + h)$; we wish to show that z_n also tends uniformly to $Z(x)$. This is certainly the case, according to the general theorem (II, 2, **28**), if $\phi(x, y)$ and $\psi(x, y)$ satisfy a Lipschitz condition with respect to y; but this last hypothesis is unnecessary, and it is sufficient to assume that the functions $\phi(x, y)$ and $\psi(x, y)$ are continuous. Indeed, we have

$$Z(x) = z_0 + \int_{x_0}^{x} \phi[t, Y(t)]Z(t) \, dt + \int_{x_0}^{x} \psi[t, Y(t)] \, dt;$$

comparing this formula with that which gives $z_n(x)$ results in

$$Z(x) - z_n(x) = \int_{x_0}^{x} \{\phi[t, Y(t)]Z(t) - \phi[t, y_{n-1}(t)]z_{n-1}(t)\} \, dt$$

$$+ \int_{x_0}^{x} \{\psi[t, Y(t)] - \psi[t, y_{n-1}(t)]\} \, dt,$$

which, setting $Z(x) - z_n(x) = \delta_n(x)$, can be written as

$$\delta_n(x) = \int_{x_0}^{x} \phi[t, y_{n-1}(t)]\delta_{n-1}(t) \, dt +$$

$$\int_{x_0}^{x} \{\phi[t, Y(t)] - \phi[t, y_{n-1}(t)]\}Z(t) \, dt$$

$$+ \int_{x_0}^{x} \{\psi(t, Y(t)] - \psi[t, y_{n-1}(t)]\} \, dt.$$

The coefficient of $\delta_{n-1}(t)$ under the integral sign is smaller in absolute value than a positive number M, for $y_{n-1}(t)$ remains between $y_0 - b$ and $y_0 + b$; moreover, the sum of the other terms under the integral sign tends uniformly to zero when n increases without bound, since y_n tends uniformly to Y. This being the case, let us choose an integer p such that the absolute value of

$$\{\phi[t, Y(t)] - \phi[t, y_{n-1}(t)]\}Z(t) + [t, \psi Y(t)] - \psi[t, y_{n-1}(t)]$$

is less than a positive number λ, for any t, whenever $n \geq p$. Having chosen the number p in this manner, let us consider a set of functions $\Delta_{p-1}(x)$, $\Delta_p(x)$, . . . , $\Delta_n(x)$, . . . determined by the recurrence relation

$$\Delta_n(x) = \int_{x_0}^{x} [M\Delta_{n-1}(t) + \lambda]\, dt \qquad (n = p, p + 1, \ldots),$$

and let us assume that we have taken $\Delta_{p-1}(x) \geq |\delta_{p-1}(x)|$. We see step by step that each of the functions $\Delta_p(x)$, $\Delta_{p+1}(x)$, . . . is respectively a dominant of $\delta_p(x)$, $\delta_{p+1}(x)$, ... Now, when n increases without bound, $\Delta_n(x)$ approaches uniformly the integral of the linear equation $y' = My + \lambda$, which is zero for $x = x_0$, that is, it approaches $\dfrac{\lambda}{M}\{e^{M(x-x_0)} - 1\}$. We can therefore find a sufficiently large integer m so that for all $n \geq p + m$ we have

$$|\Delta_n(x)| < \frac{\lambda}{M}\{e^{(Mx_1-x_0)} - 1\} + \epsilon,$$

ϵ being any positive number whatever. This inequality will hold *a fortiori* if we replace $\Delta_n(x)$ by $\delta_n(x)$. Moreover, we may assume that we have chosen p so that $\dfrac{\lambda}{M}\{e^{M(x_1-x_0)} - 1\}$ is less than ϵ, since λ can be made as small as we please.

The absolute value of $\delta_n(x) = Z(x) - z_n(x)$ is therefore $< 2\epsilon$, provided that $n \geq p + m$; $z_n(x)$ therefore approaches $Z(x)$ uniformly as n increases without bound.

Instead of an interval such as $(x_0, x_0 + h)$, it is clear that we could also apply the method to an interval $(x_0 - h, x_0 + h)$; if the approximations are uniformly convergent for the y_n, the same will be true for the z_n. The theorem can evidently be extended to a system of $n + p$ equations of the form

$$(4)\begin{cases} \dfrac{dy_i}{dx} = f_i(x, y_1, y_2, \ldots, y_n), \quad (i = 1, 2, \ldots, n),\, (k = 1, 2, \ldots, p), \\[2mm] \dfrac{dz_k}{dx} = \phi_{k1}(x, y_1, \ldots, y_n)z_1 + \ldots \phi_{kp}(x, y_1, \ldots, y_n)z_p \\[1mm] \qquad + \psi_k(x, y_1, \ldots, y_n), \end{cases}$$

where the functions f, ϕ, ψ are continuous in a certain domain D, and where the functions f satisfy in this domain a Lipschitz condition with respect to the y_i. If we apply to this system the method of successive approximations, these approximations are convergent in the same interval as the approximations for the y_i alone, and the convergence is uniform.[4]

3. Integrals considered as functions of the initial values.

Let us return for the sake of definiteness to a differential equation of the first order

$$(5) \qquad \frac{dy}{dx} = f(x, y),$$

where we shall assume that $f(x, y)$ satisfies the usual conditions in a domain D defined by the relations

$$\alpha - a \leq x \leq \alpha + a, \qquad \beta - b \leq y \leq \beta + b.$$

Let us take a set of initial values (x_0, y_0) belonging to this domain. The values of the successive approximations of the integrals y_1, $y_2, \ldots, y_n, \ldots$ stay between $\beta - b$ and $\beta + b$ provided that we have

$$|y_0 - \beta| + M|x - x_0| < b;$$

to convince ourselves of this it is sufficient to repeat the argument of II, 2, **28**, and we see in the same way that $y_n(x; x_0, y_0)$ converges uniformly to a limit $\psi(x; x_0, y_0)$ in the domain D' defined by the relations

$$\alpha - a \leq x \leq \alpha + a, \alpha - a \leq x_0 \leq \alpha + a, \beta - b \leq y_0 \leq \beta + b,$$

$$|y_0 - \beta| + M \, | \, x - x_0| < b.$$

This domain D' contains in particular the domain D'' defined by the inequalities

$$|x - \alpha| < h, \qquad |x_0 - \alpha| \leq h, \qquad |y_0 - \beta| < \frac{b}{2},$$

h being the smaller of the two numbers a and $b/4M$. The successive approximations $y_n(x; x_0, y_0)$ are clearly continuous functions of

---

[4] The properties which will be established in the following paragraphs have been the subject of a rather large number of works, which can be found cited in a paper by E. Cotton on the subject (*Bulletin de la Société mathématique*, Vol. XXXVII, 1919, p. 204, and Vol. XXXVIII, 1910, p. 4). The method which I have followed does not differ essentially from Cotton's.

x_0, y_0 in this domain, and consequently *the integral* $y = \psi(x; x_0, y_0)$, *which reduces to* y_0 *for* $x = x_0$, *is a continuous function of* x_0 *and of* y_0.

To prove that this function has derivatives with respect to x_0 and to y_0, we shall suppose that $f(x, y)$ possesses a continuous derivative $f'_y(x, y)$. Let

$$z = \frac{\partial \psi}{\partial y_0}, \qquad u = \frac{\partial \psi}{dx_0},$$

be the derivatives whose existence we wish to establish; if these derivatives do exist, they satisfy the differential equations

$$(6) \qquad \frac{dz}{dx} = zf'_y(x, y), \qquad \frac{du}{dx} = uf'_y(x, y),$$

which are deduced immediately from equation (5). We are accordingly led to study the system of three differential equations (5) and (6), and we shall take as initial values

$$y = y_0, \qquad z = 1, \qquad u = -f(x_0, y_0)$$

for $x = x_0$. Now, this system is exactly of the form studied above. Since the function $f'_y(x, y)$ is continuous, we can apply the theorem which has been established; Picard's method, applied to this system, leads to approximations uniformly convergent in the same domain D''. To apply this method, we shall take as our first approximations $y = y_0$, $z = 1$, $u = 0$, and we shall set

$$y_1(x) = y_0 + \int_{x_0}^{x} f(t, y_0)\, dt,$$

$$z_1 = 1 + \int_{x_0}^{x} f'_y(t, y_0)\, dt,$$

$$u_1 = -f(x_0, y_0),$$

and then, more generally,

$$y_n(x) = y_0 + \int_{x_0}^{x} f[t, y_{n-1}(t)]\, dt,$$

$$z_n(x) = 1 + \int_{x_0}^{x} z_{n-1}(t) f'_y[t, y_{n-1}(t)t]\, dt,$$

$$u_n(x) = -f(x_0, y_0) + \int_{x_0}^{x} u_{n-1}(t) f'_y[t, y_{n-1}(t)]\, dt.$$

We have first

$$\frac{\partial y_1}{\partial x_0} = -f(x_0, y_0) = u_1, \qquad \frac{\partial y_1}{\partial y_0} = 1 + \int_{x_0}^{x} f'_y(t, y_0)\, dt = z_1,$$

and then

$$\frac{\partial y_n}{\partial x_0} = -f(x_0, y_0) + \int_{x_0}^{x} f'_y[t, y_{n-1}(t)]\, \frac{\partial y_{n-1}}{\partial x_0}\, dt,$$

$$\frac{\partial y_n}{\partial y_0} = 1 + \int_{x_0}^{x} f'_y[t, y_{n-1}(t)]\frac{\partial y_{n-1}}{\partial y_0}\, dt;$$

we deduce from these relations

$$\frac{\partial y_n}{\partial x_0} - u_n = \int_{x_0}^{x} f'_y[t, y_{n-1}(t)]\left[\frac{\partial y_{n-1}}{\partial x_0} - u_{n-1}(t)\right] dt,$$

$$\frac{\partial y_n}{\partial y_0} - z_n = \int_{x_0}^{x} f'_y[t, y_{n-1}(t)]\left[\frac{\partial y_{n-1}}{\partial y_0} - z_{n-1}(t)\right] dt,$$

and therefore we see, step by step, that we have, whatever n may be,

$$\frac{\partial y_n}{\partial x_0} = u_n, \qquad \frac{\partial y_n}{\partial y_0} = z_n.$$

Now the limit of y_n is the integral $y = \psi(x; x_0, y_0)$; since z_n and u_n approach their limits uniformly, these limits z and u furnish the partial derivatives of the integral $\psi(x; x_0, y_0)$ with respect to x_0 and y_0, and these derivatives are continuous in the domain which has been defined above.

It is easy to get the expressions for these derivatives. Indeed, if we replace y by $\psi(x; x_0, y_0)$ in equations (6), the integrals of this system which take on the initial values 1 and $-f(x_0, y_0)$ for $x = x_0$ are obtained immediately and give us

$$z = \frac{\partial \psi}{\partial y_0} = e^{\int_{x_0}^{x} f'_y[t, \psi(t, x_0, y_0)]dt},$$

$$u = \frac{\partial \psi}{\partial x_0} = -f(x_0, y_0)e^{\int_{x_0}^{x} f'_y[t, \psi(t, x_0, y_0)]dt}.$$

These formulas prove that $\psi(x; x_0, y_0)$, considered as functions of the initial values x_0, y_0, satisfy the partial differential equation[5]

$$(7) \qquad \frac{\partial \psi}{\partial x_0} + f(x_0, y_0) \frac{\partial \psi}{\partial y_0} = 0.$$

The reasoning can be extended to a system of any number of equations. Let us take, for example, a system of two equations of the first order

$$(8) \qquad \frac{dy}{dx} = f(x, y, z), \qquad \frac{dz}{dx} = \phi(x, y, z)$$

whose second members are continuous and possess continuous partial derivatives f'_y, f'_z, ϕ'_y, ϕ'_z in a certain domain D. Picard's method again proves that the integrals

$$y = \psi(x; x_0, y_0, z_0), \qquad z = \pi(x; x_0, y_0, z_0),$$

---

[5] Let $\phi(x, y)$ be a continuous function, having a continuous derivative ϕ'_y; the function

$$Z(x_0, y_0) = \int_a^{x_0} \phi[x, \psi(x; x_0, y_0)] \, dx,$$

where a is a constant, possesses the partial derivatives

$$\frac{\partial Z}{\partial x_0} = \phi(x_0, y_0) + \int_a^{x_0} \frac{\partial \phi}{\partial \psi} \frac{\delta \psi}{\partial x_0} \, dx, \qquad \frac{\partial Z}{\partial y_0} = \int_a^{x_0} \frac{\partial \phi}{\partial \psi} \frac{\partial \psi}{\partial y_0} \, dx,$$

and, consequently, the function $Z(x_0, y_0)$ is an integral of the partial differential equation

$$(7') \qquad \frac{\partial Z}{\partial x_0} + f(x_0, y_0) \frac{\partial Z}{\partial y_0} = \phi(x_0, y_0).$$

The function $\psi(x; x_0, y_0)$ has the same symmetrical properties as in the case where the function $f(x, y)$ is analytic (II, 2, **27**). From the relation

$$y_1 = \psi(x_1; x_0, y_0),$$

where y_1 denotes the value of the integral for $x = x_1$, we conclude inversely

$$y_0 = \psi(x_0; x_1, y_1),$$

for there clearly is symmetry between the two pairs of variables (x_0, y_0) and (x_1, y_1). Suppressing the second indices, we see then that the integral of equation (5), which is equal to y_0 for $x = x_0$, satisfies the relation $y_0 = \psi(x_0; x, y)$; x_0 being supposed constant, we can say that the preceding equation represents the general integral of equation (5) in the domain which has been defined above, y_0 being the arbitrary constant.

which assume respectively the values y_0 and z_0 for $x = x_0$, are continuous functions of x; x_0, y_0, z_0 in another domain δ, which would be defined as above. To prove that the functions ψ and π possess partial derivatives with respect to the variables x_0, y_0, z_0, we shall adjoin to equations (8) a system of six linear equations

(9)

$$\frac{du}{dx} = \frac{\partial f}{\partial y}u + \frac{\partial f}{\partial z}\xi, \quad \frac{dv}{dx} = \frac{\partial f}{\partial y}v + \frac{\partial f}{\partial z}\eta, \quad \frac{dw}{dx} = \frac{\partial f}{\partial y}w + \frac{\partial f}{\partial z}\zeta$$

$$\frac{d\xi}{dx} = \frac{\partial \phi}{\partial y}u + \frac{\partial \phi}{\partial z}\xi, \quad \frac{d\eta}{dx} = \frac{\partial \phi}{\partial y}v + \frac{\partial \phi}{\partial z}\eta, \quad \frac{d\zeta}{dx} = \frac{\partial \phi}{\partial y}w + \frac{\partial \phi}{\partial z}\zeta$$

with the initial conditions $u = -f(x_0, y_0, z_0)$, $v = 1$, $w = 0$, $\xi = -\phi(x_0, y_0, z_0)$, $\eta = 0$, $\zeta = 1$ for $x = x_0$.

From an earlier remark, Picard's method, applied to the system of eight equations (8) and (9), leads to uniformly convergent approximations. Now, if we take as first approximations for y, z, u, v, w, ξ, η, ζ the values

$$y = y_0, z = z_0, u = 0, v = 1, w = 0, \xi = 0, \eta = 0, \zeta = 1,$$

we verify immediately that we have

$$\frac{\partial y_1}{\partial x_0} = u_1, \quad \frac{\partial y_1}{\partial y_0} = v_1, \quad \frac{\partial y_1}{\partial z_0} = w_1, \quad \frac{\partial z_1}{\partial x_0} = \xi_1, \quad \frac{\partial z_1}{\partial y_0} = \eta_1, \quad \frac{\partial z_1}{\partial z_0} = \zeta_1,$$

and we are then step by step assured that these formulas still hold when the index 1 is replaced by any index n. Therefore, the integrals of the auxiliary system (9), which take on the initial values given above, represent respectively the partial derivatives of the functions $\psi(x; x_0, y_0, z_0)$, $\pi(x; x_0, y_0, z_0)$ with respect to the variables x_0, y_0, z_0:

(10)
$$\begin{cases} u = \dfrac{\partial \psi}{\partial x_0}, \quad v = \dfrac{\partial \psi}{\partial y_0}, \quad w = \dfrac{\partial \psi}{\partial z_0} \\[2ex] \xi = \dfrac{\partial \pi}{\partial x_0}, \quad \eta = \dfrac{\partial \pi}{\partial y_0}, \quad \zeta = \dfrac{\partial \pi}{\partial z_0} \end{cases}$$

which proves the stated theorem.

Let us notice that (u, ξ), (v, η), (w, ζ) form three pairs of integrals of the linear system

$$\frac{dU}{dx} = f'_y(x, \psi, \pi)U + f'_z(x, \psi, \pi)V,$$

$$\frac{dV}{dx} = \phi'_y(x, \psi, \pi)U + \phi'_z(x, \psi, \pi)V,$$

corresponding respectively to the initial values $(-f_0, -\phi_0)$, $(1, 0)$, $(0, 1)$. We have, therefore,

$$u = -f_0 v - \phi_0 w, \quad \xi = -f_0 \eta - \phi_0 \zeta$$

and, consequently, the functions $\psi(x; x_0, y_0, z_0)$, $\pi(x; x_0, y_0, z_0)$ satisfy the partial differential equation[6]

(11) $$\frac{\partial F}{\partial x_0} + f(x_0, y_0, z_0)\frac{\partial F}{\partial y_0} + \phi(x_0, y_0, z_0)\frac{\partial F}{\partial z_0} = 0.$$

4. Extension to equations which depend on parameters.
The preceding properties can be further extended to systems of sections whose second members include variable parameters. Let us consider, for example, an equation of the first order depending on a parameter

(12) $$\frac{dy}{dx} = f(x, y, \lambda),$$

whose second member is a continuous function of x, y, λ, having continuous partial derivatives f'_y and f'_λ in a certain domain D. The integral which takes on the value y_0 for $x = x_0$ is again a continuous function $y = \psi(x; x_0, y_0, \lambda)$ of x_0, y_0, λ in a certain domain δ,

---

[6] We could verify as above (Footnote 5) that the function

$$Z(x; x_0, y_0, z_0) = \int_{x_0}^{x} \theta(x, \psi, \pi) \, dx$$

satisfies the partial differential equation

$$\frac{\partial Z}{\partial x_0} + f(x_0, y_0, z_0)\frac{\partial Z}{\partial y_0} + \phi(x_0, y_0, z_0)\frac{\partial Z}{\partial z_0} + \theta(x_0, y_0, z_0) = 0.$$

We see likewise that the two relations $y = \psi(x; x_0, y_0, z_0)$, $z = \pi(x; x_0, y_0, z_0)$ can also be written as

$$y_0 = \psi(x_0; x, y, z), \qquad z_0 = \pi(x_0; x, y, z).$$

We thus have two first integrals of the system (8).

for we can define it as the sum of a uniformly convergent series all of whose terms are continuous functions of x; x_0, y_0, λ in this domain. To prove that the function ψ can be differentiated with respect to λ it will be sufficient to adjoin to equation (12) the linear equations

(13)
$$\begin{cases} \dfrac{dz}{dx} = zf'_y(x, y, \lambda), \quad \dfrac{du}{dx} = uf'_y(x, y, \lambda), \\[2ex] \qquad \dfrac{dv}{dx} = vf'_y(x, y, \lambda) + f'_\lambda, \end{cases}$$

with the initial values $z = 1$, $u = -f(x_0, y_0)$, $v = 0$. Returning to the reasoning of Section 3, we see that the integrals of this new system are, respectively,

$$y = \psi(x; x_0, y_0, \lambda), \quad z = \frac{\partial \psi}{\partial y_0}, \quad u = \frac{\partial \psi}{\partial x_0}, \quad v = \frac{\partial \psi}{\partial \lambda}.$$

The method is clearly general, and we can state the following general proposition:

Given a system of n *differential equations of the first order*

(14)
$$\frac{dy_1}{dx} = f_1(x, y_1, y_2, \ldots, y_n; \lambda_1, \ldots \lambda_p), \ldots, \frac{dy_n}{dx} = f_n,$$

whose second members are continuous functions of the variables x, y_i, λ_k, *and have continuous partial derivatives* $\partial f_j / \partial y_i$, $\partial f_j / \partial \lambda_k$, *in a domain* D, *the integrals of this system which take on the initial values* y_1^0, y_2^0, ..., y_n^0 *for* x $= x_0$, *are themselves continuous functions and possess partial derivatives with respect to the variables* x_0, (y_i^0), λ_k, *which are also continuous in a sufficiently small domain* δ.

Remark. The same method will make possible the proof of the existence of the partial derivatives, up to order N, of the integrals, with respect to the variables x, (y_i^0), λ_k, provided that the functions $f_1, f_2, \ldots, f_n$ also possess continuous partial derivatives with respect to the variables y_i, λ_k, up to the same order N.

5. Variations of solutions. We reach more exact conclusions when a particular system of integrals of the differential equations considered is already known. We shall again, for definiteness, develop the theory for a single equation

(15)
$$\frac{dy}{dx} = f(x, y, \lambda)$$

about which we shall make the following hypotheses:

1. For $\lambda = 0$, this equation has a particular integral $y_1(x)$, continuous in the interval (x_0, x_1);

2. The function $f(x, y, \lambda)$ is continuous and has continuous partial derivatives $f'_y(x, y, \lambda)$, $f'_\lambda(x, y, \lambda)$ in the domain D defined by the conditions

$$x_0 \leq x \leq x_1, \quad y_1(x) - a \leq y \leq y_1(x) + a, \quad |\lambda| \leq b,$$

a and b being two positive numbers.

Let R be the strip in the xy-plane bounded by the two lines $x = x_0$, $x = x_1$, and the two curves

$$y = y_1(x) - a, \quad y = y_1(x) + a,$$

between which lies the known integral curve $y = y_1(x)$; the function $f(x, y, \lambda)$, as well as its partial derivatives f'_y, f'_λ are continuous in this strip, provided that the absolute value of λ is less than b.

This being granted, if the absolute value of λ is sufficiently small, we are going to prove that the Picard method leads to successive approximations convergent in the entire interval (x_0, x_1) to the integral which takes on the same initial value y_0 as $y_1(x)$ does for $x = x_0$. Let H and K be the upper bounds of (f'_y) and of (f'_λ) in the domain D; y' and y being between $y_1(x) - a$ and $y_1(x) + a$, and λ, λ' between $-b$ and $+b$; then we always have the Lipschitz inequality

(16) $$|f(x, y', \lambda') - f(x, y, \lambda)| < H|y' - y| + K|\lambda' - \lambda|.$$

Taking $Y_1 = y_1(x)$ as the first approximation of the desired integral, we then set

$$Y_2(x) = y_0 + \int_{x_0}^{x} f[t, Y_1(t), \lambda]\, dt, \quad x_0 \leq x \leq x_1,$$

$$Y_3(x) = y_0 + \int_{x_0}^{x} f[t, Y_2(t), \lambda]\, dt,$$

and, in general,

$$Y_n(x) = y_0 + \int_{x_0}^{x} f[t, Y_{n-1}(t), \lambda] \, dt.$$

We are going to show first of all that all of these approximations remain between $y_1(x) - a$ and $y_1(x) + a$ in the entire interval (x_0, x_1), provided that the absolute value of λ is sufficiently small. Indeed, we have

$$Y_n(x) - y_1(x) = \int_{x_0}^{x} \{f[t, Y_{n-1}(t), \lambda] - f[t, y_1(t), 0]\} \, dt;$$

if $Y_{n-1}(x)$ lies between $y_1(x) - a$ and $y_1(x) + a$, we have again, from relation (16),

$$|Y_n(x) - y_1(x)| < \int_{x_0}^{x} \{H|Y_{n-1}(t) - y_1(t)| + K|\lambda|\} \, dt.$$

Let us consider a set of functions $\Delta_n(x)$ defined by the recurrence relation

$$\Delta_n(x) = \int_{x_0}^{x} \{H\Delta_{n-1}(t) + K|\lambda|\} \, dt,$$

with the condition $\Delta_1(x) = 0$. It is clear that all the functions $\Delta_2(x), \ldots, \Delta_n(x), \ldots$ are positive between x_0 and x_1, and that we have $|Y_n(x) - y_1(x)| < \Delta_n(x)$. Now the functions $\Delta_n(x)$ are the successive approximations of the integral of the linear equation

$$u' = Hu + K|\lambda|,$$

which is zero for $x = x_0$, that is, the function

$$\frac{K|\lambda|}{H} \left\{ e^{H(x-x_0)} - 1 \right\};$$

the first approximation being zero, all the succeeding ones are less than the integral itself (Section 1), and consequently we have for any n

$$\Delta_n(x) < \frac{K|\lambda|}{H} \left\{ e^{H(x_1-x_0)} - 1 \right\}.$$

If $|\lambda|$ is such that the second member of this inequality is less than a, we see step by step that every successive approximation $Y_2(x), \ldots,$

$Y_n(x), \ldots$ remains between $y_1(x) - a$ and $y_1(x) + a$ in the entire interval (x_0, x_1). The reasoning is completed as in the general case (II, 2, **28**); when n increases indefinitely, $Y_n(x)$ has as a limit an integral $Y(x, \lambda)$ which assumes the value y_0 for $x = x_0$, is continuous in the interval (x_0, x_1), and remains between $y_1 - a$ and $y_1 + a$ in this interval. The integral curve therefore remains within the strip R when x varies from x_0 to x_1. The methods of Sections **3** and **4** prove, moreover, that $Y(x, \lambda)$, considered as a function of the two variables x and λ, is continuous, as well as its partial derivatives Y'_x and Y'_λ, when x remains in the interval (x_0, x_1), and $|\lambda|$ remains less than a suitably chosen number η.

The reasoning is clearly general, and the theorem can be extended to a system composed of any number whatever of differential equations, whose second members depend on any number whatever of parameters.

When the equations (14) *have for* $\lambda_1 = 0, \ldots, \lambda_p = 0$ *a particular system of integrals* $y_i = y_i^0(x)$, *continuous in the interval* (x_0, x_1) *and if the second members* $f_1, f_2, \ldots, f_n$ *are continuous and possess continuous partial derivatives with respect to the variables* y_i, λ_k, *in the interval* D *defined by the conditions*

$$x_0 \leq x \leq x_2, \qquad y_i^0(x) - a \leq y_i \leq y_i^0(x) + a, \qquad |\lambda_k| < b,$$

a and b *being two positive numbers, then the integrals of this system which, for* $x = x_0$, *take on the same values as*

$$y_i^0(x), \ldots, y_n^0(x),$$

are continuous functions, as are the first partial derivatives with respect to x *and the parameters* λ_k *in a domain* D' *defined by the conditions*

$$x_0 \leq x \leq x_1, \qquad |\lambda_k| < \mu, \qquad k = 1, 2, \ldots, p,$$

μ *being a suitably determined positive number.*

In the particular case when the second members f_i are analytic functions of the unknowns y_i and of the parameters λ_k, the integrals of the system are represented, in the Picard method, by sums of uniformly convergent series all of whose terms are analytic functions[7] of the parameters λ_k. These integrals are therefore also analytic

---

[7] Indeed few modifications in the reasoning suffice to show that the conclusions remain valid when the parameters have complex values, provided that the moduli are sufficiently small.

functions of these parameters, and we are thus led to a theorem of H. Poincaré, which will be proven directly a little later.

We can again generalize the preceding theorem by supposing that the initial values of y_1, y_2, . . ., y_n for $x = x_0$ are so many independent variables. If we represent the initial value of $y_i(x)$ by $y_i^0(x_0) = \beta_i$, it is sufficient to set

$$y_i(x) = \beta_i + Y_i(x)$$

to be led to a system of the same form as system (14), but including in addition n parameters β_1, β_2, . . ., β_n. The integrals of this new system which at $x = x_0$ take on the initial values $y_i^0(x)$ are continuous functions and have continuous partial derivatives with respect to the new parameters β_1, β_2, . . ., β_n, provided that the absolute values of these parameters remain sufficiently small.

Finally, we can also suppose that the initial value of x is itself variable while admitting the continuity of f_x. For example, if in the equation (15) we set

$$x = X + \alpha, \quad y = Y + \beta,$$

the equation becomes

$$\frac{dY}{dX} = f(X + \alpha, \quad Y + \beta, \quad \lambda),$$

and the integral of this equation which takes on the value y_0 for $X = x_0$ is a continuous function of α, β, λ when x varies from x_0 to x_1, always assuming the conditions given above are satisfied, and provided that $|\alpha|$, $|\beta|$, $|\lambda|$ are sufficiently small. We conclude from this that in the same domain the integral of equation (15), which takes on the value $y_0 + \beta$ for $x = x_0 + \alpha$, is a continuous function, having continuous partial derivatives with respect to the variables α, β, λ.

Examples. Let $y_1(x)$ be a particular integral of an equation of the first order $y' = f(x, y)$, continuous from x_0 to x_1, and having the value y_0 for $x = x_0$.

The integral of the same equation which takes on the value $y_0 + \lambda$ for $x = x_0$ is a function $F(x, \lambda)$ of the two variables x, λ, continuous and having continuous partial derivatives as x varies from x_0 to x_1, and λ from $- h$ to $+ h$, the positive number h being chosen sufficiently small. Let AB be the segment of the line $x = x_0$ contained between the two points A and B with ordinates $y_0 - h$

and $y_0 + h$. At each point of the segment AB begins an arc of the integral curve going from this point with abscissa x_0 to a point with abscissa x_1, and the totality of these arcs fills the strip included between the two lines $x = x_0$, $x = x_1$, and the two arcs beginning from the points A and B.

Indeed, let λ' and λ'' be two values of λ contained between $- h$ and $+ h$; the two integral curves $C_{\lambda'}$, $C_{\lambda''}$, which correspond to these values of λ, cannot have any common point between the two lines $x = x_0$, $x = x_1$, for there would pass through this common point two integral curves. If these curves are intersected by the parallel to the y-axis, $x = \alpha$, $(x_0 < \alpha < x_1)$, the function $F(\alpha, \lambda)$ can only be increasing with λ; if we had at the same time

$$\lambda' > \lambda'', \quad F(\alpha, \lambda') < F(\alpha, \lambda''),$$

it is clear that the two curves $C_{\lambda'}$, $C_{\lambda''}$ would intersect between the two lines $x = x_0$, $x = \alpha$. The function $F(\alpha, \lambda)$ therefore passes once and only once through every value included between $F(\alpha, - h)$ and $F(\alpha, h)$ when λ increases from $- h$ to $+ h$.

Let us consider again a system of two equations of the first order whose second members do not contain any variable parameter, and let $y_1(x)$, $z_1(x)$ be a particular system of integrals continuous in the interval (x_0, x_1), and taking on the values y_0 and z_0 for $x = x_0$. The integrals which take on the initial values $y_0 + \lambda$, $z_0 + \mu$ for $x = x_0$ are continuous functions, as are their derivatives, in the entire interval (x_0, x_1) provided that $|\lambda|$ and $|\mu|$ are less than a suitable positive number. In the plane $x = x_0$, let us consider a small closed curve γ surrounding the point M_0, with coordinates (x_0, y_0, z_0). From each point of the region σ, bounded by γ, there comes a segment of the integral curve ending at a point of the plane $x = x_1$. The set of these segments fills a region of space, bounded by the surface formed by the segments coming from the different points of γ.

6. Equations of variation. Let us consider, for the sake of definiteness, a system of two equations

$$(17) \qquad \frac{dy}{dx} = f(x, y, z, \lambda), \quad \frac{dz}{dx} = \phi(x, y, z, \lambda),$$

and let $y = y_1(x)$, $z = z_1(x)$ be a system of solutions corresponding to the value $\lambda = 0$ of the parameter, solutions which we are assuming to be continuous in the interval (x_0, x_1), the other hypotheses on the second members f and ϕ being kept. From what we have just seen, equations (17) have an infinity of systems of solutions, depending upon the parameter λ, continuous in the same interval, and reducing to $y_1(x)$ and $z_1(x)$, respectively, for $\lambda = 0$. It will suffice to take as initial values the functions $y_0(\lambda)$, $z_0(\lambda)$, continuous and with continuous derivatives, and reducing for $\lambda = 0$ to $y_1(x_0)$ and $z_1(x_0)$, respectively. We can even assume that the parameter λ does not occur explicitly in the functions f and ϕ, in such a way that these integrals depend on λ only through the medium of the initial values. Let

$$y = F(x, \lambda), \quad z = \Phi(x, \lambda)$$

be one of these systems of integrals; for $\lambda = 0$ we have identically

(18) $$F(x, 0) = y_1(x), \quad \Phi(x, 0) = z_1(x),$$

while for $x = x_0$ we have

(19) $$F(x_0, \lambda) = y_0(\lambda), \quad \Phi(x_0, \lambda) = z_0(\lambda).$$

Differentiating the two members of equations (17) with respect to the parameter λ, we get

(20)
$$\begin{cases} \dfrac{\partial^2 F}{\partial x \partial \lambda} = \dfrac{\partial f}{\partial y}\dfrac{\partial F}{\partial \lambda} + \dfrac{\partial f}{\partial z}\dfrac{\partial \Phi}{\partial \lambda} + \dfrac{\partial f}{\partial \lambda}, \\[2mm] \dfrac{\partial^2 \Phi}{\partial x \partial \lambda} = \dfrac{\partial \phi}{\partial y}\dfrac{\partial F}{\partial \lambda} + \dfrac{\partial \phi}{\partial z}\dfrac{\partial \Phi}{\partial \lambda} + \dfrac{\partial \phi}{\partial \lambda}; \end{cases}$$

let us represent by $\xi(x)$ and $\eta(x)$ the derivatives $F'_\lambda (x, \lambda)$ and $\Phi'_\lambda (x, \lambda)$, where we have made $\lambda = 0$, and let us give to λ the value $\lambda = 0$ in the preceding relations. We see that these functions $\xi(x)$ and $\eta(x)$ satisfy the linear equations

(21)
$$\begin{cases} \dfrac{d\xi}{dx} = f'_y(x, y_1, z_1; 0)\xi + f'_z(x, y_1, z_1; 0)\eta + f'_\lambda(x, y_1, z_1; 0), \\[2mm] \dfrac{d\eta}{dx} = \phi'_y(x, y_1, z_1; 0)\xi + \phi'_z(x, y_1, z_1; 0)\eta + \phi'_\lambda(x, y_1, z_1; 0), \end{cases}$$

which Poincaré has called *equations of variation*. These equations determine the functions $\xi(x)$, $\eta(x)$ in the entire interval (x_0, x_1) if their values for $x = x_0$ are known. The name *equations of variation* is explained by the fact that if the variation $\delta\lambda$ of the parameter is taken to be extremely small, these equations determine the principal part of the expansion of the integrals $y(x)$ and $z(x)$ as x varies from x_0 to x_1.

In general, integration of system (21) presents the same difficulties as the integration of any linear system. But if the general integral of system (17) is known, with two arbitrary constants a and b,

$$(22) \qquad y = G(x, \lambda, a, b), \quad z = H(x, \lambda, a, b),$$

we can immediately deduce from it the general integral of system (21). Indeed, let us suppose, to be definite, that the integrals $y_1(x)$, $z_1(x)$ correspond to the values a_0, b_0 of the constants of integration. Differentiating successively equations (17) with respect to the parameters a, b, y and then setting $\lambda = 0$, $a = a_0$, $b = b_0$ in the relations thus derived, we see immediately that the functions $G'_\lambda(x, 0; a_0, b_0)$ and $H'_\lambda(x, 0; a_0, b_0)$ constitute a particular system of integrals of equations (21), while the functions (G'_a, H'_a) and (G'_b, H'_b) form two particular systems of integrals of the same equations after the suppression of the terms independent of ξ and of η.

In applications, it often happens that the functions f and ϕ do not depend on λ, and the equations of variation form a homogeneous system. From what we have just remarked, we shall immediately have the general integral of this linear system if the general integral of system (17) is known.

7. Poincaré's theorem.

We have already observed that when the second members of the differential equations are analytic functions of the unknowns y_i and of the parameters, the integrals are also analytic functions of the parameters (Section 5). This theorem, due to H. Poincaré, can also be proven directly, by the ordinary methods of the calculus of limits.[8]

Let us consider, to be definite, a system of two differential equations

$$(23) \qquad \begin{cases} \dfrac{dy}{dx} = f(x, y, z, \lambda) = \Sigma a_{\alpha\beta\gamma} y^\alpha z^\beta \lambda^\gamma, \\[2mm] \dfrac{dz}{dx} = \phi(x, y, z, \lambda) = \Sigma b_{\alpha\beta\gamma} y^\alpha z^\beta \lambda^\gamma, \end{cases}$$

where the second members are entire series in y, z, λ, whose coefficients $a_{\alpha\beta\gamma}$, $b_{\alpha\beta\gamma}$ are continuous functions of the variable x in a certain interval (x_0, x_1). These series are assumed to be convergent,

[8] Picard has given a slightly different proof (*Cours d'Analyse*, Vol. III, Chap. VIII).

whatever the value of x in this interval, provided that the moduli of y, z, λ do not exceed a positive number ρ; moreover, these series contain no terms independent of y, z, λ, so that for $\lambda = 0$ equations (23) have the system of particular integrals $y = z = 0$.

We propose first of all to find two power series in λ,

(24)
$$y = \lambda y_1(x) + \lambda^2 y_2(x) + \ldots + \lambda^n y_n(x) + \ldots,$$
$$z = \lambda z_1(x) + \lambda^2 z_2(x) + \ldots + \lambda^n z_n(x) + \ldots,$$

satisfying equations (23) *formally*, and all of whose coefficients $y_n(x)$, $z_n(x)$ vanish for $x = x_0$. Substituting these expansions for y and z in equations (23) and identifying, we have at first the relations

(25)
$$\frac{dy_1}{dx} = a_{100}y_1(x) + a_{010}z_1(x) + a_{001},$$

$$\frac{dz_1}{dx} = b_{100}y_1(x) + b_{010}z_1(x) + b_{001},$$

which, taken with the conditions $y_1(x_0) = z_1(x_0) = 0$, determine the functions $y_1(x)$ and $z_1(x)$. These equations are precisely the equations of variation which correspond to the particular system of integrals $y = z = 0$. Generally, equating the coefficients of λ^n in the two members after the substitution, we obtain for the determination of the coefficients $y_n(x)$ and $z_n(x)$ the two linear equations

(26)
$$\begin{cases} \dfrac{dy_n}{dx} = a_{100}y_n(x) + a_{010}z_n(x) + u_n, \\[2mm] \dfrac{dz_n}{dx} = b_{100}y_n(x) + b_{010}z_n(x) + v_n, \end{cases}$$

u_n and v_n being two polynomials, with positive, integral coefficients, in the coefficients $a_{\alpha\beta\gamma}$, $b_{\alpha\beta\gamma}$, and in the functions $y_i(x)$ and $z_i(x)$ for which $i < n$. We see, therefore, reasoning step by step, that all the functions y_n and z_n are continuous and have continuous derivatives y'_n and z'_n, in the interval (x_0, x_1). We may remark that all these functions can be determined by quadratures if we have integrated equations (25).

In order to establish the convergence of the expansions (24) thus obtained, let us imagine an auxiliary system

$$(27) \quad \begin{cases} \dfrac{dY}{dx} = F(x, Y, Z; \lambda) = \Sigma A_{\alpha\beta\gamma} Y^\alpha Z^\beta \lambda^\gamma, \\[2mm] \dfrac{dZ}{dx} = \Phi(x, Y, Z; \lambda) = \Sigma B_{\alpha\beta\gamma} Y^\alpha Z^\beta \lambda^\gamma, \end{cases}$$

in which the coefficients $A_{\alpha\beta\gamma}$, $B_{\alpha\beta\gamma}$ are dominant functions for $a_{\alpha\beta\gamma}$ and $b_{\alpha\beta\gamma}$, respectively, in the interval (x_0, x_1).

Once more we can seek expansions of the form

$$(28) \quad \begin{cases} Y = Y_1(x)\lambda + \ldots + Y_n(x)\lambda^n + \ldots, \\[1mm] Z = Z_1(x)\lambda + \ldots + Z_n(x)\lambda^n + \ldots, \end{cases}$$

formally satisfying the auxiliary system (27), and in which all the coefficients $Y_n(x)$ and $Z_n(x)$ vanish for $x = x_0$. Let us suppose $x_1 > x_0$; these coefficients Y_n and Z_n are determined successively by systems of linear equations; Y_1 and Z_1, for example, must satisfy the system

$$(29) \quad \begin{aligned} \frac{dY_1}{dx} &= A_{100}Y_1 + A_{010}Z_1 + A_{001}, \\[2mm] \frac{dZ_1}{dx} &= B_{100}Y_1 + B_{010}Z_1 + B_{001} \end{aligned}$$

and vanish for $x = x_0$. If we compare this system with the analogous system (25) which determines $y_1(x)$ and $z_1(x)$, we see immediately that $Y_1(x)$ and $Z_1(x)$ are dominant functions for $y_1(x)$ and $z_1(x)$ in the interval (x_0, x_1) (Section 1). Consequently, dY_1/dx and dZ_1/dx are themselves dominants for dy_1/dx and dz_1/dx. The reasoning can be continued step by step, and we see that the functions Y_n, Z_n, dY_n/dx, dZ_n/dx are dominants respectively for the functions y_n, z_n, dy_n/dx, dz_n/dx in the interval (x_0, x_1). It will suffice, therefore, for us to show that by suitably choosing the dominant functions $A_{\alpha\beta\gamma}$, $B_{\alpha\beta\gamma}$, the series (28) and those derived from them by differentiating term by term are uniformly convergent when the absolute value of λ is small enough.

That granted, let M be an upper bound of the modulus of the two functions f and ϕ when x varies from x_0 to x_1, and the moduli of y, z, λ do not exceed the positive number ρ. The coefficients of the general term in $y^\alpha z^\beta \lambda^\gamma$ is less than or at most equal to the coefficient of the same term in the expansion of

$$\frac{M(y + z + \lambda)}{1 - (y + z + \lambda)/\rho}$$

in powers of y, z, λ. We can therefore *a fortiori* take for the auxiliary system (28) the system

$$(30) \qquad \frac{dY}{dx} = \frac{dZ}{dx} \cdot \frac{M(Y + Z + \lambda) \cdot \left(1 + \dfrac{Y + Z + \lambda}{\rho}\right)}{1 - \dfrac{Y + Z + \lambda}{\rho}},$$

and everything reduces to proving that the integrals of this system, which are zero for $x = x_0$, can be expanded in increasing powers of λ in the entire interval (x_0, x_1), provided that $|\lambda|$ is sufficiently small. Taking account of the initial conditions and setting $Y + Z + \lambda = \rho t$, system (30) reduces to the single equation

$$\frac{dt}{dx} = \frac{2Mt(1 + t)}{1 - t},$$

with the condition $t = \lambda/\rho$ for $x = x_0$. The variables are separable, and the integral sought is the root of the equation $t = \alpha (t + 1)^2$, where $\alpha = \rho\lambda e^{2M(x-x_0)}/(\rho + \lambda)^2$, which reduces to λ/ρ for $x = x_0$. For $\lambda = 0$, we also have $\alpha = 0$, and the root of the equation in t which is zero for $\alpha = 0$ is, as is easily seen, a holomorphic function of α as long as $|\alpha| < \frac{1}{4}$. Now, in order that this be so, it is sufficient to take $|\lambda|$ small enough so that $\rho\lambda e^{2M(x-x_0)}/(\rho + \lambda)^2$ is less than $\frac{1}{4}$. If λ satisfies this condition, the integrals Y and Z will then be expandable in a power series in λ, convergent in the entire interval (x_0, x_1). Formulas (30) show in the same way that the derivatives dY/dx, dZ/dx are developable in entire series in λ in the same interval.

The proof can clearly be extended to any number of equations, depending on any number of parameters. We can also extend it to the case where the variable x is given complex values if the coefficients are analytic functions of x. Let us assume, for example, that equations (23) contain no variable parameter, and that we wish to expand the integrals in powers of the initial values y_0, z_0, which correspond to $x = x_0$.

Let us set

$$y = \Sigma\alpha_{mn}y_0{}^m z_0{}^n, \quad z = \Sigma\beta_{mn}y_0{}^m z_0{}^n;$$

the coefficients α_{mn}, β_{mn}, will be determined successively by the systems of linear equations, with the initial conditions $\alpha_{mn}(x_0) = \beta_{mn}(x_0) = 0$, for $m + n > 1$. As for the coefficients $(\alpha_{10}, \beta_{10})$ and $(\alpha_{01}, \beta_{01})$, they form two systems of solutions of the equations of variation, determined respectively by the initial conditions $\alpha_{10}(x_0) = 1$, $\beta_{10}(x_0) = 0$, and $\alpha_{01}(x_0) = 0$, $\beta_{01}(x_0) = 1$. The series thus obtained will certainly be convergent in the entire interval (x_0, x_1), provided that the absolute values of y_0 and of z_0 are less than a sufficiently small positive number. This new problem is indeed only a special case of the first, for the method is essentially tantamount to setting $y = Y + y_0$, $z = Z + z_0$, and then expanding in powers of the parameters y_0, z_0 the integrals of the new system which are zero for $x = x_0$.

Remark. When system (23) is a linear system in y, z, with coefficients linear in λ, we can take as our auxiliary system a system of the form

$$\frac{dY}{dx} = \frac{dZ}{dx} = (A + B\lambda)(Y + Z) + C\lambda,$$

A, B, C being positive constants. The integrals of this auxiliary system which are zero for $x = x_0$, are *entire functions of the parameter* λ, and consequently the same is true of the integrals of the linear system considered. It would evidently be the same if the coefficients of the linear system were entire functions of λ (cf. II, 2, **29**).

II. PERIODIC AND ASYMPTOTIC SOLUTIONS. STABILITY

8. Periodic solutions. We shall henceforth designate the independent variable by t, which we may regard as representing time, for the sake of definiteness. Let

(31) $$\frac{dx_i}{dt} = (x_1, x_2, \ldots x_n, t) \quad (i = 1, 2, \ldots, n)$$

the equations defining the motion of a body in n-dimensional space; the X_i are assumed to be periodic functions of t with period ω. Let us consider a system of solutions corresponding to the initial values $x_1^0, x_2^0, \ldots, x_n^0$, for $t = t_0$, or, using geometric language, the path starting from the point with coordinates $(x_1{}^0, x_2{}^0, \ldots, x_n{}^0)$. If, for $t = t_0 + \omega$, these integrals take on again respectively the initial values $x_1{}^0, \ldots, x_n{}^0$, the body returns to its initial position in the time $t_0 + \omega$; since, moreover, equations (31) do not change when t changes to $t + \omega$, it is clear that the system of solutions under consideration is periodic. Let $x_i = \phi_i(t)$ $(i = 1, 2, \ldots, n)$ be this system of solutions, the functions $\phi_1(t), \ldots, \phi_n(t)$ being periodic functions of period ω. If the second members of equations (31) depend on certain variable parameters, it may happen that for values of these parameters close to the values which correspond to the known periodic solution, and for suitably chosen initial values, system (31) possesses new periodic solutions close to the first one. We shall develop the reasoning for a system of three equations. Let

$$(32) \quad \begin{cases} \dfrac{dx}{dt} = X(x, y, z; t, \mu), & \dfrac{dy}{dt} = Y(x, y, z; t, \mu), \\ \dfrac{dz}{dt} = Z(x, y, z; t, \mu), \end{cases}$$

be a system of three differential equations whose second members are periodic functions of the time t of period ω. Let us suppose that for $\mu = 0$ these equations have a system of solutions

$$(33) \qquad x = \phi_1(t), \quad y = \phi_2(t), \quad z = \phi_3(t),$$

ϕ_1, ϕ_2, ϕ_3 being periodic functions of t of period ω. Let us take for μ a value close to zero, and let

$$(34) \quad x = \Phi_1(t, \alpha_1, \alpha_2, \alpha_3, \mu), \quad y = \Phi_2(t, \ldots), \quad z = \Phi_3(t, \ldots)$$

be the integrals of equations (32) which for $t = 0$ assume the values $\phi_1(0) + \alpha_1, \phi_2(0) + \alpha_2, \phi_3(0) + \alpha_3$, respectively. The values of these integrals for $t = \omega$ are themselves continuous functions of $\alpha_1, \alpha_2, \alpha_3, \mu$, provided that the absolute values of these quantities are sufficiently small, and if we have

$$(35) \quad \psi_i = \Phi_i(\omega, \alpha_1, \alpha_2, \alpha_3, \mu) - \phi_i(0) - \alpha_i = 0 \quad (i = 1, 2, 3)$$

the body will occupy at time $t = \omega$ the same position as at time $t = 0$. Accordingly we shall find ourselves in exactly the same conditions as at the beginning of the motion and, therefore, we shall have a periodic solution of equations (32) corresponding to these values of $\alpha_1, \alpha_2, \alpha_3, \mu$.

Equations (35) are satisfied for $\mu = 0$ by zero values of α_1, α_2, α_3, which provide the periodic solution assumed known *a priori*. We shall be able to assert that these equations (35) still possess solutions in α_1, α_2, α_3, for values of μ close to zero, if the Jacobian of the first members with respect to α_1, α_2, α_3 is not zero for $\mu = 0$, $\alpha_1 = 0$.

Let us set

$$\xi_i = \left(\frac{\partial \Phi_1}{\partial \alpha_i}\right)_0, \quad \eta_i = \left(\frac{\partial \Phi_2}{\partial \alpha_i}\right)_0, \quad \zeta_i = \left(\frac{\partial \Phi_3}{\partial \alpha_i}\right)_0,$$

where the zero index indicates that we have replaced α_1, α_2, α_3, and μ by zero after the differentiation; we know that (ξ_i, η_i, ζ_i) are three systems of particular integrals of the equations of variation

$$(36) \quad \begin{cases} \dfrac{d\xi}{dt} = \dfrac{\partial X}{\partial x}\xi + \dfrac{\partial X}{\partial y}\eta + \dfrac{\partial X}{\partial z}\zeta, \\[2mm] \dfrac{d\eta}{dt} = \dfrac{\partial Y}{\partial x}\xi + \dfrac{\partial Y}{\partial y}\eta + \dfrac{\partial Y}{\partial z}\zeta, \\[2mm] \dfrac{d\zeta}{dt} = \dfrac{\partial Z}{\partial x}\xi + \dfrac{\partial Z}{\partial y}\eta + \dfrac{\partial Z}{\partial z}\zeta, \end{cases}$$

where we have replaced in the second members x, y, z by $\phi_1(t)$, $\phi_2(t)$, $\phi_3(t)$, and μ by zero, after the differentiation. Now we know the initial values of these three systems of solutions

$$\xi_1 = 1, \quad \eta_1 = 0, \quad \zeta_1 = 0, \quad \xi_2 = 0, \quad \eta_2 = 1, \quad \zeta_2 = 0,$$

$$\xi_3 = 0, \quad \eta_3 = 0, \quad \zeta_3 = 1.$$

We should have the values of these three functions for $t = \omega$, if we could integrate system (36); such is always the case, in particular, whenever we know the general integral of system (32) for $\mu = 0$. However, for the purpose we have in view, this integration is not necessary. In fact, the Jacobian which occurs in the discussion is

$$(37) \quad \Delta = \begin{vmatrix} \xi_1(\omega) - 1 & \eta_1(\omega) & \zeta_1(\omega) \\ \xi_2(\omega) & \eta_2(\omega) - 1 & \zeta_2(\omega) \\ \xi_3(\omega) & \eta_3(\omega) & \zeta_3(\omega) - 1 \end{vmatrix};$$

equating this determinant to zero, we have the necessary and sufficient condition for equations (36) to have a system of solutions

$$\xi = A\xi_1 + B\xi_2 + C\xi_3, \quad \eta = A\eta_1 + B\eta_2 + C\eta_3,$$

$$\zeta = A\zeta_1 + B\zeta_2 + C\zeta_3,$$

providing the same values for $t = 0$ and for $t = \omega$, that is, a system of periodic solutions.

In order that this be so, it would be necessary for one of the characteristic exponents (II, 2, **55**) of equations (36) to be zero. To be brief, let us agree to say that these characteristic exponents are the characteristic exponents of the known periodic solution $x_1 = \phi_1(t)$, $x_2 = \phi_2(t)$, $x_3 = \phi_3(t)$; we shall then be able to state the following theorem:

If no one of the characteristic exponents of the known periodic solution is equal to zero, then for every value of μ near to zero there corresponds a periodic solution of equations (32) close to the first solution.

When one of the characteristic exponents of the known periodic solution is zero, the preceding reasoning no longer applies, but we are not able to conclude from this that there does not exist, for small values of μ, periodic solutions close to the first. Let us suppose, for example, that the Jacobian of the first members of equations (35) with respect to α_1, α_2, μ is not zero for $\alpha_1 = \alpha_2 = \alpha_3 = \mu = 0$; then to values of α_3 close to zero there corresponds a set of values of α_1, α_2, μ, satisfying relations (35). We therefore see, inversely, that to a value of μ close to zero there correspond also values of α_1, α_2, α_3, tending to zero with μ; but there are, in general, several sets of values of α_1, α_2, α_3, corresponding to the same value of μ, and consequently several families of periodic solutions close to the first. The conclusion will be invalid only if all the Jacobians of the first members of equations (35) are zero for $\alpha_i = 0$, $\mu = 0$. Even in this case, one cannot state, without further investigation, that there do not exist periodic solutions close to the first. It might happen, for example, that the three equations (35) are not distinct; it is clear that when this circumstance occurs, all the Jacobians in question will be zero, and yet there will be, in general, a double or triple infinity of periodic solutions, according as the three equations reduce to two distinct equations, or to a single one. For a detailed discussion, as well as for an investigation of the case when equations (31) do not explicitly involve the time, I shall refer the reader to the works of H. Poincaré, or to the *Traité d'Analyse* of É. Picard (Vol. III, Chap. VIII). The preceding suffices to show how the study of periodic solutions reverts to the study of a system of three equations in three unknown functions of a parameter, in the neighborhood of a solution known *a priori*.

9. Stable and unstable solutions. Let

$$x_i = \phi_i(t) \quad (i = 1, 2, \ldots, n)$$

be a system of solutions of the differential equations

$$(38) \qquad \frac{dx_i}{dt} = X_i(x_1, x_2, \ldots, x_n; t);$$

the functions $\phi_i(t)$ are continuous for all values of $t > t_0$, and we assume further that these solutions do not pass through a singular point of the differential equations (38). Let us consider another system of integrals assuming for $t = t_0$ the initial values

$$\phi_i(0) + \alpha_i.$$

From what we already know, we can choose the absolute values of $\alpha_1, \alpha_2, \ldots, \alpha_n$ small enough so that the new solution differs from the first by as little as we wish, during a time period as long as we wish. But it is possible that, when t increases indefinitely, the new solution ends by differing considerably from the first, however small the absolute values of α_i are. This possibility leads us to a new, important notion, that of the stability of integrals of differential equations.

To give a precise formulation, we shall suppose that the known solution reduces to $x_1 = 0, \ldots, x_n = 0$, which clearly does not restrict the generality, for we can always take for new unknowns the variables $x'_i = x_i - \phi_i(t)$. We shall moreover restrict ourselves to the very general case where the equations have the form

$$(39) \qquad \frac{dx_i}{dt} = \Sigma P^{(i)}{}_{m_1 m_2} \ldots {}_{mn} x_1{}^{m_1} x_2{}^{m_2} \ldots x_n{}^{m_n} \begin{pmatrix} m_1 \geq 0, \ldots m_n \geq 0 \\ i = 1, 2, \ldots n \end{pmatrix},$$

the second members being power[9] series in $x_1, \ldots, x_n$ whose coefficients are continuous functions of t, which remain bounded for real

---

[9] The question has been recently treated, with much more general hypotheses, by E. Cotton, who replaces the differential equations (39) by a system of integral equations (*Annales de l'École Normale supérieure*, 3rd series, Vol. XXVIII, 1911, p. 473). I should also cite an important paper by P. Bohl (*Bulletin de la Société mathématique*, Vol. XXVIII, 1910).

values of $t \geq t_0$. Finally, we shall suppose that these series are convergent for all real or complex values of the variables x_i with moduli less than a suitably chosen positive number H, and for all values of $t \geq t_0$. If M is a positive number, greater than the absolute value of any one whatever of the second members in the domain thus defined, we have, for all values of $t \geq t_0$ (II, 1, **93**),

$$|P^i{}_{m_1 m_2 \ldots m_n}| < \frac{M}{H^{m_1 + m_2 + \ldots + m_n}}.$$

When the coefficients P are independent of t, we have the equations of steady motion, that is, equations defining the motion, in an n-dimensional space, of a moving point whose velocity at each instant is independent of the time and depends only upon the position of the moving body at each instant. Another very important case to consider is that in which the coefficients of P are periodic functions of the time; it is to this latter case that we are led when we wish to study the stability of a known periodic solution $x_i = \phi_i(t)$ of equations (38), the second members being either independent of t or periodic functions. The transformation $x_i = \phi_i(t) + x'_i$ will indeed lead to equations (39) where the second members will be periodic functions of t, even though the X_i are independent of t.

Let us consider the integrals of equations (39) $x_1(t), \ldots, x_n(t)$ which take on for $t = t_0$ initial values $x_1{}^0, \ldots, x_n{}^0$, less than H in absolute value. Given any positive number whatever $\epsilon < H$, if it is possible to associate with it another positive number $\eta \leq \epsilon$ such that the conditions $|x_n{}^0| < \eta$ imply as consequences the inequalities

(40) $|x_1(t)| < \epsilon, \quad |x_n(t)| < \epsilon,$

for all values of t greater than t_0, we say that the solution $x_i = 0$ is a *stable* solution. If there exists a positive number ϵ such that it is impossible to associate with it another positive number η in such a way as to satisfy the preceding conditions, the solution is *unstable*. It is clear that we can replace the definition of stability by the following: with every positive number $\epsilon < H$, we can associate another positive number η such that the condition

$$(x_1{}^0)^2 + \ldots + (x_n{}^0)^2 < \eta^2$$

implies the inequality $\{x_1(t)\}^2 + \ldots + \{x_n(t)\}^2 < \epsilon$ for $t < t_0$. The definition of instability can be similarly modified.

Linear equations with constant coefficients readily provide examples. The solutions of the system $dx/dt = -y$, $dy/dt = x$ which assume the initial values x_0, y_0 for $t = 0$ are

$$x = x_0 \cos t - y_0 \sin t, \quad y = x_0 \sin t + y_0 \cos t,$$

and we have $x^2 + y^2 = x_0{}^2 + y_0{}^2$. It would suffice to have $x_0{}^2 + y_0{}^2 < \epsilon^2$ in order to have, for any value of t, $x^2 + y^2 < \epsilon^2$. The solution $x = y = 0$ is therefore *stable*.

The integrals of the system

$$\frac{dx}{dt} = y, \quad \frac{dy}{dt} = 2x + y,$$

which take on the values x_0, y_0 for $t = 0$ are expressed as

$$x = \frac{x_0 + y_0}{3} e^{2t} + \frac{2x_0 - y_0}{3} e^{-t},$$

$$y = \frac{2(x_0 + y_0)}{3} e^{2t} - \frac{2x_0 - y_0}{3} e^{-t}.$$

The solution $x = y = 0$ is *unstable*, for if we take, for example, $y_0 = 2x_0$, $|x|$ and $|y|$ increase indefinitely with t, no matter how small x may be, provided that it is not zero. This example gives rise to several remarks. If the initial values x_0, y_0 satisfy the condition $x_0 + y_0 = 0$, $|x|$ and $|y|$ become small and approach zero when t increases from 0 to $+\infty$; we have *conditional stability*. Similarly, if we take initial values such that the difference $2x_0 - y_0$ is zero, x and y approach zero when t decreases from 0 to $-\infty$. If x_0, y_0 satisfy none of these conditions, $|x|$ and $|y|$ increase indefinitely when t grows indefinitely, whether through positive or negative values.

The integrals of the system $dx/dt = y$, $dy/dt = -2y - 2x$, which take on the values x_0, y_0 for $t = 0$, are expressed as

$$x = e^{-t}[x_0 \cos t + (x_0 + y_0) \sin t], \quad y = e^{-t}[y_0 \cos t -$$
$$(2x_0 + y_0) \sin t];$$

whatever x_0, y_0 are, these functions tend to zero when t increases indefinitely. Not only is the solution $x = y = 0$ stable, but every integral approaches arbitrarily close to the first when t approaches $+\infty$; we shall say to be brief that they are asymptotic to the solution $x = y = 0$.

10. General theorems on stability.[10] When the coefficients of the terms of first degree in $x_1, \ldots, x_n$ in the second members of equations (39) are independent of t, the equations of variation which correspond to the known solution $x_i = 0$ are linear equations with constant coefficients, and the study of this system permits us in general to determine whether this solution is stable or unstable.

Let $V(x_1, x_2, \ldots, x_n)$ be a quadratic form with constant coefficients; if in it we replace $x_1, x_2, \ldots, x_n$ by a system of solutions of equations (39), the result of the substitution is a function of t, whose derivative V', taking account of equations (39) themselves, has the expression

$$(41) \qquad V' = V_1(x_1, x_2, \ldots, x_n) + \Phi(x_1, x_2, \ldots, x_n; t),$$

V_1 being a new quadratic form with constant coefficients, and Φ a power series in $x_1, x_2, \ldots, x_n$, beginning with terms of at least the third degree. If we can choose the coefficients of $V(x_1, x_2, \ldots, x_n)$ such that $V_1(x_1, x_2, \ldots, x_n)$ is a *positive definite form*, we have the following theorems:

1. *The solution* $x_i = 0$ *is stable, if the corresponding form* $V(x_1, x_2, \ldots, x_n)$ *is a negative definite form*;
2. *The solution* $x_i = 0$ *is unstable, if the form* V *is a positive definite form, or an indefinite form.*[11]

To facilitate the argument, we shall employ geometric language, and we shall call every set of values for the n variables $(x_1, x_2, \ldots, x_n)$ a *point*. The set of points whose coordinates satisfy the relation $x_1^2 + \ldots + x_n^2 = \rho^2$ will be called a *hypersphere S_ρ* of radius ρ and the set of points for which we have $x_1^2 + \ldots + x_n^2 < \rho^2$ will similarly be called the *interior* of the hypersphere S_ρ.

This being granted, if the form $V_1(x_1, x_2, \ldots, x_n)$ is a positive definite form, it follows from the hypotheses on the coefficients of equations (39) made above, that we can find a positive number R such that in the interior of the hypersphere of radius R the derivative V' will be positive and that it will vanish only at the origin.

---

[10] I have followed, aside from a few modifications of detail, the method of proof of Liapounoff, in the paper already cited (*Annales de la Faculté de Toulouse*, 2nd series, Vol. IX, p. 403).

[11] When $V_1(x_1, x_2, \ldots, x_n)$ is a definite form, the Hessian of the corresponding form V cannot be zero; for if this Hessian were zero, the n equations $dV/dx_i = 0$, and consequently the equation $V_1 = 0$, could not be satisfied by values of the unknowns x_i not all zero. The form V is accordingly the sum of n squares of distinct linear functions, multiplied by constant factors different from zero.

Indeed, we can represent the coordinates $x_1, \ldots, x_n$ by $\rho\alpha_1, \rho\alpha_2, \ldots,$ $\rho\alpha_n$, ρ being a positive number, and $\alpha_1, \alpha_2, \ldots, \alpha_n$ being numbers which satisfy the relation $\alpha_1{}^2 + \ldots + \alpha_n{}^2 = 1$. Making these substitutions in V' we obtain

$$V' = \rho^2[V_1(\alpha_1, \alpha_2, \ldots, \alpha_n) + \rho W],$$

W being a function of $\alpha_1, \alpha_2, \ldots, \alpha_n, \rho, t$, which is continuous provided that ρ remains less than a certain bound H and that $t > t_0$. When the point $(\alpha_1, \alpha_2, \ldots, \alpha_n)$ describes the hypersphere of unit radius, the form $V_1(\alpha_1, \alpha_2, \ldots, \alpha_n)$ remains positive and greater than a certain minimum m. Besides, let M be the maximum of the absolute value of W. If we take for R a positive number less than m/M, it is clear that in the interior of the hypersphere of radius R, V' will be positive, except for the origin, where we shall have $V' = 0$. We shall suppose in the following argument that the number R has been so chosen.

That being so, let us examine first the case where $V(x_1, x_2, \ldots, x_n)$ is a negative definite form. Let ϵ be any positive number less than R; when the point $(x_1, x_2, \ldots, x_n)$ describes the hypersphere of radius ϵ, $V(x_1, x_2, \ldots, x_n)$ remains negative and consequently is smaller than a maximum value $- K$. Moreover, this function V vanishes for $x_1 = \ldots = x_n = 0$; we can therefore fix a number $\lambda > \epsilon$ such that in the interior of the hypersphere S_λ of radius λ, $V > - K$. Let λ be so chosen; then if for $t = t_0$, the initial values $x_1{}^0, x_2{}^0, \ldots, x_n{}^0$ are the coordinates of an interior point of the hypersphere with radius λ, *the point* $(x_1, x_2, \ldots, x_n)$ *will always remain in the interior of the hypersphere of radius* ϵ, *as* t *increases from* t_0 *to* $+ \infty$. Indeed, the point $(x_1, x_2, \ldots, x_n)$ begins by being in the interior of this hypersphere; if it does not remain there indefinitely, let us suppose it attains the hypersphere S_ϵ for the first time in time $T > t_0$. Let V_0 and V_T be the values of $V(x_1, x_2, \ldots, x_n)$ at the times t_0 and T; we have $V_0 > - K$, $V_T \leq - K$ (from the way in which we have defined the numbers K and λ), and therefore $V_0 > V_T$. Now such a relation is impossible since, from time t_0 to time T, the derivative V' is positive. We are thus led to a contradiction by supposing that the point $(x_1, \ldots, x_n)$ attains the hypersphere S_ϵ; consequently, *the solution* $x_i = 0$ *is stable*.

In the case considered, not only is the solution stable, but also every solution sufficiently nearby is asymptotic to the first. Indeed, when t increases from t_0 to $+ \infty$, the function V, which starts out with a negative value and increases steadily, tends toward zero or towards a negative value $- l$. I say that this last hypothesis must be rejected. Indeed, since the function V vanishes at the origin, there exists a number λ' such that in the interior of the hypersphere with radius λ', we have $V > -l$. The point $(x_1, x_2, \ldots, x_n)$ therefore remains exterior to this hypersphere $S_{\lambda'}$. Now when the point $(x_1, x_2, \ldots, x_n)$ remains included between $S_{\lambda'}$ and S_ϵ, V' remains greater than a certain minimum $\mu > 0$. We shall therefore have at time T,

$$V_T > V_0 + \mu(T - t_0);$$

such a relation is impossible, for the second member increases indefinitely with T, while V_T must remain less than $-l$. It is therefore necessary that $V(x_1, x_2, \ldots, x_n)$ approach zero when t increases indefinitely, and consequently that $x_1, x_2, \ldots, x_n$ tend to zero.

It is to be noticed that the reasoning employed above proves that *there is stability when* V *is a negative definite form, provided that* V' *can take on only positive or zero values for values of* x_i *in the neighborhood of zero.* But we can no longer affirm in this case that solutions in the neighborhood of the first one are asymptotic to it. For example, in the elementary case of two equations

$$\frac{dx}{dt} = y, \quad \frac{dy}{dt} = -x,$$

if we take $V = -(x^2 + y^2)$, we have $V' = 0$; there is stability, but no asymptotic behavior.

Let us suppose in the second place that, V_1 being a positive definite form, V is a positive definite form or an indeterminate form. With the number R having the same meaning as above, let ϵ be a positive number less than R, and λ another positive number $\leq \epsilon$. However small λ may be, we are going to prove that it is always possible to take in the interior of the hypersphere with radius λ a point $(x_1^0, \ldots, x_n^0)$ such that, the initial values of the variables x_i being $x_1^0, x_2^0, \ldots, x_n^0$, respectively, the point $(x_1, x_2, \ldots, x_n)$ ultimately attains the surface of the hypersphere of radius ϵ. Indeed, let $(x_1^0, x_2^0, \ldots, x_n^0)$ be the coordinates of a point interior to this hypersphere such that we have $V_0 = V(x_1^0, x_2^0, \ldots, x_n^0) > 0$. Since the form V vanishes at the origin, there exists a number $\lambda' < \lambda$ such that in the interior of the hypersphere of radius λ' we have $V < V_0$. Let us consider the system of integrals of equations (39) which assume for $t = t_0$ the values $x_1^0, x_2^0, \ldots, x_n^0$; we wish to show that the point $(x_1, x_2, \ldots, x_n)$ will ultimately emerge from the hypersphere S_ϵ after a finite time. The contrary hypothesis indeed leads to an absurd result. If the point $(x_1, x_2, \ldots, x_n)$ remains interior to this hypersphere, V' always being positive, V will go on increasing and will not be able to take on a value less than V_0. The point $(x_1, x_2, \ldots, x_n)$ therefore will remain included between the two hyperspheres S_ϵ and $S_{\lambda'}$; but in this domain, V' has a positive minimum m. For every value of $T > t_0$, we shall therefore have $V_T > V_0 + m(T - t_0)$; now such an inequality is impossible, for the second member increases indefinitely with T, while V remains less than a certain limit, when the point $(x_1, x_2, \ldots, x_n)$ is in the interior of the hypersphere S_ϵ.

11. Application of general theorems. In order to apply the preceding theorems, it is clear that we can carry out on the variables x_i a linear substitution with any constant coefficients whatever, whose determinant is different from zero. We shall choose the coefficients of this substitution in such a manner as to reduce the equations of variation, corresponding to the solution $x_i = 0$, to a simple canonical form. Let

$$(42) \qquad \frac{dx_i}{dt} = a_{i1}x_1 + \ldots + a_{in}x_n \quad (i = 1, 2, \ldots, n)$$

be these equations of variation for the system designated (39); they are obtained by reducing the second members to terms of the first degree. We have seen (II, 2, **59**) how we could reduce system (42) to its canonical form; this form depends above all on the nature of the roots of the characteristic equation

$$(43) \qquad D(\lambda) = \begin{vmatrix} a_{11} - \lambda & a_{12} & \ldots & a_{1n} \\ a_{21} & a_{22} - \lambda & \ldots & a_{2n} \\ \ldots & \ldots & \ldots & \ldots \\ a_{n1} & a_{n2} & \ldots & a_{nn} - \lambda \end{vmatrix} = 0.$$

If this equation has n real and distinct roots, $\lambda_1, \ldots, \lambda_n$, we can reduce equations (42) to the form

$$(44) \qquad \frac{dy_1}{dt} = \lambda_1 y_1, \quad \frac{dy_2}{dt} = \lambda_2 y_2, \ldots, \quad \frac{dy_n}{dt} = \lambda_n y_n,$$

by a linear substitution with real coefficients. The same substitution, applied to equations (39), would lead to a system which would be obtained by adjoining to the second members of equations (44) power series in $y_1, \ldots, y_n$, beginning with terms of at least second degree. *If no one of the coefficients* λ_i *is equal to zero, we obtain at once a quadratic* form $V(y_i)$ whose associated form $V_1(y_i)$ is a positive definite form. It is sufficient to take

$$V = \tfrac{1}{2}(\lambda_1 y_1{}^2 + \ldots + \lambda_n y_n{}^2),$$

which gives

$$V_1 = \lambda_1{}^2 y_1{}^2 + \lambda_2{}^2 y_2{}^2 + \ldots + \lambda_n{}^2 y_n{}^2.$$

If all the coefficients λ_i are *negative*, V is a negative definite form, and there is *stability*. If at least one of the coefficients λ_i is *positive*, the form V is a positive definite form or an indefinite form capable of assuming positive values; here we have *instability*. When one of the coefficients λ_i is zero, it is clear that we cannot obtain a positive definite form for V_1, whatever the quadratic form V may be, since V_1 vanishes for values of y_i not all zero.

Let us suppose in the second place that the characteristic equation has multiple roots, all of these roots being real, and *none of them being zero*. We can then (II, 2, **59**) carry out on the variables x_i a linear substitution with real coefficients such that the new equations of variations divide into a certain number of groups having a simple form (several groups can be made up from a single equation.) Let us consider, to be definite, a group of three equations of the form

$$(45) \quad \frac{dy_1}{dt} = \lambda_1 y_1 \quad \frac{dy_2}{dt} = \lambda_1 y_2 + \mu y_1 \quad \frac{dy_3}{dt} = \lambda_1 y_3 + \nu_1 y_1 + \nu_2 y_2;$$

λ_1 not being zero, we can, without changing this coefficient, replace μ, ν_1, ν_2 by numbers whose absolute values are less than any given positive number, for, if we change y_1 into $\rho\sigma y_1$, y_2 into σy_2, ρ and σ being two non-zero constant factors, system (45) is replaced by a system of the same form, where λ_1 has not changed, and where μ, ν_1, ν_2 have been replaced by $\mu\rho$, $\nu_1\sigma\rho$, $\nu_2\sigma$, respectively. If λ_1 is not zero, we can then always assume μ, ν_1, ν_2 small enough so that the quadratic form

$$\mathfrak{v}_1 = \lambda_1{}^2(y_1{}^2 + y_2{}^2 + y_3{}^2) + \lambda_1 \mu y_1 y_2 + \lambda_1 \nu_1 y_1 y_3 + \lambda_1 \nu_2 y_2 y_3$$

is a positive definite form, for it reduces to the form

$$\lambda_1{}^2(y_1{}^2 + y_2{}^2 + y_3{}^2)$$

for $\mu = \nu_1, = \nu_2 = 0$, and this quadratic form $\mathfrak{v}_1(y_1, y_2, y_2)$ can be deduced from the form $\mathfrak{v} = \frac{1}{2}\lambda_1(y_1{}^2 + y_2{}^2 + y_3{}^2)$, by taking the derivative with respect to t and then replacing dy_1/dt, dy_2/dt, dy_3/dt by their expressions (45). Operating in the same way with every group similar to group (45), we shall evidently construct a form

$$V_1(y_1, y_2, \ldots, y_n),$$

which will be definite and positive, provided that no one of the numbers λ_i is zero. The corresponding form V which will be the sum of forms like $\frac{1}{2}\lambda_1(y_1{}^2 + y_2{}^2 + y_3{}^2)$, extended to all groups of equations similar to group (45), will be a definite negative form when all the numbers λ_i are negative, and only in this case. The conclusion is the same as before. *The solution is stable if all the roots of the characteristic equation are negative, and unstable if one of them is positive.*

Finally, let us suppose that some of the roots of the characteristic equation are imaginary. These roots are then conjugate in pairs, and to each group of equations, such as (45), corresponds a conjugate group

$$(45')\qquad \frac{dy'_1}{dt} = \lambda'_1 y'_1, \quad \frac{dy'_2}{dt} = \lambda'_1 y'_2 + \mu' y'_1,$$

$$\frac{dy'_3}{dt} = \lambda'_1 y'_3 + \nu'_1 y'_1 + \nu'_2 y'_2,$$

the variables y_1 and y'_1, y_2 and y'_2, y_3 and y'_3, being conjugate imaginaries, just as are the coefficients λ_1 and λ', μ and μ', ν and ν'. For the same reason as before, the absolute values of the coefficients μ, ν_1, ν_2 can be assumed smaller than any preassigned positive number. We could replace the system of equations (45) and (45') by a system of six linear equations with real coefficients, by setting $y_1 = u_1 + iv_1$, $y'_1 = u_1 - iv_1$, $\ldots$, but this transformation is useless for our purpose. Let us set in fact

$$\mathfrak{v} = y_1 y'_1 + y_2 y'_2 + y_3 y'_3;$$

taking equations (45) and (45') into consideration, we have

$$\frac{d\mathfrak{v}}{dt} = (\lambda_1 + \lambda'_1)(y_1 y'_1 + y_2 y'_2 + y_3 y'_3) + \mu y_1 y'_2 + \mu' y'_1 y_2$$

$$+ \nu_1 y_1 y'_3 + \nu'_1 y'_1 y_3 + \nu_2 y_2 y'_3 + \nu'_2 y'_2 y_3;$$

the quadratic form in the second member is a definite form, when the absolute values of μ, ν_1, ν_2, are sufficiently small, provided that

$\lambda_1 + \lambda'_1$ is not zero, that is, provided that the real part of α_1 is not zero. Let $\lambda_1 = \alpha + \beta - \sqrt{-1}$, α not being zero; then, setting

$$\mathfrak{v} = 2\alpha(y_1y'_1 + y_2y'_2 + y_3y'_3) = 2\alpha(u_1^2 + v_1^2 + u_2^2 + v_2^2 + u_3^2 + v_3^2),$$

we see that $d\mathfrak{v}/dt$ will be a definite positive form if we have first of all required the absolute values of the coefficients μ, ν_1, ν_2 to be small enough, and the form $\mathfrak{v}$ itself will be a definite form, positive or negative according to the sign of α. Proceeding similarly with every group of equations having real roots or pairs of conjugate imaginary roots, we see that we can always construct a quadratic form $V(x_1, x_2, \ldots, x_n)$ such that the associated quadratic form $V_1(x_1, x_2, \ldots, x_n)$ will be a positive definite form *provided that none of the roots λ_i of the characteristic equation has a zero real part.* If every real part is *negative*, the form V is itself a negative definite form, and the solution $x_i = 0$ is *stable*; if at least one of these real parts is *positive*, the form V can take on positive values, and the solution $x_i = 0$ is *unstable*.

Examination of the doubtful case. When one of the roots λ_i has its real part equal to zero, there is uncertainty; this is the only case where the solution $x_i = 0$ can be stable without every nearby solution being asymptotic to it. We can remove the doubt, except in the case where the real parts of all the other roots are zero or negative. Let us suppose, in fact, that some of the roots of the characteristic equation have their real parts equal to zero, while others have their real parts positive. The roots of the characteristic equation $D'(s)=0$ of the auxiliary system

$$(46) \qquad \frac{dx'_i}{dt} = a_{i1}x'_1 + \ldots + \left(a_{i1} - \frac{\mu}{2}\right)x'_1 + \ldots + a_{in}x'_n$$

$$(i = 1, 2, \ldots, n),$$

which is derived from system (42) by replacing a_{ii} in it by $a_{ii} - \frac{1}{2}\mu$, are equal to the roots of equation (43) diminished by $\frac{1}{2}\mu$. Under the hypothesis we are making we can accordingly choose for μ a real positive number such that none of the roots of the equation $D'(s) = 0$ has its real part equal to zero, and some of these roots have a positive real part. From the case we have just considered, there exists a quadratic form

$$V(x_1, x_2, \ldots, x_n),$$

which can assume positive values, while the form

$$W(x_1, x_2, \ldots, x_n)$$

$$= \sum_{i=1}^{n} \left[a_{i1}x_1 + \ldots + \left(a_{ii} - \frac{\mu}{2} \right) x_i + \ldots + a_{in}x_n \right] \frac{\partial V}{\partial x_i}$$

is itself a positive definite form. If in $V(x_1, x_2, \ldots, x_n)$ we replace $x_1, x_2, \ldots, x_n$ by integrals of system (39), the result of the substitution is a function of t, whose derivative can be expressed, taking account of the definition of $W(x_1, \ldots, x_n)$, as

$$V' = \mu V + W + \Phi (x_1, x_2, \ldots, x_n, t),$$

Φ being a power series in $x_1, x_2, \ldots, x_n$, which contains no term of degree lower than the second. Since W is a positive definite form, we can determine, as we have seen above (Section 10), a positive number R such that in the interior of the hypersphere with radius R we have, for $t \geq t_0$, $W + \Phi > 0$; and consequently $V' > \mu V$. Let ϵ be any positive number less than R, and η another positive number $\leq \epsilon$. In the interior of the hypersphere with radius η, there exist points for which the form V has a positive value.

Let $(x_1{}^0, x_2{}^0, \ldots, x_n{}^0)$ be one of these points and V_0 the corresponding value of V; we are going to show that the path starting at the point $(x_1{}^0, x_2{}^0, \ldots, x_n{}^0)$ reaches the hypersphere of radius ϵ in a finite time. Indeed, let us assume that this is not so; V is then a function of the time satisfying an equation of the form $V' = \mu V + \phi(t)$, $\phi(t)$ being a positive function of the time. This function V is therefore greater than the integral of the equation $V' = \mu V$, assuming the same value V_0 for $t = t_0$, that is, greater than $V_0 e^{\mu(t-t_0')}$. Now, this expression increases indefinitely with t; it is therefore impossible that the point $(x_1, x_2, \ldots, x_n)$ remain constantly in the interior of the hypersphere of radius ϵ, since $V(x_1, x_2, \ldots, x_n)$ remains bounded in this domain.

In a word, *there is stability when the real part of every root λ_i of the characteristic equation is negative; there is instability if the real part of one of these roots is positive. The only doubtful case is that in which p of these roots (p > 0) have their real parts zero, all the others having their real parts negative.*

In order to recognize whether there is stability or instability it is therefore necessary to take account of the terms of degree higher than the first in the second members of equations (39). We have already seen an example (Section **9**) where there is stability; there is instability for the system

$$\frac{dx}{dt} = 0, \quad \frac{dy}{dt} = x.$$

12. Stability of equilibrium. Let $U(x_1, x_1, \ldots, x_n)$ be an analytic function of the variables $x_1, x_2, \ldots, x_n$, independent of t, vanishing with its partial derivatives of the first order for $x_1 = \ldots = x_n = 0$, and holomorphic in this neighborhood. The equations

$$(47) \qquad \frac{dx_1}{dt} = \frac{\partial U}{\partial x_1}, \ldots, \frac{dx_n}{dt} = \frac{\partial U}{\partial x_n}$$

possess the solution $x_i = 0$. This solution is *stable* if the function

$$U(x_1, x_2, \ldots, x_n)$$

is *maximum* for $x_i = 0$; indeed, when we substitute in this function for the variables x_i the integrals of system (47), the result is a function of t whose derivative is the expression $\Sigma(dV/dx_i)^2$, and therefore cannot assume negative values. The reasoning of Section **10** proves that the solution $x_i = 0$ is stable if $U(x_1, x_2, \ldots, x_n)$ has a *proper* maximum at the origin, since this function cannot take on positive values in the neighborhood of the origin.

To consider the inverse question, let us designate by $V(x_1, \ldots, x_n)$ the quadratic form made up by the set of terms of second degree in the development of U, and let us restrict ourselves to the case where the Hessian of this form is not zero. If we apply the general theorem of Section **10** to this form

$$V(x_1, x_2, \ldots, x_n),$$

the associated form V_1 is precisely $\Sigma(dV_1/dx_i)^2$, that is, a *positive definite form*. In order to have stability, it is necessary and sufficient that $V(x_1, x_2, \ldots, x_n)$ be a negative definite form, which is also the necessary and sufficient condition for $U(x_1, x_2, \ldots, x_n)$ to have a maximum at the point $x_i = 0$. Thus, when the Hessian of the form V is not zero, *we can have stability only if* U *is a maximum at the origin*.

In this particular case, we have to set, in the characteristic equation,

$$a_{ih} = a_{hi} = \frac{\partial^2 V}{\partial x_i \partial x_h},$$

and, from the well known properties of quadratic forms, the roots of this equation are always *real* whatever the form V may be; there cannot be a zero root if the Hessian is different from zero.

In a dynamical problem, where there exists a function of forces independent of the time, we know, from a theorem of Lagrange, that if this function of forces is maximum for certain values of the parameters, the corresponding position of the system is a position of stable equilibrium. The reasoning of Section **10** is fundamentally only the extension of the classic demonstration of Dirichlet. The study of the converse proposition presents much greater difficulties. We shall examine only one particular case. Let us suppose that we have chosen the parameters on which the position of the system depends in such a way that the differential equations of the motion have the form

$$(48) \qquad \frac{d^2x_1}{dt^2} = \frac{\partial U}{\partial x_1}, \quad \frac{d^2x}{dt^2} = \frac{\partial U}{\partial x_2}, \quad \ldots, \quad \frac{d^2x_n}{dt^2} = \frac{\partial U}{\partial x_n},$$

$U(x_1, \ldots, x_n)$ being a function of $x_1, \ldots, x_n$, regular in the neighborhood of the origin, and vanishing with its first derivatives for $x_i = 0$. In order to find out whether the solution $x_i = 0$ is stable, we shall again restrict ourselves to the case where the Hessian of the form $V(x_1, \ldots, x_n)$, which is made up of the group of terms of the second degree of U, is different from zero. System (48) is equivalent to the system of $2n$ equations of the first order

$$(49) \qquad \frac{dx_i}{dt} = y_i, \quad \frac{dy_i}{dt} = \frac{\partial V}{\partial x_i} + \ldots \ (i = 1, 2, \ldots, n).$$

We can obtain directly the characteristic equation of the linear system obtained by neglecting the terms of higher order in the second members; it suffices to look for integrals of this system of the form

$$x_i = \alpha_i e^{\mu t}, \quad y_i = \beta_i e^{\mu t},$$

which lead, in order to determine μ, to the equation

$$D(\mu) = \begin{vmatrix} a_{11} - \mu^2 & a_{12} & \ldots & a_{1n} \\ a_{21} & a_{22} - \mu^2 & \ldots & a_{2n} \\ \ldots & \ldots\ldots\ldots & \ldots & \ldots \\ a_{n1} & a_{n2} & \ldots & a_{nn} - \mu^2 \end{vmatrix} = 0.$$

The roots of this equation are $\pm \sqrt{\lambda_i}$, the λ_i being the roots of the first characteristic equation, relative to equations (47). All these numbers λ_i are real, and by hypothesis none of them is zero; if one of them were positive, the equation in μ would have a positive root, and the solution $x_i = y_i = 0$ of equations (49) could not be stable, from the general theorem. The result of this discussion can therefore be stated as follows: *When study of the terms of second degree of* $U(x_1, \ldots, x_n)$ *permits us to recognize whether this function is maximum or not, for the values* $x_i = 0$, *it is necessary that* U *be a maximum in order that the equilibrium be stable.*[12]

Remark. When all the numbers λ_i are negative, the real parts of all the roots of $D(\mu) = 0$ are zero. We therefore have the case where it is not possible to claim stability *a priori* if one does not pay attention to the special form of equations (49).[13]

13. Applications to more general systems. We can extend the preceding results to systems (39), just as the linear equations (42) form a *reducible system* (II, 2, **62**). We remember that this is what we call linear systems reducible to linear systems with constant coefficients by a linear substitution made on the unknowns x_i, the coefficients of this substitution being continuous and bounded functions of the variable t for $t > t_0$, along with their derivatives with respect to t, and the inverse of the determinant of these coefficients being bounded. It is clear that if the system (42) is reducible, in completely applying to system (39) the linear substitution we have just defined, we shall replace this system by a system of the same kind in which the coefficients of the terms of first degree in the second member will be independent of t.

In particular, when the coefficients of system (39) are periodic functions of t, we have seen that system (42) is reducible. It is a result of the proof which has been given of this theorem that the roots of the characteristic equation of the transformed system are

---

[12] The converse of the theorem of Lagrange had been established in the most general case by Liapounoff (*Journal de Liouville*, 1896), Painlevé (*Comptes rendus*, Vol. 125, p. 1021), Hadamard (*Journal de Liouville*, 1897), and more recently by E. Cotton (*Comptes rendus*, Vol. 153, p. 1029).

[13] The definition of stability given above (Section **9**) is concerned only with the *future*, t varying from t_0 to $+ \infty$. But it is possible to conceive of another one, concerned both with the *future* and the *past*, t then varying from $- \infty$ to $+ \infty$. When we change t into $- t$, the roots of the characteristic equation are multiplied by $(- 1)$; we can therefore have stability both in the future and in the past only if the real parts of all these roots are zero. We find ourselves in a situation where the study of the equations of variation does not suffice to decide whether there is stability or not.

precisely the characteristic exponents of system (42) with periodic coefficients (II, 2, 55). There will therefore be stability if all the characteristic exponents have their real parts negative, instability if one of these exponents has its real part positive.

14. Asymptotic series. Conditional stability. We can confirm the results obtained in the preceding sections by the direct study of the series representing the integrals, these series being arranged according to powers of the initial values, when the real parts of the numbers λ_i are all negative (see Exercise 1, p. 45). Poincaré and Lyapunov have introduced series of another kind, which make clear the asymptotic character of the solutions. We shall study only the most simple case, that of a system which we can express in the reduced form

$$(50) \quad \frac{dx_1}{dt} = \lambda_1 x_1 + \ldots, \quad \frac{dx_p}{dt} = \lambda_p x_p + \ldots, \quad \frac{dx_n}{dt} = \lambda_n x_n + \ldots,$$

the non-written terms forming entire series in $x_1, \ldots, x_n$, beginning with terms of the second degree, whose coefficients are independent of t. Let us set

$$u_1 = C_1 e^{\lambda_1 t}, \quad u_2 = C_2 e^{\lambda_2 t}, \ldots, \quad u_p = C_p e^{\lambda_p t} \quad (p \leq n),$$

$C_1, C_2, \ldots, C_p$ being constants *different from zero*, and let us propose to find power series with constant coefficients, arranged in powers of $u_1, u_2, \ldots, u_p$ and formally satisfying equations (50),

$$(51) \quad x_i = \sum L^i{}_{m_1 m_2} \ldots {}_{m_p} u_1{}^{m_1} u_2{}^{m_2} \ldots u_p{}^{m_p} \quad (i = 1, 2, \ldots, n),$$

the coefficients $L^i{}_{m_1 m_2} \ldots {}_{m_p}$ being constants we propose to determine. To get a precise statement of the problem, we shall suppose that the terms of first degree in $x_1, x_2, \ldots, x_p$ are respectively $u_1, \ldots, u_p$, while $x_{p+1}, \ldots, x_n$ include no term of first degree in $u_1, \ldots, u_p$. We have, in a general way,

$$\frac{d}{dt} (u_1{}^{m_1} u_2{}^{m_2} \ldots u_p{}^{m_p}) = (m_1 \lambda_1 + \ldots + m_p \lambda_p) u_1{}^{m_1} u_2{}^{m_2} \ldots u_p{}^{m_p};$$

upon substituting the expansions (51) in equations (50), and stating that we have an identity, we obtain for the determination of the coefficient $L^i{}_{m_1 m_2} \ldots {}_{m_p}$ the relation

$$(52) \quad (m_1 \lambda_1 + \ldots + m_p \lambda_p - \lambda_i) L^i{}_{m_1} \ldots {}_{m_p} = H^i{}_{m_1} \ldots {}_{m_p},$$

the second member being deduced by the addition and multiplication of the coefficients of series (50) and the coefficients already determined in series (51), arising from the terms of lower degree in $u_1, \ldots, u_p$. We shall therefore be able to determine step by step all the coefficients L^i without ever being stopped, provided that there does not exist among the λ any relation of the form

$$(53) \qquad m_1 \lambda_1 + \ldots + m_p\lambda_p - \lambda_i = 0,$$

$m_1, \ldots, m_p$ being positive integers whose sum is at least equal to 2, and the index i assuming all the values $1, 2, \ldots, n$. Let us make this hypothesis and further let us suppose that the absolute value of expression (53) has a *positive* lower limit l. In order to prove the convergence of the series (51) thus obtained, let us consider the system of auxiliary equations, where η is between 0 and 1, and less than l,

$$(54) \quad \begin{cases} \eta y_1 = u_1 + \sum Q^1{}_{m_1 \ldots m_n} y_1{}^{m_1} \cdots y_n{}^{m_n}, \\ \qquad \ldots \ldots \ldots \ldots \ldots \ldots \ldots \ldots \ldots \ldots \ldots, \\ \eta y_p = u_p + \sum Q^p{}_{m_1 \ldots m_n} y_1{}^{m_1} \cdots y_n{}^{m_n}, \\ \eta y_{p+1} = \sum Q^{p+1}{}_{m_1 \ldots m_n} y_1{}^{m_1} \cdots y_n{}^{m_n}, \\ \qquad \ldots \ldots \ldots \ldots \ldots \ldots \ldots \ldots \ldots \ldots \ldots \\ \eta y_n = \sum Q^n{}_{m_1 \ldots m_n} y_1{}^{m_1} \cdots y_n{}^{m_n}, \end{cases}$$

the second members being majorizing series for the series which occur in equations (50). Equations (54) are satisfied by convergent power series in $u_1, u_2, \ldots, u_p$, and it is easily verified, step by step, from the way in which the number η has been defined, that these new series are majorants for the series (51). As a result series (51) are themselves convergent for the values of t between 0 and a positive number T, provided that the absolute values of the coefficients $C_1, \ldots, C_p$ are less than a suitable bound.

This being so, let us suppose that the real parts of the numbers $\lambda_1, \lambda_2, \ldots, \lambda_p$ are negative, and that equality (53) never holds for integral and positive values of the numbers $m_1, m_2, \ldots, m_p$, whose sum is greater than two. In this case, as the real part of $\lambda_1 m_1 + \ldots + \lambda_p m_p$ decreases indefinitely when the numbers $m_1, m_2, \ldots, m_p$ increase indefinitely, there is a positive minimum for the modulus of the first member of relation (53) and we can apply the result which precedes. There exist series (51) formally satisfying equations (50), arranged according to powers of $C_1 e^{\lambda_1 t}, \ldots, C_p e^{\lambda_p t}$; these series are convergent for $t = 0$ provided that the moduli of $C_1, C_2, \ldots, C_p$ are

small enough, and consequently they are convergent for all positive
values of t. It is evident that the corresponding integrals are asymptotic to the solution $x_i = 0$. If $p = n$, the result is in good agree-
ment with the general theorem on stability, but we obtain new results
by supposing that, among the numbers $\lambda_1, \ldots, \lambda_n$ there are only p
of them whose real part is negative. If we have taken for $\lambda_1, \lambda_2, \ldots,$
λ_p these p roots and if relation (53) is never satisfied by integral,
positive values of the coefficients $m_1, \ldots, m_p$, we obtain integrals
asymptotic to the solution $x_i = 0$, depending upon p arbitrary constants $C_1, C_2, \ldots, C_p$. We then say that that is *conditional stability*.
The totality of these paths form in n-dimensional space a sub-space
of p dimensions (E_p), which is also a locus of points such that paths
coming from one of these points are asymptotic to the solution
$x_i = 0$.

The same series also enable us to prove that we cannot have
stability there, in the absolute sense of the word, if one of the numbers
λ_i has a positive real part. Indeed, let λ_1 be one of the roots of
$D(\lambda) = 0$, whose real part is positive, and at least equal to the real
part of some one of the other roots. None of the numbers $m_1\lambda_1 - \lambda_i$
can be zero, if we have $m_1 > 1$; therefore there exist solutions of
system (50) for which $x_1, x_2, \ldots, x_n$ are represented by power series
arranged in powers of $u_1 = C_1 e^{\lambda_1 t}$ with a radius of convergence ρ
different from zero. The series which gives x_1 begins with the term
u_1, while the other series begin with terms of the second degree.
The initial value $x_1{}^0$ of x_1 for $t = 0$ is equal to the sum of a power
series in C_1, beginning with C_1, and we can derive from it by inversion a power series in $x_1{}^0$ from C_1, beginning with $x_1{}^0$, and such that
$(x_1{}^0)^2 + \ldots + (x_n{}^0)^2$ approaches zero with $x_1{}^0$. Let us suppose, for
definiteness, that λ_1 is real, and that h is a positive number $< \rho$,
such that the value of x_1 (u_1) for $u_1 = h$ is not zero. In addition, let
η be any positive number whatever. It is always possible to take for
$x_1{}^0$ a positive number less than η such that the corresponding value
c of C_1 will be positive and less than h, since the ratio $C_1/x_1{}^0$ approaches unity when $x_1{}^0$ tends to zero. The corresponding integral
$x_1(c e^{\lambda_1 t})$, which assumes the value of $x_1{}^0$ for $t = 0$, will attain the
value $x_1(h)$ in the time T given by the equality $h = c e^{\lambda_1 T}$, that is,
for the positive value $T = 1/\lambda_1 \log (h/c)$. The solution $x_i = 0$ is
therefore unstable. We should reason in an analogous fashion if λ_1
were a complex number with its real part positive. There would then
be another root λ_2 conjugate to the first, and we should consider the
series arranged in powers of $C_1 e^{\lambda_1 t}$ and of $C_2 e^{\lambda_2 t}$, taking conjugate
imaginary values for C_1 and C_2.

For the study of asymptotic series in the most general cases, one should consult, in addition to Lyapunov's paper, Chapter VII of Volume I of *Méthodes nouvelles de la Mécanique céleste* by Poincaré, and Chapter III of Volume III of the *Traité d'Analyse* of Picard.

Comments and Exercises

1. Prove, by the direct study of the series, in powers of the initial values, which represent the integrals, that there is stability, when the real parts of all the roots of the characteristic equation $D(\lambda) = 0$ are negative.

Solution: Let us consider a system of the form

$$\text{(A)} \qquad \frac{dx_i}{dt} = -\lambda_i x_i + \sum P^i_{m_1 m_2 \ldots m_n} x_1{}^{m_1} x_2{}^{m_2} \ldots x_n{}^{m_n},$$

the real parts of the λ_i all being positive. Let μ be a positive number smaller than the real parts of every λ_i. We consider the auxiliary system

$$\text{(A')} \qquad \frac{dX_i}{dt} = -\mu X_i + \sum Q^i_{m_1 \ldots m_n} X_1{}^{m_1} X_2{}^{m_2} \ldots X_n{}^{m_n},$$

the Q_t being dominant functions for the functions P_i for $t \geq t_0$. Setting $x_i = e^{-kt} y_i$, $X_i = e^{kt} Y_i$, the two systems (A) and (A') are replaced by two systems of the same kind in which the coefficient of Y_i will be greater than the modulus of the coefficient of y_i provided that the positive number k is suitably chosen. It will therefore suffice to prove the stated property for an auxiliary system of the form

$$\frac{dX_i}{dt} = -\mu X_i + M \frac{(X_1 + X_2 + \ldots + X_n)^2}{1 - \dfrac{X_1 + \ldots + X_n}{\rho}},$$

M, λ, and ρ being positive numbers; this is done easily by expanding the integrals in powers of the initial values.

2. Apply the general theorems on stability to the study of the integrals of the equation $X\,dy - Y\,dx = 0$ in the neighborhood of the origin; X and Y are power series in x and y, with no constant term.

We are led to the study of the system

$$\frac{dx}{dt} = X = a'x + b'y + \ldots, \quad \frac{dy}{dt} = Y = ax + by + \ldots$$

and we observe that the integral curve starting from the point (x_0, y_0) will pass through the origin when x and y approach zero as the absolute value of t increases indefinitely, and only in this case.

CHAPTER II

EQUATIONS OF MONGE-AMPÈRE[1]

I. CHARACTERISTICS. INTERMEDIATE INTEGRALS

15. Cauchy's problem for an equation of the second order.

In the case of a partial differential equation of the second order in two independent variables, the general existence theorem of Cauchy (II, 2, **94**) is stated as follows:

Given an equation

$$(1) \quad r = F(x, y, z, p, q, s, t), \quad \left(r = \frac{\partial^2 z}{dx^2}, s = \frac{\partial^2 z}{\partial x \, \partial y}, t = \frac{\partial^2 z}{\partial y^2} \right),$$

whose second member is an analytic function holomorphic in the neighborhood of the values x_0, y_0, z_0, p_0, q_0, s_0, t_0, *let* ϕ_0 (y) *and* ϕ_1 (y) *be two functions of* y, *holomorphic in the neighborhood of* y = y_0, *and such that we have*

$$\phi_0(y_0) = z_0, \quad \phi'_0(y_0) = q_0, \quad \phi''_0(y_0) = t_0,$$

$$\phi_1(y_0) = p_0, \quad \phi'_1(y_0) = s_0;$$

then equation (1) *has an integral* z(x, y), *holomorphic in the domain of the point* (x_0, y_0), *and such that, for* x = x_0, *we have*

$$z(x_0, y) = \phi_0(y), \quad \left(\frac{\partial z}{\partial x} \right)_{x_0} = \phi_1(y).$$

There exists only one integral satisfying these conditions.

---

[1] I restrict myself to the essential points of the theory; for more details, one may consult my *Leçons sur l'intégration des équations aux dérivées partielles du second ordre* (Hermann, 1896–1898).

The conditions which determine the integral surface have an obvious geometrical meaning. The two equations $x = x_0$, $z = \phi_0(y)$ represent a plane curve C; and we see that this curve C belongs to an infinitude of integral surfaces depending upon an arbitrary function $\phi_1(y)$. If we are also given this function $\phi_1(y)$, the tangent plane to the integral surface is known for that particular one all along C.

More generally, let us consider any curve whatever, Γ, plane or skew, and a developable surface Δ passing through this curve, in such a way that to each point M of Γ corresponds a plane passing through the tangent at M to this curve; an integral of an equation of the second order

$$(2) \qquad\qquad F(x, y, z, p, q, r, s, t) = 0$$

is in general completely determined if we require it to pass through the curve Γ and to be tangent to the developable surface Δ all along this curve. Let us suppose indeed that, in the neighborhood of a point (x_0, y_0, z_0) of Γ, the equations of this curve are put in the form $y = f(x)$, $z = \phi(x)$, the functions $f(x)$ and $\phi(x)$ being holomorphic in the domain of the point x_0. Let us take three new variables u, v, w, related to the variables x, y, z by the relations

$$x = u, \quad y = f(u) + v, \quad z = \phi(u) + w,$$

and let us consider u and v as the new independent variables and w as the new unknown function. From the relation $dz = p\, dx + q\, dy$, we deduce (I, **42**)

$$p = \frac{\partial w}{\partial u} + \phi'(u) - \frac{\partial w}{\partial v} f'(u), \quad q = \frac{\partial w}{\partial v};$$

it follows next, as a consequence of the identities $dp = r\, dx + s\, dy$, $dq = s\, dx + t\, dy$,

$$r = \frac{\partial^2 w}{\partial u^2} - 2f'(u)\,\frac{\partial^2 w}{\partial u\, \partial v} + \{f'(u)\}^2\,\frac{\partial^2 w}{\partial v^2} - f''(u)\,\frac{\partial w}{\partial v} + \phi''(u),$$

$$s = \frac{\partial^2 w}{\partial u\, \partial v} - f'(u)\,\frac{\partial^2 w}{\partial v^2}, \quad t = \frac{\partial^2 w}{\partial v^2}.$$

Equation (2) is changed into a new equation of the second order

$$(3) \qquad \mathscr{F}\left(u, v, w, \frac{\partial w}{\partial u}, \frac{\partial w}{\partial v}, \frac{\partial^2 w}{\partial u^2}, \frac{\partial^2 w}{du\, \partial v}, \frac{\partial^2 w}{\partial v^2}\right) = 0,$$

while the geometric conditions which the desired integral must satisfy have been replaced by the following ones. Since z must reduce to $\phi(x)$ for $y = f(x)$, w must be zero for $v = 0$, whatever the value of u; besides, since the tangent plane to the surface is given all along Γ, q is a known function of x, and therefore $\partial w/\partial v$ is a known function of u for $v = 0$. We are therefore led to a simpler problem:

To determine an integral of equation (3) *which reduces to zero for* y = 0, *while the derivative* ∂w/∂v *reduces to a known function of* u.

These conditions make the values of w, $\partial w/\partial u$, $\partial w/\partial v$, $\partial^2 w/\partial u^2$, $\partial^2 w/\partial u\partial v$ known for $u = x_0$, $v = 0$; to have the right to apply the general existence theorem, it is sufficient that we can solve equation (3) for $\partial^2 w/\partial v^2$, in such a way as to put the equation in normal form (1). It suffices for this that this equation (3) have in $\partial^2 w/\partial v^2$ a root which is a holomorphic function of the other variables in the neighborhood of the preceding initial values. In order to verify that such is indeed the case in general, if the curve Γ and the developable surface Δ have not been chosen in a particular way, let us observe that all along Γ, the direction coefficients p and q of the tangent plane to the developable surface Δ are functions of x satisfying the condition $\phi'(x) = p + qf'(x)$, which expresses the fact that this plane contains the tangent to Γ.

The values of the second derivatives r, s, t of the unknown function $z(x, y)$ must satisfy, at each point of Γ, equation (2) and the two relations

$$(4) \qquad p'(x) = r + sf'(x), \quad q'(x) = s + tf'(x).$$

Let r_0, s_0, t_0 be a system of solutions of equations (2) and (4) where we have set $x = x_0$, $y = y_0$, $z = z_0 = \phi(x_0)$. To this system of solutions of equation (2) corresponds a system of solutions of equation (3), and it is immediately verifiable, from the formulas for change of variable which give r, s, t, that we have

$$(5) \qquad \left\{ \frac{\partial \mathscr{F}}{\partial\left(\dfrac{\partial^2 w}{\partial v^2}\right)} \right\}_0 = \left(\frac{\partial F}{\partial r}\right)_0 \{f'(x_0)\}^2 - \left(\frac{\partial F}{\partial s}\right)_0 f'(x_0) + \left(\frac{\partial F}{\partial t}\right)_0.$$

If the second member of this relation is not zero, equation (3) can be solved for $\partial^2 w/\partial v^2$, and the general existence theorem is applicable.

To sum up, the proposed problem has as many holomorphic

solutions as the equations (2) and (4) have systems of solutions in r, s, t for which the expression

$$\frac{\partial F}{\partial r}\{f'(x)\}^2 - \frac{\partial F}{\partial s}f'(x) + \frac{\partial F}{\partial t}$$

is different from zero.

A study of exceptional cases where this expression is zero is going to be made in detail for a particular class of equations.

The preceding considerations justify the definition of the general integral proposed by M. Darboux and since adopted: *An integral is general if one can prescribe the arbitrary functions or arbitrary constants, possibly infinite in number, occurring in it, in such a way as to obtain any solution whose existence is guaranteed by Cauchy's theorem, that is, in such a way as to assign to the unknown function and one of its derivations any values, given in advance, at every point of the curve, subject only to the requirement of continuity.*

The actual determination of the integral satisfying these conditions constitutes the *Cauchy problem*, for an equation of the second order. The preceding reasoning assumes that the equation and the given values are analytic; by extension, we keep the name of Cauchy problem, even when the given values are not analytic. We shall see later on that in many cases the condition of analyticity does not occur in the solution (Chap. IV).

Remark I. Once we have discovered the existence of a solution satisfying the Cauchy conditions, we can calculate step by step the values of the successive derivatives of the unknown function $z(x, y)$ at any point of Γ. The third order derivatives, for example, would be obtained by solving the system of five compatible linear equations:

$$\frac{\partial F}{\partial x} + \frac{\partial F}{\partial z}p + \frac{\partial F}{\partial p}r + \frac{\partial F}{\partial q}s + \frac{\partial F}{\partial r}p_{30} + \frac{\partial F}{\partial s}p_{21} + \frac{\partial F}{\partial t}p_{12} = 0,$$

$$\frac{\partial F}{\partial y} + \frac{\partial F}{\partial z}q + \frac{\partial F}{\partial p}s + \frac{\partial F}{\partial q}t + \frac{\partial F}{\partial r}p_{21} + \frac{\partial F}{\partial s}p_{12} + \frac{\partial F}{\partial t}p_{03} = 0,$$

$$\left(p_{ik} = \frac{\partial^{i+k}z}{\partial x^i \partial y^k}\right),$$

$$\frac{dr}{dx} = p_{30} + p_{21}f'(x), \quad \frac{ds}{dx} = p_{21} + p_{12}f'(x), \quad \frac{dt}{dx} = p_{12} + p_{03}f'(x),$$

r, s, t having already been calculated, and so on. We easily verify that the derivatives of order n are furnished by a system of linear equations, in which the determinant of the coefficients of the unknowns is a power of the expression

$$\frac{\partial F}{\partial r} [f'(x)]^2 - \frac{\partial F}{\partial s} f'(x) + \frac{\partial F}{\partial t},$$

which, by hypothesis, is different from zero.

Remark II. Given an integral surface S of equation (2), the differential equation

$$(6) \qquad \frac{\partial F}{\partial r} dy^2 - \frac{\partial F}{\partial s} dx\, dy + \frac{\partial F}{\partial t} dx^2 = 0,$$

in which we assume z, p, q, r, s, t, expressed in terms of the variables x and y, determines on this surface two families of curves, which we call *characteristic curves*. If we consider one of these curves Γ and the developable surface Δ tangent to S all along Γ, we cannot apply in this situation the general existence theorem, since we find ourselves exactly in the exceptional case which has been excluded from our reasoning. We see in particular that if there exists an infinity of integral surfaces, depending on one or more arbitrary constants, tangent all along a curve, this curve is necessarily a characteristic curve on each of these surfaces.

Remark III. We often say that the general integral of a partial differential equation of the second order in two independent variables depends on *two* arbitrary functions of one variable. This manner of speaking does not have a precise meaning unless one refers directly to Cauchy's theorem, and indeed it is necessary to keep from judging the degree of generality of an integral from the number of arbitrary functions which occur in its expression. Let us consider, for example, the equation $\partial^2 z/\partial x^2 = \partial z/\partial y$, and the integral of this equation which, for $x = x_0$, is equal to a given function $\phi(y)$, while $\partial z/\partial x$ reduces to another given function $\phi(y)$, these two functions being holomorphic in the neighborhood of the point y_0

$$\phi(y) = a_0 + a_1(y - y_0) + \ldots + a_n(y - y_0)^n + \ldots,$$

$$\psi(y) = b_0 + b_1(y - y_0) + \ldots + b_n(y - y_0)^n + \ldots.$$

This integral is easily obtained and if we express the expansion in powers of $x - x_0$, we can write it in the form

$$z = \phi(y) + (x - x_0)\,\psi(y) + \frac{(x - x_0)^2}{1.2}\,\phi'(y) + \frac{(x - x_0)^3}{1.2.3}\,\psi'(y) + \cdots$$

$$+ \frac{(x - x_0)^{2n}}{(2n)!}\,\phi^{(n)}(y) + \frac{(x - x_0)^{2n+1}}{(2n + 1)!}\,\psi^{(n)}(y) \cdots,$$

where the two arbitrary functions $\phi(y)$ and $\psi(y)$ occur explicitly. But, if we express the development in powers of $y - y_0$, we can also write it as

$$z = F(x) + (y - y_0)\,F''(x) + \frac{(y - y_0)^2}{1.2}\,F^{(\text{IV})}(x) + \cdots$$

$$+ \frac{(y - y_0)^n}{n!}\,F^{(2n)}(x) \cdots,$$

$F(x)$ denoting the holomorphic function

$$F(x) = a_0 + b_0(x - x_0) + a_1\frac{(x - x_0)^2}{1.2} + b_1\frac{(x - x_0)^3}{1.2.3} + \cdots$$

$$+ a_n\frac{(x - x_0)^{2n}}{(n + 1)\ldots(2n - 1)2n} + b_n\frac{(x - x_0)^{2n+1}}{(n + 1)\ldots(2n + 1)} + \cdots,$$

and, in this new expression, there does not appear more than a single function $F(x)$. This result is easily explained by observing that from a purely formal point of view it is absolutely the same to be given the two power series $\phi(y)$ and $\psi(y)$ or to be given the single series $F(x)$ (cf. I, 44).

This remark leads to an important property of integrals of the equation $r = q$. The function $F(x)$ is the function to which the integral reduces for $y = y_0$; we see that this integral is completely determined as soon as we know the single function $F(x)$, which fact appears to contradict the Cauchy theorem. But this apparent contradiction is resolved when we observe that the curves $y = C$ of an integral surface are the characteristic curves, for which the theorem is not valid. Let us also observe that this function $F(x)$ cannot be chosen arbitrarily, if one supposes the integral holomorphic in the neighborhood of the point (x_0, y_0). In fact, the series $\phi(y)$ and $\psi(y)$ then have a finite radius of convergence, and there exist two positive numbers M and ρ such that we have, for any n, $(a_n) < M\rho^{-n}$, $|b_n| < M\rho^{-n}$. Upon replacing a_n and b_n by $M\rho^{-n}$ in $F(x)$, we obtain an *entire function*, and consequently every integral of the equation $r = q$, which is an analytic function of the two variables x, y, holomorphic in the neighborhood of a point (x_0, y_0), is an *entire function of the variable x*, for $y = y_0$. It follows that we cannot find an analytic integral which, for $y = y_0$, reduces to a given holomorphic function of x, if this holomorphic function is arbitrary; it is necessary in particular that it be an entire function of x. This example is often cited to show that one cannot apply Cauchy's existence theorem to an equation which is not put into the normal form required by the proof.

16. Surface elements. Manifold *M*.

To abbreviate our language, we shall give the name *surface element*, or more simply, *element*, to the combination of a point with coordinates (x, y, z) and of a plane $Z - z = p(X - x) + q(Y - y)$ passing through this point. When the five coordinates x, y, z, p, q of an element are functions of one or several independent variables, we obtain a manifold of elements, but we have to consider here only manifolds such that the functions x, y, z, p, q and their differentials satisfy identically the relation

$$(7) \qquad dz = p\,dx + q\,dy;$$

we say then that two neighboring elements of such a manifold are *united*. Relation (7) expresses the fact that the point $(x + dx, y + dy, z + dz)$ is situated in the plane with direction coefficients p, q, passing through the point (x, y, z). Manifolds of this type are represented by the letter M_i, the index i indicating the number of dimensions of the manifold, that is, the number of independent variables on which x, y, z, p, q depend.

Let us consider first of all a manifold M_1; x, y, z, p, q are then functions of one independent variable α, satisfying relation (7). The point x, y, z describes a curve Γ, and condition (7) states that the plane with the direction coefficients p, q corresponding to each point of Γ passes through the tangent to Γ at this point. The manifold M_1 is therefore composed of the combination of a curve Γ and of a developable surface Δ passing through this curve, each point of Γ being associated with a tangent plane to Δ at this point. It may happen, as a special case, that the curve Γ reduces to a point; the manifold M_1 is then composed of the set of elements obtained by associating a fixed point of space with the tangent planes of any cone whatever having its vertex at that point.

If with each point of a surface S we associate the tangent plane at this point, we obtain a manifold of elements depending upon two parameters, identically satisfying relation (7); that is, a manifold M_2. Conversely, given five functions of two independent variables, satisfying condition (7), three cases can occur: 1. In general, the point (x, y, z) describes a surface S; the plane with direction coefficients p, q is then the tangent plane at the point (x, y, z) to this surface, and the manifold M_2 is obtained by associating each point of a surface with the tangent plane at this point; 2. If a point x, y, z describes a curve Γ, the manifold M_2 is composed of all the elements which we obtain by associating each point of Γ with any plane whatever passing through the tangent at this point; this combination indeed depends upon two parameters; 3. It may also happen that the point (x, y, z) is fixed, p and q being the two variable parameters. Relation (7) is still satisfied, and the manifold M_2 is composed of all the elements obtained by associating a fixed point of space with any plane whatever passing through that point. It is of interest, for the sake of the generality of certain theorems, to consider manifolds M_2 of the three types. But in the sequel we shall concern ourselves only with manifolds M_1 composed of a curve and of tangent planes to a developable surface passing through this curve, and with manifolds M_2 in which each element is composed of a point of the surface S associated with the tangent plane at this point. It is clear that a surface S or, more exactly, the corresponding manifold M_2, may be generated in an infinite number of ways by a family of manifolds M_1 depending upon an arbitrary constant. In fact, it suffices to take on S any arbitrary family of curves depending upon a parameter, and to associate with each of its curves the developable surface tangent to S all along this curve.

With the terminology which has just been explained, Cauchy's problem for an equation of the second order in two independent variables can be stated as follows: *Given a manifold* M_1, *to find an integral surface to which belong all the elements of this manifold.*

17. Equations of Monge-Ampère. Characteristics. We are
going to discuss this problem when the equation of the second order is linear in r, s, t, or of the more general form considered by Ampère

$$(8) \qquad Hr + 2Ks + Lt + M + N(rt - s^2) = 0,$$

H, K, L, M, N being functions of x, y, z, p, q. Let $x(\lambda)$, $y(\lambda)$, $z(\lambda)$, $p(\lambda)$, $q(\lambda)$ be the coordinates of an element of a manifold M_1, composed of a curve Γ, each point of which is associated with the tangent plane at this point to a developable surface Δ passing through this curve. The second derivatives r, s, t of the unknown function $z(x, y)$ at any point whatever of Γ must satisfy equation (8) and the two conditions

$$(9) \qquad dp = r\,dx + s\,dy, \quad dq = s\,dx + t\,dy,$$

where x, y, z, p, q are functions of the parameter λ, and we have first of all to solve this system of three equations in r, s, t. In order to examine this case more readily, it is convenient to employ the following geometric representation. If we regard x, y, z, p, q, dx, dy, dp, dq as given constants, r, s, t as the rectangular coordinates of a point, equations (9) represent a line D, parallel to one of the generatrices of the cone (T) which has $rt - s^2 = 0$ for its equation, while equation (8) represents a surface of the second degree S, of which the cone (T) is the director cone, if N is not zero, or a plane P, if $N = 0$. This being granted, the only cases which can occur are the following ones:

1. In general, the line D intersects the surface S or the plane P in a single point at a finite distance, and therefore equations (8) and (9) possess a single system of solutions in r, s, t. Cauchy's problem has one and only one solution.[2]

2. It can happen that the line D does not intersect the surface S or the plane P in any finitely distant point. Cauchy's problem does not have a holomorphic solution.

3. Finally, it can happen that the line D lies entirely on the surface S or in the plane P, so that equations (8) and (9) possess an infinity of systems of solutions in r, s, t, for each point of the curve Γ. We say then that the manifold M_1 being considered is a *characteristic manifold*, or a *characteristic*.

To form the equations which define these manifolds, it is enough to express the fact that the line D lies entirely on the surface represented by equation (8). Let us suppose first of all that $N \neq 0$; we can write equation (8), after multiplying every term by N, as

$$(Nr + L)\,(Nt + H) - N^2 s^2 + 2KNs + MN - HL = 0,$$

or again, as

$$(10) \qquad (Nr + L)\,(Nt + H) - (Ns + \lambda_1)\,(Ns + \lambda_2) = 0,$$

---

[2] Indeed, expression (5) (III, **15**) is not zero for this system of solutions, for $\partial F/\partial r$, $\partial F/\partial s$, $\partial F/\partial t$ are the direction numbers of the normal to S or to P, and dy^2, $-dx\cdot dy$, dx^2 are the direction numbers of the line D.

λ_1 and λ_2 being the two roots of the equation of second degree

(11) $$\lambda^2 + 2K\lambda + HL - MN = 0,$$

(12) $$\lambda_1 = -K + \sqrt{K^2 - HL + MN},$$
$$\lambda_2 = -K - \sqrt{K^2 - HL + MN}.$$

Equation (10) exhibits the two systems of rectilinear genera-trices of S; we obtain all these generatrices by assigning to the parameter μ all possible values in one of the systems of equations

(A) $\begin{cases} Nr + L = \mu(Ns + \lambda_1), \\ Ns + \lambda_2 = \mu(Nt + H), \end{cases}$ (B) $\begin{cases} Nr + L = \mu(Ns + \lambda_2), \\ Ns + \lambda_1 = \mu(Nt + H). \end{cases}$

In order that the line D, represented by equations (9), belong to one of these systems of generatrices, it is necessary and sufficient that we be able to determine μ in such a way that we have

$$\frac{dx}{N} = \frac{dy}{-\mu N} = \frac{dp}{\mu\lambda_1 - L} = \frac{dq}{\mu H - \lambda_2},$$

or the analogous relations obtained by permuting λ_1 and λ_2.

The elimination of μ from between the preceding equations leads to the two equations

$$Ndp + Ldx + \lambda_1 dy = 0, \quad Ndq + \lambda_2 dx + Hdy = 0.$$

In a word, every characteristic M_1 of equation (8) is made up of a system of *five* functions x, y, z, p, q of an independent variable satisfying one of the two following systems of *three* equations

(13)$_1$ $\begin{cases} Ndp + Ldx + \lambda_1 dy = 0, \quad Ndq + \lambda_2 dx + Hdy = 0, \\ \quad\quad dz - pdx - qdy = 0, \end{cases}$

(13)$_2$ $\begin{cases} Ndp + Ldx + \lambda_2 dy = 0, \quad Ndq + \lambda_1 dx + Hdy = 0, \\ \quad\quad dz - pdx - qdy = 0, \end{cases}$

which are derived one from the other by permuting λ_1 and λ_2. We see that there are in general *two* distinct families of characteristics, which are identical if we have $\lambda_1 = \lambda_2$, that is to say, if S reduces to a cone, and in this case only.

Let us suppose now that $N = 0$; equation (8) is therefore linear in r, s, t,

(8') $$Hr + 2Ks + Lt + M = 0.$$

The parallel to the line D drawn through the origin has for equations

$$\frac{r}{(dy)^2} = \frac{s}{-\,dx\,dy} = \frac{t}{(dx)^2};$$

this parallel must be in the plane $Hr + 2Ks + Lt = 0$, drawn through the origin parallel to the plane P, which requires that we have

$$(14) \qquad H\,dy^2 - 2K\,dx\,dy + L\,dx^2 = 0.$$

Once again we shall distinguish several cases:

First case. Let $H \neq 0$. We derive from equation (14) two finite values λ_1, λ_2 for dy/dx. Let us take, for example, $dy = \lambda_1 dx$; equations (9) give then

$$s = \frac{dq}{dx} - \lambda_1 t, \qquad r = \frac{dp}{dx} - \lambda_1 \frac{dq}{dx} + \lambda_1^2 t,$$

and, putting these values of r and of s in equation (8'), the resulting condition, taking account of the relations between the roots and the coefficients of equation (14), can be written as

$$H\,dp + H\lambda_2\,dq + M\,dx = 0.$$

The differential equations of the two systems of characteristics are therefore the following:

$$(15)_1 \qquad \begin{cases} dy = \lambda_1 dx, & H\,dp + H\lambda_2 dq + M\,dx = 0, \\ dz - p\,dx - q\,dy = 0, \end{cases}$$

$$(15)_2 \qquad \begin{cases} dy = \lambda_2 dx, & H\,dp + H\lambda_1 dq + M\,dx = 0, \\ dz - p\,dx - q\,dy = 0, \end{cases}$$

λ_1 and λ_2 being the two roots of the equation

$$(16) \qquad H\lambda^2 - 2K\lambda + L = 0.$$

Second case. Let $H = 0$, $L \neq 0$. An entirely similar calculation gives the differential equations of the two systems of characteristics

$$(17)_1 \quad dz - p\,dx - q\,dy = 0, \quad dx = 0, \quad M\,dy + 2K\,dp + L\,dq = 0,$$

$$(17)_2 \quad dz - p\,dx - q\,dy = 0, \qquad 2K\,dy - L\,dx = 0,$$

$$M\,dy + L\,dq = 0.$$

Third case. Let $H = L = 0$. We have two systems of *always distinct* characteristics, whose differential equations are respectively

$$(18)_1 \quad dz - p\,dx - q\,dy = 0, \qquad dx = 0, \qquad 2K\,dp + M\,dy = 0,$$

$$(18)_2 \quad dz - p\,dx - q\,dy = 0, \qquad dy = 0, \qquad 2K\,dq + M\,dx = 0.$$

We shall remark that the relation

$$(19) \qquad\qquad K^2 - HL + MN = 0$$

expresses in all cases the necessary and sufficient condition that the two systems of characteristics reduce to a single one.

The characteristics of each system depend upon an arbitrary function, and not on a finite number of arbitrary constants, as in the case of an equation of the first order. Indeed, we have only three relations among five functions of one variable and their derivatives; we can choose for one of the variables y, z, p, q an arbitrary function of x, and there remains a system of three differential equations of the first order to determine the three other functions. Let us take for example an equation of the form

$$s = f(x, y, z, p, q);$$

the differential equations of one of the systems are

$$dx = 0, \qquad dz = q\,dy, \qquad dp = f(x, y, z, p, q)\,dy.$$

The first, $dx = 0$, shows that x is constant all along the characteristic, that is to say, the curve Γ is in a plane parallel to the yz-plane. Conversely, let Γ be any plane curve whatever represented by the two equations $x = x_0$, $z = \phi(y)$. We deduce from the second of the equations $q = \phi'(y)$, while p must be an integral of the differential equation

$$\frac{dp}{dy} = f[x_0, y, \phi(y), p, \phi'(y)];$$

we can again arbitrarily choose the value of p for a given value y_0 of y. Every plane curve, whose plane is parallel to the yz-plane, belongs therefore to an infinity of characteristic manifolds depending upon an arbitrary constant.[3] It is clear, from symmetry, that the same is true for every plane curve whose plane is parallel to the xz-plane.

---

[3] The general equations of the characteristics of an equation $s = f(x, y, z)$ can be obtained explicitly. In fact, if we take $x = x_0$, $p = \phi(y)$, the last equation $dq = f\,dy$ will give z, and the second then gives $q = dz/dy$.

18. Properties of characteristics. The importance of characteristics in the theory of equation (8) is a consequence of the following theorem: *Every integral of this equation can be generated, in two different ways, by characteristics.*

We can state this property again in a more precise way: *Every element of an integral belongs to a characteristic of each of the systems all of whose elements belong to this integral.*

Let us suppose, for the sake of definiteness, that $N \neq 0$. Let $z = f(x, y)$ be an integral of equation (8); if we replace in the first two equations of $(13)_1$ z, p, q, r, s, t by $f(x, y)$, $\partial f/\partial x$, ..., $\partial^2 f/\partial y^2$, respectively, we obtain two differential equations of the first order

$$(20) \quad \begin{cases} (Nr + L)\, dx + (Ns + \lambda_1)\, dy = 0, \\ (Ns + \lambda_2)\, dx + (Nt + H)\, dy = 0, \end{cases}$$

which reduce to a single one, since the elimination of dy/dx leads precisely to equation (10). There exists therefore, on the integral surface considered, a family of curves, depending upon one arbitrary constant, and satisfying the two equivalent equations (20). Let C be one of these curves; the elements of first order of the integral along C form a manifold M_1, which is a characteristic manifold. Indeed, by virtue of the relations

$$dp = r\, dx + s\, dy, \qquad dq = s\, dx + t\, dy,$$

we can conversely go back from equations (20) to the differential equations $(13)_1$ of the characteristics. Through each point of the integral surface there passes therefore a curve C such that the elements of the surface along this curve form a characteristic manifold of the first system. We should see in the same way that, through each point of the surface, there passes a curve C' such that the elements of the integral along C' form a characteristic of the second system. The curves C and C' make up the two families of *characteristic curves* on the integral surface considered. These two families of curves are given by a differential equation of the first order and of the second degree. We deduce, as a matter of fact, from the first of equations (20)

$$\lambda_1 = -\, (Nr + L) \frac{dx}{dy} - Ns,$$

and, replacing λ_1 by this expression in equation (11), we end up with the differential equation

$$(Nt + H)\, dy^2 + 2(Ns - K)\, dx\, dy + (Nr + L)\, dx^2 = 0,$$

which we can again write (cf. III, **15**)

(21) $R\,dy^2 - S\,dx\,dy + T\,dy^2 = 0,$

R, S, T designating the partial derivatives of the first member of
equation (8), with respect to r, s, t, respectively.

Entirely similar calculations apply to the case where N is zero.
On every integral surface there exist two families of characteristic
curves, in general distinct, which are defined by the differential
equation of first order and second degree

(22) $H\,dy^2 - 2K\,dx\,dy + L\,dx^2 = 0;$

the elements of the integral surface along one of these curves form
a characteristic manifold.[4]

Conversely, *if a manifold* M_2, *each of whose elements consists of a
point of a surface* S *and of the tangent plane at this point, is generated
by a family of characteristic manifolds depending upon one arbitrary
constant, the corresponding surface* S *is an integral surface.*

In our reasoning, we shall always suppose that N is not zero.
By hypothesis, through each point of the surface S passes a curve C
such that the manifold M_1 formed by the elements of the surface S
all along C is a characteristic manifold. Let us suppose, for example,
that the values of x, y, z, p, q along C satisfy system $(13)_1$. The
first two equations of $(13)_1$ can be expressed in the equivalent
form (20) and, in order that the values of dy/dx found from these
two equations should be the same, it is necessary that the values
r, s, t satisfy equation (10), that is, that S be an integral surface of
the equation under discussion. The proof would be exactly the same
if N were zero.

As a result of these theorems, every system of three differential
equations

(23) $\begin{cases} dz = p\,dx + q\,dy, \quad A\,dp + B\,dq + F\,dx + G\,dy = 0, \\ \quad A_1 dp + B_1 dq + F_1 dx + G_1 dy = 0, \end{cases}$

A, B, . . ., G_1 being arbitrary functions of x, y, z, p, q (but at least
one of the coefficients A, B, A_1, B_1 not being zero) defines one of
the systems of characteristics of a Monge-Ampère equation; we

---

[4] The reasoning is not valid for integrals which simultaneously satisfy the
three equations $R = S = T = 0$. Such integrals, if any exist, are the *singular*
integrals, to which we cannot apply the Cauchy theorem, whatever be the
manifold M_1 taken on one of them.

should obtain this equation if we replaced dp by $r\, dx + s\, dy$, dq by $s\, dx + t\, dy$, and eliminated dy/dx. The equation will contain a term in $rt - s^2$ if $AB_1 - BA_1$ is not zero, and will be linear in r, s, t in the contrary case.

We have also studied the characteristics from the point of view of the Cauchy problem. We have seen above that, when we wish to solve this problem for a characteristic manifold M_1, one of the derivatives of second order may be taken arbitrarily. If we go on to the calculation of successive derivatives, we find in the same way that for each order the value of one derivative may be taken arbitrarily, at least when the two systems of characteristics are distinct. *The indeterminateness is inherent;* this results from the following propositions, of which we shall give only the statement,[5] and which are proved by the usual methods of the calculus of limits.

When the two families of characteristics are distinct:

I. Each characteristic belongs to an infinity of integrals, depending upon an infinite number of arbitrary constants.

II. When two integrals, possessing all the elements of a characteristic, have contact of the nth order at one point of this characteristic, they have contact of the nth order at all points of the characteristic.

III. A characteristic and a curve Γ intersecting the characteristic curve at a point M determine one and only one integral, provided that the tangent to Γ at M is in the plane of the corresponding element.

IV. In particular, two characteristics of different systems, having an element in common, determine one and only one integral surface.

The statements are less simple when the two families of characteristics are not distinct.

19. Intermediate integrals. The three differential equations which define the characteristics, containing five variables x, y, z, p, q, cannot be integrated as a system of ordinary differential equations. Nevertheless one can investigate whether there exist *first integrals* for these equations; we shall say that the relation $V(x, y, z, p, q) =$ a constant is a first integral of equations $(13)_1$, for example, when the relation $dV = 0$ is a consequence of these three equations. When such is the case, it is clear that the function $V(x, y, z, p, q)$ preserves the same value all along any characteristic whatever of the system, this value varying from one characteristic to another.

---

[5] E. Goursat, *Leçons sur les équations aux dérivées partielles du second ordre*, (I, Chap. 4; II, Chap. 10).

If in dV we replace dz, dp, dq by expressions for them derived from formulas $(13)_1$, we find

$$dV = \left(\frac{\partial V}{\partial x} + p \frac{\partial V}{dz} - \frac{L}{N} \frac{\partial V}{\partial p} - \frac{\lambda_2}{N} \frac{\partial V}{\partial q} \right) dx$$

$$+ \left(\frac{\partial V}{\partial y} + q \frac{\partial V}{\partial z} - \frac{\lambda_1}{N} \frac{\partial V}{\partial p} - \frac{H}{N} \frac{\partial V}{\partial q} \right) dy;$$

in order that equations $(13)_1$ imply the relation $dV = 0$, it is necessary and sufficient that V satisfy the two conditions

$$(24) \quad \begin{cases} N \left(\dfrac{\partial V}{\partial x} + p \dfrac{\partial V}{\partial z} \right) - L \dfrac{\partial V}{\partial p} - \lambda_2 \dfrac{\partial V}{\partial q} = 0, \\[2ex] N \left(\dfrac{\partial V}{\partial y} + q \dfrac{\partial V}{\partial z} \right) - \lambda_1 \dfrac{\partial V}{\partial p} - H \dfrac{\partial V}{\partial q} = 0. \end{cases}$$

We should reason similarly in all the other cases, and the result obtained can be stated thus: *In order that* V(x, y, z, p, q) = C *be a first integral of the differential equations of one of the systems of characteristics, it is necessary and sufficient that the function* V *be an integral of the system of two linear equations which arise upon replacing in the differential equations of the characteristics of the other system,* dx, dy, dp, dq *by*

$$\frac{\partial V}{\partial p}, \frac{\partial V}{\partial q}, - \left(\frac{\partial V}{\partial x} + p \frac{\partial V}{\partial z} \right), - \left(\frac{\partial V}{\partial y} + q \frac{\partial V}{\partial z} \right)$$

respectively.

If $V(x, y, z, p, q)$ is an integral of equations (24), we have identically, in the same way in which we obtained this system,

$$dV = \frac{\partial V}{\partial z} (dz - p \, dx - q \, dy) + \frac{1}{N} \frac{\partial V}{\partial p} (N \, dp + L \, dx + \lambda_1 dy),$$

$$+ \frac{1}{N} \frac{\partial V}{\partial q} (N \, dq + \lambda_2 dx + H \, dy);$$

conversely, if we have obtained, by any means whatever, three multipliers μ_1, μ_2, μ_3, such that we have identically

$$dU = \mu_1 (dz - p \, dx - q \, dy) + \mu_2 (N \, dp + L \, dx + \lambda_1 dy)$$

$$+ \mu_3 (N \, dq + \lambda_2 dx + H \, dy),$$

it is clear that $U = C$ is a first integral for this system of characteristics. The investigation of first integrals thus also comes down to the investigation of the integrable combinations of the differential equations of the characteristics.

When the functions L, H, N, λ_1, λ_2 are arbitrary, system (24) possesses no other solution than the trivial solution $V = C$. We have already seen how we can tell whether this system has other integrals, and how to obtain these integrals by integrating ordinary differential equations (II, 2, **88–89**).

The knowledge of a first integral permits us to find integrals of the second order equation (8). Indeed, *if* V(x, y, z, p, q) = C *is a first integral of the differential equations of one of the systems of characteristics, every integral of the first order partial differential equation* V(x, y, z, p, q) = C *(except perhaps for singular integrals) is also an integral of the second order equation* (8).

Let us suppose always that $N \neq 0$, and let V be an integral of system (24). Every non-singular integral S of the first order equation $V = C$ is a source of characteristic curves, and the manifold M_1, formed by the elements of the surface along one of these curves, satisfies the differential equations (II, 2, **84**)

$$(25) \quad \frac{dx}{\dfrac{\partial V}{\partial p}} = \frac{dy}{\dfrac{\partial V}{\partial q}} = \frac{dz}{p\dfrac{\partial V}{\partial p} + q\dfrac{\partial V}{\partial q}} = \frac{-dp}{\dfrac{\partial V}{\partial x} + p\dfrac{\partial V}{\partial z}} = \frac{-dq}{\dfrac{\partial V}{\partial y} + q\dfrac{\partial V}{\partial z}}.$$

Comparing these equations to relations (24), we see that the elements of the manifold M_1 satisfy the differential equations obtained by replacing, in formulas (24), $\partial V/\partial p$, $\partial V/\partial q$, $(\partial V/\partial x) + p(\partial V/\partial z)$, $(\partial V/\partial y) + q(\partial V/\partial z)$ by dx, dy, $-dp$, $-dq$ respectively, that is, satisfy equations $(13)_2$. The manifolds M_1 are therefore also the characteristic manifolds for equation (8) and, consequently (III, **18**), the surface S is an integral of this equation.

Conversely, *if all the non-singular integrals of the equation* V(x, y, z, p, q) = C *are also integrals of equation* (8), *for any value of the constant* C, dV = 0 *is an integrable combination of the differential equations of one of the systems of characteristics of equation* (8). Indeed, let M_1 be a characteristic manifold of the equation $V = C$; all the elements of M_1 belong to an infinity of non-singular integrals of the equation $V = C$ and, consequently, to an infinity of integrals of equation (8). Every manifold M_1, defined by the differential equations (25), must therefore belong to one of the systems of characteristics, and, therefore, the function V must satisfy the relations which we derive from the differential equations of one of these systems by replacing dx, dy, dp, dq in it by the corresponding denominators of formulas (25).[6]

If system (24), or one of the systems formed in the same way utilizing the differential equations of one of the systems of characteristics, possesses two distinct integrals, u and v, $\phi(u, v)$ is also an integral, whatever the function ϕ (II, 2, **89**) and all the non-singular integrals of the equation $\phi(u, v) = 0$ are also integrals of the second order equation. Conversely, if S is an integral of equation (8), we can choose the function ϕ so that it is also an integral of the first order equation $\phi(u, v) = 0$. Indeed, let us consider on the surface S the characteristics of the system for which $u = C$ and $v = C'$ are two first integrals, and let Γ be another curve of this surface, different from these characteristics. Along this curve Γ u and v are functions of a single variable parameter and are connected, consequently, by a relation $\phi(u, v) = 0$; *this relation holds at all points of* S. Let M be a point of S; the characteristic of the system considered which passes through M intersects Γ in a point

---

[6] We can also establish this property directly. From the equation

$$V(x, y, z, p, q) = C$$

we derive, differentiating with respect to x and to y,

$$(e) \quad \frac{\partial V}{\partial x} + \frac{\partial V}{\partial z}p + \frac{\partial V}{\partial p}r + \frac{\partial V}{\partial q}s = 0, \quad \frac{\partial V}{\partial y} + \frac{\partial V}{\partial z}q + \frac{\partial V}{\partial p}s + \frac{\partial V}{\partial q}t = 0.$$

If from these relations we take two of the second order derivatives, r and s for example, and substitute them in equation (8), the result of the substitution must reduce to an identity. Indeed, if this result is not independent of t, we could find from it the value of t, and, therefore we should have the three second order derivatives expressed in terms of x, y, z, p, q. Successive differentiations would permit us to express, step by step, all the partial derivatives of z in terms of x, y, z, p, q, and the integrals common to equation (8) and to $V = C$ could depend only upon a *finite* number of arbitrary constants. If the result of the substitution is independent of t, since this result does not contain C, equation (8) cannot possess all the integrals of $V = C$, unless the result is not identically zero.

If then we return to the geometric interpretation of the text, we can say that the line D, represented by equations (e), in which we regard r, s, t as the running coordinates, must lie on the surface represented by equation (8). It follows that V must satisfy one of the systems which we obtain by replacing dx, dy, dp, dq by

$$-\frac{\partial V}{\partial p}, \quad -\frac{\partial V}{\partial q}, \quad \frac{\partial V}{\partial x} + p\frac{\partial V}{\partial z}, \quad \frac{\partial V}{\partial y} + q\frac{\partial V}{\partial z},$$

respectively, in the differential equations of one of the systems of characteristics.

M_0, and, since u and v keep the same value along this characteristic, we also have $\phi(u, v) = \phi(u_0, v_0) = 0$. We see therefore that *every integral of the second order equation* (8) *also satisfies a first order equation of the form* $\phi(u, v) = 0$, *and conversely*.

The equation $\phi(u, v) = 0$, which we can also write as $v = \psi(u)$ and which depends upon an arbitrary function, is called an *intermediate integral*[7] of the second order equation.

We can verify by a direct calculation that the equation $\phi(u, v) = 0$ is equivalent to equation (8). Let us represent by du/dx, dv/dx, du/dy, dv/dy the derivatives of u and v, taken by regarding z as a function of the variables x and y, p and q as its partial derivatives; from the equation $\phi(u, v) = 0$ we derive a second order equation, independent of the function ϕ,

$$\frac{du}{dx}\frac{dv}{dy} - \frac{du}{dy}\frac{dv}{dx} = 0,$$

or, upon expanding,

$$\left(\frac{\partial u}{\partial x} + \frac{\partial u}{\partial z}p + \frac{\partial u}{\partial p}r + \frac{\partial u}{\partial q}s\right) \left(\frac{\partial v}{\partial y} + \frac{\partial v}{\partial z}q + \frac{\partial v}{\partial p}s + \frac{\partial v}{\partial q}t\right)$$

$$- \left(\frac{\partial v}{\partial x} + \frac{\partial v}{\partial z}p + \frac{\partial v}{\partial p}r + \frac{\partial v}{\partial q}s\right) \left(\frac{\partial u}{\partial y} + \frac{\partial u}{\partial z}q + \frac{\partial u}{\partial p}s + \frac{\partial u}{\partial q}t\right) = 0.$$

Let us always suppose that equation (8) has a term in $rt - s^2$ and that u and v are two integrals of system (24). Let us multiply each of the terms of the preceding equation by N^2 and then replace

$$N\left(\frac{\partial u}{\partial x} + p\frac{\partial u}{\partial z}\right), \quad N\left(\frac{\partial v}{\partial x} + p\frac{\partial v}{\partial z}\right), \ldots$$

by their expressions in formulas (24); then, taking account of the values of $\lambda_1 + \lambda_2$ and $\lambda_1\lambda_2$, we end up, after several easy reductions, with the equation

$$N\frac{D(u, v)}{D(p, q)}[Hr + 2Ks + Lt + M + N(rt - s^2)] = 0,$$

which differs from equation (8) by only a factor.

---

[7] We sometimes also call *intermediate integrals* every first order equation $V = C$, all of whose non-singular integrals satisfy equation (8).

To sum up, *when the differential equations of one of the systems of characteristics have two distinct integrable combinations, the integration of Monge-Ampère is reduced to the integration of a first order equation depending upon an arbitrary function.* We can, in general, effect the integration of this first order equation only after having taken a fixed form for the arbitrary function. But the solution of Cauchy's problem always reduces, in this case, to the integration of a system of ordinary differential equations. Indeed, if we are given a manifold M_1, the coordinates of an element (x, y, z, p, q) are functions of a variable parameter α. Replacing x, y, z, p, q by their expressions in u and v, the results obtained are functions $U(\alpha)$ and $V(\alpha)$ of α. In order for all the elements of M_1 to belong to an integral of the equation $v = \psi(u)$, the function ψ must satisfy the relation $V(\alpha) = \psi[U(\alpha)]$ which in general determines this function. The function ψ once known, we are reduced to Cauchy's problem for a first order equation.

Equations (24) have at most *three* distinct integrals; for this to be so, they must form a complete system (II, 2, **89**). We shall easily verify, in making the calculations, that this cannot take place if $\lambda_1 = \lambda_2$, and this condition is not sufficient. Let u, v, w be three distinct integrals; equation (8) then possesses two distinct intermediate integrals, $v = \psi(u)$, $w = \pi(u)$. Equation (8) also has two intermediate integrals when the two systems of characteristics are distinct, if the differential equations of each of the systems have two integrable combinations. Let us suppose, for the sake of definiteness, that equations (24) have two distinct integrals u and v, and that equations (24'), obtained by permuting λ_1 and λ_2,

$$(24') \quad \begin{cases} N\left(\dfrac{\partial V_1}{\partial x} + p\,\dfrac{\partial V_1}{\partial z}\right) - L\,\dfrac{\partial V_1}{\partial p} - \lambda_1\,\dfrac{\partial V_1}{\partial q} = 0, \\[2mm] N\left(\dfrac{\partial V_1}{\partial y} + q\,\dfrac{\partial V_1}{\partial z}\right) - \lambda_2\,\dfrac{\partial V_1}{\partial p} - H\,\dfrac{\partial V_1}{\partial q} = 0, \end{cases}$$

have themselves two distinct integrals, u_1 and v_1; equation (8) then has the two intermediate integrals $v = \psi(u)$, $v_1 = \pi(u_1)$. But we deduce from equations (24) and (24')

$$\begin{aligned} [V, V_1] = \ & \frac{\partial V}{\partial p}\left(\frac{\partial V_1}{\partial x} + p\,\frac{\partial V_1}{\partial z}\right) - \frac{\partial V_1}{\partial p}\left(\frac{\partial V}{\partial x} + p\,\frac{\partial V}{\partial z}\right) \\[2mm] & + \frac{\partial V}{\partial q}\left(\frac{\partial V_1}{\partial y} + q\,\frac{\partial V_1}{\partial z}\right) - \frac{\partial V_1}{dq}\left(\frac{\partial V}{\partial y} + q\,\frac{\partial V}{\partial z}\right) = 0, \end{aligned}$$

and therefore $[v - \psi(u), v_1 - \pi(u_1)] = 0$, whatever be the arbitrary functions ψ and π. It follows (II, 2, **80**) that the two simultaneous equations of the first order

$$v = \psi(u), \qquad v_1 = \pi(u_1)$$

form a completely integrable system. Since we cannot in general solve these two equations for the derivatives p and q, inasmuch as the functions ψ and π do not have a definite value, we introduce two new independent variables α and β, by setting $u = \alpha$, $u_1 = \beta$, which gives $v = \psi(\alpha)$, $v_1 = \pi(\beta)$. From these four relations we can now express x, y, p, q as functions of z, α, β, $\psi(\alpha)$, $\pi(\beta)$; replacing p, q, dx, dy by their values in the relation $dz = p\,dx + q\,dy$, we get finally an equation in total differentials

$$dz = P\,d\alpha + Q\,d\beta,$$

where P and Q depend upon z, α, β, $\psi(\alpha)$, $\psi'(\alpha)$, $\pi(\beta)$, $\pi'(\beta)$, which is completely integrable, whatever the functions $\psi(\alpha)$ and $\pi(\beta)$. Once this equation has been integrated, we will have x, y, z expressed in terms of two parameters α and β.

20. Miscellaneous applications. Examples.

1. The two systems of characteristics of the equation $rt - s^2 = 0$ are identified and the differential equations

$$dp = 0, \qquad dq = 0, \qquad dz - p\,dx - q\,dy = 0$$

have three integrable combinations, for we can write the last as $d(z - px - qy) = 0$. We therefore have two intermediate integrals

$$q = \phi(p), \qquad z - px - qy = \psi(p);$$

in order to derive the general integral from it, it is sufficient to return to the calculations already made. (I, **215**.)

2. The equation $q^2 r - 2pqs + p^2 t = 0$ likewise has only one system of characteristics, for equation (16) here becomes $q^2 \lambda^2 + 2pq\lambda + p^2 = 0$ and has the double root $- p/q$. In this case differential equations (15) become

$$dz - p\,dx - q\,dy = 0, \qquad p\,dx + q\,dy = 0, \qquad q\,dp - p\,dq = 0;$$

we notice readily three integral combinations

$$dz = 0, \qquad d\left(\frac{q}{p}\right) = 0, \qquad d\left(x + \frac{q}{p}\,y\right) = 0.$$

The equation therefore possesses the two intermediate integrals $q + p\,\phi(z) = 0$, $x + (q/p)y + \psi(z) = 0$ which are integrated without difficulty. But we obtain immediately the general integral of the equation under consideration by eliminating q/p between the two intermediate integrals. We are thus led to the equation

$$x - y\phi(z) + \psi(z) = 0,$$

which represents the ruled surfaces having the xy-plane as directing plane (II, 2, **93**).

3. The equation $(1 + q^2)s - pqt = 0$ expresses the fact that the sections of the surface $z = f(x, y)$ made by planes parallel to the plane $x = 0$ are lines of curvature. Formulas $(17)_1$ and $(17)_2$ give us for the differential equations of the two systems of characteristics,

$(17')_1$ $dz - p\,dx - q\,dy = 0, \qquad dx = 0,$

$$(1 + q^2)\,dp - pq\,dq = 0,$$

$(17')_2$ $dz - p\,dx - q\,dy = 0, \qquad (1 + q^2)\,dy + pq\,dx = 0,$

           $dq = 0.$

Each of these has two integrable combinations; indeed, we derive from equations $(17')_1$ $dx = 0$, $d(p/\sqrt{1 + q^2}) = 0$, and from equations $(17')_2$, $dq = 0$, $d(y + qz) = 0$. Consequently, the equation of second order has two intermediate integrals which we can write as

$$p = \sqrt{1 - q^2}\,f'(x), \qquad y + qz = \phi(q),$$

f and ϕ being arbitrary functions. We would have been able to obtain the first immediately by writing the second order equation in the form

$$\frac{s}{p} = \frac{qt}{1 + q^2}$$

and observing that the two members are the derivatives, with respect to y, of $\log p$ and of $\tfrac{1}{2}\log(1 + q^2)$. This first order equation has the complete integral

$$z = \sqrt{1 + a^2}\,f(x) + ay + b,$$

and the general integral is represented by the system of two equations

$$z = \sqrt{1 + a^2}\,f(x) + ay + \phi(a), \qquad y + \phi'(a) + \frac{a}{\sqrt{1 + a^2}}\,f(x) = 0,$$

which permit the expression of y and z in terms of x and of the auxiliary parameter a. The reader will verify without difficulty that this solution differs only in notation from that which has been given.

4. The equation $rt - s^2 + a^2 = 0$ which arises in the mechanical theory of heat, has two systems of characteristics whose differential equations are respectively

$$\text{(I)} \begin{cases} dz - p\,dx - q\,dy = 0, \\ dp + a\,dy = 0, \\ dq - a\,dx = 0; \end{cases} \qquad \text{(II)} \begin{cases} dz - p\,dx - q\,dy = 0, \\ dp - a\,dy = 0, \\ dq + a\,dx = 0. \end{cases}$$

We notice at once two integrable combinations for each of these systems, and consequently two intermediate integrals, which we shall write as

$$q - ax = \phi'(p + ay), \qquad q + ax = \psi'(p - ay),$$

ϕ and ψ being arbitrary functions. Applying the method explained at the close of the preceding paragraph, let us set $p + ay = \alpha$, $p - ay = \beta$; we then derive from the preceding equations

$$x = \frac{\psi'(\beta) - \phi'(\alpha)}{2a}, y = \frac{\alpha - \beta}{2a}, p = \frac{\alpha + \beta}{2}, q = \frac{\phi'(\alpha) + \psi'(\beta)}{2},$$

and putting these values of x, y, p, q into $dz = p\,dx + q\,dy$, we get

$$dz = \frac{\alpha + \beta}{4a}(d\psi' - d\phi') + \frac{\phi' + \psi'}{4a}(d\alpha - d\beta)$$

$$= \frac{\phi' + \psi' - (\alpha + \beta)\,\phi''(\alpha)}{4a}\,d\alpha$$

$$+ \frac{(\alpha + \beta)\,\psi''(\beta) - \phi'(\alpha) - \psi'(\beta)}{4a}\,d\beta.$$

From this we deduce by integration by parts

$$z = \frac{[\phi'(\alpha) + \psi'(\beta)]\,(\alpha - \beta)}{4a} - \frac{1}{2a}\int \alpha\phi''(\alpha)\,d\alpha + \frac{1}{2a}\int \beta\psi''(\beta)\,d\beta,$$

and finally

$$z = \frac{(\alpha + \beta)\,[\psi'(\beta) - \phi'(\alpha)] + 2\phi(\alpha) - 2\psi(\beta)}{4a}.$$

We thus have expressions for x, y, z as functions of two variable parameters α and β, and the arbitrary functions $\phi(\alpha)$ and $\psi(\beta)$.

5. Let us again consider the equation $s = kpz$, which we can write as

$$\frac{\partial q}{\partial x} = \tfrac{1}{2}\,k\,\frac{\partial z^2}{\partial x},$$

and which has consequently the intermediate integral

(26)
$$\frac{\partial z}{\partial y} - \frac{kz^2}{2} = \phi(y),$$

ϕ being an arbitrary function. We can put this function ϕ in such a form that the general integral of Riccati's equation (26) is obtained explicitly. We know, indeed, that this general integral is a rational function of first degree of the constant of integration, which here is an arbitrary function of x; it is therefore of the form

$$z = \Theta_1(y) + \frac{\Theta_2(y)}{X + \Theta_3(y)},$$

Θ_1, Θ_2, Θ_3 being definite functions of y and X an arbitrary function of x. It will suffice to choose the functions Θ_1, Θ_2, Θ_3 in such a way that the first member of equation (26) does not contain X in order for z to be the general integral of an equation of this form (26). We thus find the conditions

$$\Theta'_2 - k\Theta_1\Theta_2 = 0, \qquad 2\Theta_2\Theta'_3 + k\Theta_2{}^2 = 0,$$

which permit us to express Θ_2 and Θ_1 in terms of Θ_3, Θ'_3, Θ''_3. Setting $\Theta_3 = Y$, we get $\Theta_2 = -(2/k)Y'$, then $\Theta_1 = (1/k)(Y''/Y')$, and the general integral of the equation $s = kpz$ consequently is

(27)
$$z = \frac{1}{k}\frac{Y''}{Y'} - \frac{2Y'}{k(X + Y)},$$

X and Y being arbitrary functions of x and y, respectively.

6. Liouville's equation $s = e^{kz}$ is reducible to the preceding. Indeed let us consider the system of two simultaneous equations

$$\frac{\partial u}{\partial y} = z, \qquad \frac{\partial z}{\partial x} = e^{ku}.$$

The elimination of u leads to the equation $s = kpz$, while the elimination of z leads to the equation $\partial^2 u / \partial x \partial y = e^{ku}$. We conclude from this that the general integral of this last equation is given by the formula

$$(28) \qquad e^{ku} = \frac{2X'Y'}{k(X + Y)^2},$$

whose second member is the derivative with respect to x of the second member of formula (27).

7. When the second order equation does not have any intermediate integral depending upon an arbitrary function, we cannot find the general integral by this method. But if the differential equations of one of the systems of characteristics have *one* integrable combination $dU = 0$, we obtain integrals depending upon an arbitrary function by integrating the first order equation $U = C$. Let us suppose, for example, that in the linear equation in r, s, t,

$$(29) \qquad Hr + 2Ks + Lt = 0,$$

H, K, L depend only upon the variables p, q. From equations (14) and (15), which define the characteristics, we deduce that all along a characteristic we have the relation

$$H\,dp^2 + 2K\,dp\,dq + L\,dq^2 = 0;$$

for each system of characteristics, we have a differential equation of the form

$$\lambda_1 dp + \mu_1 dq = 0, \qquad \lambda_2 dp + \mu_2 dq = 0,$$

λ_1, μ_1, λ_2, μ_2 depending only upon p and q. Each of these systems therefore has an integrable combination $d[u_1(p, q)] = 0$, $d[u_2(p, q)] = 0$ and consequently equation (29) has the integrals of the two first order equations

$$u_1(p, q) = C_1, \qquad u_2(p, q) = C_2;$$

these integral surfaces are developable (II, 2, **80**).

In his works on the rectilinear motion of gases, Hugoniot[8] (see below, III, **36**) has been led to look for an integral of an equation of the form (29), tangent to the plane $z = 0$ all along a curve. The theory of characteristics easily provides the solution of this problem. The curve of contact L is necessarily a characteristic curve lying on the solution $z = 0$, and therefore this curve is an integral of the differential equation

$$H(0, 0) \, dy^2 - 2 \, K(0, 0) \, dx \, dy + L(0, 0) \, dx^2 = 0,$$

since we also have $p = q = 0$ at every point of the integral $z = 0$. This curve is therefore a straight line D. This being granted, let S be an integral surface tangent to the xy-plane all along D; this surface is generated by the characteristics of the system different from the one to which D belongs, coming from different points of D. If $du_1 = 0$ is an integrable combination of the differential equations of this system, $u_1(p, q)$ is constant all along each of these characteristics, and consequently is equal to $u_1(0, 0)$ at all points of S. It follows that the surface S is an integral of the first order equation $u_1(p, q) = u_1(0, 0)$, and conversely, every integral surface of this equation is a solution of the problem, provided that it is tangent to the xy-plane. To resolve the question, we must be given one further condition, for example to require the surface sought for to pass through a curve which, naturally, must be tangent to the xy plane. The problem then reduces to the determination of a developable surface passing through a given curve, and having as its directrix cone a given cone. We shall obtain this surface by taking for each tangent to the curve a plane parallel to a tangent plane to the directrix cone (II, 2, **81**).

We would obtain another family of solutions by starting from the first order equation $u_2(p, q) = u_2(0, 0)$.

II. LAPLACE'S METHOD. CLASSIFICATION OF LINEAR EQUATIONS

21. Intermediate integrals of a linear equation. The two systems of characteristics of the equation

$$(30) \qquad\qquad s + ap + bq + cz + g = 0,$$

where a, b, c, g are functions of x, y, are always distinct, and their

[8] *Journal de l'École Polytechnique*, Vol. 33, Official Reports 57 and 58, 1887.

differential equations are respectively

$(31)_1$
$$\begin{cases} dz - p\,dx - q\,dy = 0, \quad dx = 0, \\ dp + (ap + bq + cz + g)\,dy = 0, \end{cases}$$

$(31)_2$
$$\begin{cases} dz - p\,dx - q\,dy = 0, \quad dy = 0, \\ dq + (ap + bq + cz + g)\,dx = 0. \end{cases}$$

Each of these systems has an integrable combination $dx = 0$ or $dy = 0$; in order that there be an intermediate integral, it is necessary and sufficient that one of them possess a second integrable combination. According to a general proposition stated above (III, **19**) and easy to verify in the present case, in order that the relation $dV = 0$ be a consequence of equations (31), for example, the function V must satisfy the two conditions

$$\frac{\partial V}{\partial p} = 0, \qquad \frac{\partial V}{\partial x} + \frac{\partial V}{\partial z}p - \frac{\partial V}{\partial q}(ap + bq + cz + g) = 0.$$

The first shows that V must be independent of p, and therefore it will be necessary that the coefficient of p and the term independent of p be zero separately in the second relation; this permits us to replace the preceding system by the system

$$(32) \qquad A(V) = \frac{\partial V}{\partial x} - (bq + cz + g)\frac{\partial V}{\partial q} = 0,$$

$$B(V) = \frac{\partial V}{\partial z} - a\frac{\partial V}{\partial q} = 0,$$

where V is an unknown function of x, y, z, q. This system already has the solution $V = y$; in order for it to have another solution, not reducing to a function of y, it is necessary and sufficient that it be a Jacobian system (II, 2, **89**); that is, that we have identically $A[B(V)] = B[A(V)]$, where $A(a) = B(bq + cz + g)$. This condition is reducible to $(\partial a/\partial x) + ab - c = 0$.

Without the necessity of integrating system (32), we can see directly that this condition is sufficient for the existence of an intermediate integral, for the equation under consideration, (30), can always be written

$$(33) \qquad \frac{\partial}{\partial x}\left(\frac{\partial z}{\partial y} + az\right) + b\left(\frac{\partial z}{\partial y} + az\right) - \left(\frac{\partial a}{\partial x} + ab - c\right)z + g = 0.$$

When $(\partial a/\partial x) + ab - c$ is zero, equation (33) reduces to a linear equation of the first order

$$(34) \qquad \frac{\partial u}{\partial x} + bu + g = 0,$$

where we have taken $u = (\partial z/\partial y) + az$ as an auxiliary unknown. The general integral of equation (34)

$$u = e^{-\int b \, dx} \left[Y - \int g \, e^{\int b \, dx} \, dx \right]$$

leads us then to an intermediate integral of equation (30)

$$(35) \qquad \frac{\partial z}{\partial y} + az = e^{-\int b \, dx} \left[Y - \int g \, e^{\int b \, dx} \, dx \right],$$

where Y is an arbitrary function of y. This first order equation can in turn be integrated as an ordinary differential equation in which y is the independent variable, and the general integral of equation (30) is represented by the formula

$$e^{\int a \, dy} \, z = X + \int e^{\int a \, dy - \int b \, dx} \left[Y - \int g \, e^{\int b \, dx} \, dx \right] dy,$$

X being an arbitrary function of x. We see that this integral is of the form

$$(36) \qquad z = \alpha X + \beta + \int \gamma \, Y \, dy,$$

α, β, γ being determinate functions of x and y; one of the arbitrary functions X occurs here explicitly, while the second arbitrary function Y is involved under the integral sign.

Interchanging the role of the variables x and y, we shall see similarly that there is an intermediate integral when $(\partial b/\partial y) + ab - c$ is zero. The general integral is represented by a formula analogous to formula (36), which would be derived from it by permuting x and y, X and Y.

The two expressions $h = (\partial a/\partial x) + ab - c$, $k = (\partial b/\partial y) + ab - c$ are called the *invariants* of equation (30); it is easily verified that these invariants do not change when we make a change of the unknowns such that $c = \lambda(x, y)z'$ for any function $\lambda(x, y)$. The result we have just established may be stated thus: *In order that equation* (30) *have an intermediate integral, it is necessary and sufficient that one of the invariants* h *or* k *be zero.*

Example. Let us take the equation $(x - y)s - q = 0$, for which the invariant h is zero; it has the intermediate integral $q = Y(x - y)$, and consequently the general integral has as its expression

$$z = X + \int Y(x - y) \, dy.$$

In order to dispense entirely with integral signs, it is enough to replace the arbitrary function Y by the second derivative Y'' of an arbitrary function, which gives us as the general integral an entirely explicit form

$$z = X + Y + (x - y)Y'.$$

Remark. It may happen that the two invariants h and k are simultaneously zero. If this is so, we have $(\partial a/\partial x) = (\partial b/\partial y)$ and a and b are the partial derivatives of a function $\lambda(x, y)$, $a = (\partial\lambda/\partial y)$, $b = (\partial\lambda/\partial x)$, and in addition we have

$$c = \frac{\partial^2\lambda}{\partial x \, \partial y} + \frac{\partial\lambda}{\partial x} \frac{\partial\lambda}{\partial y}.$$

Setting $z = e^{-\lambda}u$, equation (30) reduces to an equation whose integration is immediate: $(\partial^2 u/\partial x \partial y) + g(x, y)e^\lambda = 0$.

22. Laplace transformations.

If neither of the invariants h and k is zero, equation (30) does not have an intermediate integral. Laplace[9] made known a method of transformation which permits us to integrate the equation in an unlimited number of new cases. Let us suppose, for the sake of definiteness, that $h \neq 0$. Then upon setting

$$(37) \qquad \frac{\partial z}{\partial y} + az = z_1,$$

[9] *Recherches sur le calcul intégral aux différences partielles* (Mémoires de l'Académie, 1773). We are indicating only the principle of the method, and we shall refer the reader desirous of thoroughly examining this subject to the excellent chapters which M. Darboux has devoted to it (*Leçons sur la Théorie générale des surfaces*, Vol. II).

we have already seen that equation (30) can be written as

(38)
$$\frac{\partial z_1}{\partial x} + b z_1 + g = h z.$$

Let us consider equations (37) and (38) as a system of two simultaneous equations in the two unknowns z and z_1. Elimination of z_1 clearly leads to equation (30), which we shall henceforth call *equation* (E). On the other hand, upon eliminating z we are led to an equation of the form (E$_1$), where the unknown is z_1

(E$_1$)
$$\frac{\partial^2 z_1}{\partial x \, \partial y} + a_1 \frac{\partial z_1}{\partial x} + b_1 \frac{\partial z_1}{\partial y} + c_1 z_1 + g_1 = 0,$$

the coefficients a_1, b_1, c_1, and g_1 having the values below:

(39)
$$\begin{cases} a_1 = a - \dfrac{\partial \log h}{\partial y}, \quad b_1 = b, \quad c_1 = c - \dfrac{\partial a}{\partial x} + \dfrac{\partial b}{\partial y} - b \dfrac{\partial \log h}{\partial y}, \\[2mm] \qquad\qquad g_1 = g \left(a - \dfrac{\partial \log h}{\partial y} \right) + \dfrac{\partial g}{\partial y}. \end{cases}$$

It is clear that the integration of equation (E$_1$) and that of equation (E) constitute two equivalent problems, for formulas (37) and (38) provide a one-to-one correspondence between the integrals of the two equations. Now the invariants h_1 and k_1 of (E$_1$) have for their values, as an easy calculation shows,

(40)
$$\begin{cases} h_1 = \dfrac{\partial a_1}{\partial x} + a_1 b_1 - c_1 = 2h - k - \dfrac{\partial^2 \log h}{\partial x \, \partial y}, \\[2mm] k_1 = \dfrac{\partial b_1}{\partial y} + a_1 b_1 - c_1 = h; \end{cases}$$

k_1 cannot be zero since we have supposed $h \neq 0$, but it may happen that h_1 is zero without either of the invariants h and k being zero. If this is so, equation (E$_1$) has an intermediate integral and the general integral is represented by a formula such as (36), with two arbitrary functions X and Y. According to formula (38), we can derive from it an expression for the general integral of (E) of the form

$$z = A_0 X + A_1 X' + B + \int C Y \, dy,$$

A_0, A_1, B, C being definite functions of x and y, and X' being the derivative of X.

Entirely in the same way, if the invariant k is not zero, the two simultaneous equations

$$(41) \qquad \frac{\partial z}{\partial x} + bz = z_{-1}, \qquad \frac{\partial z_{-1}}{\partial y} + az_{-1} + g = kz$$

will lead, by the elimination of z_{-1}, to equation (E) itself, and, by elimination of z, to a new equation (E_{-1})

$$(E_{-1}) \qquad \frac{\partial^2 z_{-1}}{\partial x \, \partial y} + a_{-1} \frac{\partial z_{-1}}{\partial x} + b_{-1} \frac{\partial z_{-1}}{\partial y} + c_{-1} z_{-1} + g_{-1} = 0,$$

with the following expressions for a_{-1}, b_{-1}, c_{-1}, g_{-1}:

$$(42) \quad \begin{cases} a_{-1} = a, \qquad b_{-1} = b - \dfrac{\partial \log k}{\partial x}, \\[2mm] \quad c_{-1} = c - \dfrac{\partial b}{\partial y} + \dfrac{\partial a}{\partial x} - a \dfrac{\partial \log k}{\partial x}, \\[2mm] \quad g_{-1} = g \left(b - \dfrac{\partial \log k}{\partial x} \right) + \dfrac{\partial g}{\partial x}. \end{cases}$$

The invariants of (E_{-1}) are respectively

$$(43) \qquad h_{-1} = k, \qquad k_{-1} = 2k - h - \frac{\partial^2 \log k}{\partial x \, \partial y}.$$

If the invariant k_{-1} is zero, we shall be able to integrate the equation (E_{-1}) and consequently equation (E).

When any of the invariants h_{-1}, k_{-1} is not equal to zero, we cannot integrate equation (E) in this way; we can then apply the same transformations to the two equations (E_1), (E_{-1}), but it is to be noticed that each of these will not give rise to two new equations. Let us take for example equation (E_1), and let us apply to it the second Laplace transformation by setting

$$z' = \frac{\partial z_1}{\partial x} + b_1 z_1 = \frac{\partial z_1}{\partial x} + bz_1.$$

Referring back to formula (38) we see that we shall have

$z' = hz - g$, so that the equation obtained in z' reduces, by a simple transformation, to equation (E) itself. The first transformation applied to (E$_{-1}$) will lead similarly to an equation which differs from (E) only by a very simple change of variable. As far as integration is concerned, it is clear that these equations can be considered as identical. Therefore, the repeated application of Laplace's method will only lead to a linear sequence of equations

$$\ldots (E_{-2}), (E_{-1}), (E), (E_1), (E_2), \ldots$$

with positive and negative indices, in which each equation (E$_i$), where $i > 0$ is derived from (E$_{i-1}$) by the first transformation and where each equation (E$_{-j}$) where $j > 0$ is derived from (E$_{1-j}$) by the second. The sequence of equations with positive index can be extended so long as we do not come to an equation (E$_i$) for which h_i is zero. If we do come, after i transformations, to an equation (E$_i$) for which $h_i = 0$, this equation is integrable, and, going back step by step, we can derive from it the general integral of the equations (E$_{i-1}$), (E$_{i-2}$), . . ., up to equation (E). The same will be true if we come to an equation (E$_{-j}$) for which the invariant k_{-j} is zero, by applying j times the second Laplace transformation.

Example. Let us apply the method to the equation

$$(x - y)s + p - q = 0,$$

which does not have an intermediate integral. Let us set

$$z_1 = \frac{\partial z}{\partial y} + \frac{z}{x - y};$$

the equation becomes

$$\frac{\partial z_1}{\partial x} - \frac{z_1}{x - y} + \frac{2z}{(x - y)^2} = 0,$$

and the elimination of z leads to an equation in z_1

$$\frac{\partial^2 z_1}{\partial x \, \partial y} - \frac{\dfrac{\partial z_1}{\partial x} + \dfrac{\partial z_1}{\partial y}}{x - y} = \frac{2z_1}{(x - y)^2} = 0.$$

This new equation is integrable, for we can write it as

$$\frac{\partial}{\partial x}\left(\frac{\partial z_1}{\partial y} - \frac{z_1}{x - y}\right) - \frac{1}{x - y}\left(\frac{\partial z_1}{\partial y} - \frac{z_1}{x - y}\right) = 0,$$

and we deduce from this that it has the intermediate integral

$$\frac{\partial z_1}{\partial y} - \frac{z_1}{x - y} = Y(x - y),$$

Y being an arbitrary function of y. The general integral is therefore

$$z_1 = \frac{2X + \displaystyle\int Y(x - y)^2 \, dy}{x - y};$$

in order to dispense altogether with the integral sign, it is sufficient to replace Y by Y'', which yields

$$z_1 = 2\frac{X + Y}{x - y} + 2\,Y' + (x - y)Y''.$$

Finally, we have as the general integral of the equation in z

$$z = (x - y)\,(Y' - X') + 2X + 2Y.$$

Laplace's method is only a particular application of a more general method, due to G. Darboux, who extends it to all second order equations in two independent variables. Despite all the interest of this method, equations whose integration it permits form a very special class, and second order equations capable of formal integration are exceptional. Also, instead of looking for the general integral, we seek chiefly to determine particular integrals satisfying given conditions, sufficient to determine them. These conditions, borrowed most often from problems of mathematical physics, are very different, according as the characteristics are real or imaginary. This fact leads us to indicate a classification of second order equations based on this property.

23. The three types of linear equations. Let us consider in particular an equation of the form

(44) $Ar + 2Bs + Ct + F(x, y, z, p, q) = 0,$

the coefficients A, B, C depending only upon the independent variables x and y. On every integral surface, the two families of characteristic curves are obtained by the integration of the differential equation

$$(45) \qquad A\,dy^2 - 2B\,dx\,dy + C\,dx^2 = 0,$$

which is independent of the integral under consideration. These curves are therefore projected onto the xy-plane as the two families of curves which satisfy the first order, second degree equation (45). Conversely, every curve of this type is the projection on the xy-plane of an infinity of characteristics of equation (30).

Indeed, equation (45) decomposes into two equations of the first order and of first degree

$$(45)_1 \qquad\qquad a_1 dy + b_1 dx = 0,$$

$$(45)_2 \qquad\qquad a_2 dy + b_2 dx = 0,$$

a_1, b_1, a_2, b_2 being functions of x and y, each one of which belongs to one of the systems of characteristics. Let us consider in particular one of these systems defined by the three equations

$$dz = p\,dx + q\,dy, \quad a_1 dy + b_1 dx = 0, \quad E\,dp + G\,dq + H\,dx = 0,$$

E, G, H being functions of x, y, z, p, q whose precise expression it is unnecessary to write. Let Γ be a space curve which projects on the xy-plane as a curve C along which we have

$$a_1 dy + b_1 dx = 0;$$

x, y, z being known functions of a parameter α, the relation $dz = p\,dx + q\,dy$ permits the expression of one of the two unknowns, say p, as a function of q and of α. Putting these values of x, y, z, p into the last equation

$$E\,dp + G\,dq + H\,dx = 0,$$

we arrive at a first order differential equation for the determination of q. We see therefore that the curve Γ belongs in general to an infinity of characteristic manifolds of equation (44), depending upon an arbitrary constant. We shall often for brevity call the two families of plane curves in the xy-plane, defined by the differential equation (45), *the characteristic curves of equation* (44); it is an abbreviated expression whose meaning can present no ambiguity.

When the coefficients A, B, C are real functions of the real variables x and y, we are led to introduce the following distinction. If $B^2 - AC$ is *positive*, the two families of characteristics are real and distinct; equation (44) is the *hyperbolic type*. If $B^2 - AC$ is *negative*, the two families of characteristics are imaginary; equation (44) is the *elliptic type*. Finally, if $B^2 - AC$ is *zero*, there is only one family of characteristics, and it is real; the equation belongs to the *parabolic type*. It is evident that the same equation can belong to different types depending upon the plane region being considered.

The two families of characteristics being assumed distinct, let $\xi(x, y) = \text{const.}$, $\eta(x, y) = \text{const.}$, be the formulas which represent the general integral of equations $(45)_1$ and $(45)_2$, respectively; $\xi(x, y)$ and $\eta(x, y)$ satisfy respectively the two equations

$$a_1 \frac{\partial \xi}{\partial x} - b_1 \frac{\partial \xi}{\partial y} = 0, \qquad a_2 \frac{\partial \eta}{\partial x} - b_2 \frac{\partial \eta}{\partial y} = 0,$$

and consequently are the integrals of the first order equation

$$(46) \qquad A \left(\frac{\partial f}{\partial x} \right)^2 + 2B \frac{\partial f}{\partial x} \frac{\partial f}{\partial y} + C \left(\frac{\partial f}{\partial y} \right)^2 = 0.$$

This granted, let us suppose that we take $\xi(x, y)$ and $\eta(x, y)$ as new independent variables; equation (44) is transformed into a new equation of the same form

$$(47) \qquad A_1 \frac{\partial^2 z}{\partial \xi^2} + 2B_1 \frac{\partial^2 z}{\partial \xi \, \partial \eta} + C_1 \frac{\partial^2 z}{\partial \eta^2} + F_1 \left(\xi, \eta, z, \frac{\partial z}{\partial \xi}, \frac{\partial z}{\partial \eta} \right) = 0,$$

whose characteristics are the integral curves of the differential equation

$$A_1 \, d\eta^2 - 2B_1 \, d\xi \, d\eta + C_1 \, d\xi^2 = 0.$$

Now, according to the very definition of characteristic manifolds (III, **17**), it is clear that the characteristics of the new equation (47) correspond to the characteristics of the first. They are therefore the two families of lines $\xi = \text{const.}$, $\eta = \text{const.}$, and we have $A_1 = C_1 = 0$, so that equation (47) contains only the second order derivative $\partial^2 z / \partial \xi \, \partial \eta$. We say then that *the equation is referred to these characteristics*.

When equation (44) is of parabolic type, we shall take for $\xi(x, y)$ an integral of equation (46), the second variable $\eta(x, y)$ being any function whatever distinct from ξ. The new equation ought to have only one system of characteristics, composed of the lines $\xi = \text{const.}$ The two coefficients A_1 and B_1 must therefore be zero, and equation (47) contains only one second order derivative, $(\partial^2 z / \partial \eta^2)$. These results, which the general theory of characteristics makes intuitive,

are easy to verify by computation. Indeed, we find according to the
general formulas of change of variable that the coefficients A_1, B_1, C_1
have the following values, whatever the functions $\xi(x, y)$, $\eta(x, y)$:

$$(48) \quad \begin{cases} A_1 = A \left(\dfrac{\partial \xi}{\partial x}\right)^2 + 2B \dfrac{\partial \xi}{\partial x} \dfrac{\partial \xi}{\partial y} + C \left(\dfrac{\partial \xi}{\partial y}\right)^2, \\[2mm] B_1 = A \dfrac{\partial \xi}{\partial x} \dfrac{\partial \eta}{\partial x} + B \left(\dfrac{\partial \xi}{\partial x} \dfrac{\partial \eta}{\partial y} + \dfrac{\partial \xi}{\partial y} \dfrac{\partial \eta}{\partial x}\right) + C \dfrac{\partial \xi}{\partial y} \dfrac{\partial \eta}{\partial y}, \\[2mm] C_1 = A \left(\dfrac{\partial \eta}{\partial x}\right)^2 + 2B \dfrac{\partial \eta}{\partial x} \dfrac{\partial \eta}{\partial y} + C \left(\dfrac{\partial \eta}{\partial y}\right)^2; \end{cases}$$

the coefficients A_1 and C_1 are indeed zero when we take for ξ, η two
distinct integrals of equation (46). If $B^2 - AC = 0$, equation (46)
can be written in the two equivalent forms

$$A \frac{\partial f}{\partial x} + B \frac{\partial f}{\partial y} = 0, \qquad B \frac{\partial f}{\partial x} + C \frac{\partial f}{\partial y} = 0,$$

and A_1 and B_1 will be zero, provided that ξ is an integral of this
equation.

When equation (44) belongs to the elliptic type, the preceding
transformation introduces two conjugate imaginary variables
$\xi(x, y)$ and $\eta(x, y)$. If we wish to employ only real transformations
and real variables, it suffices to take in place of ξ, η the two real
variables $X = \xi + \eta$, $Y = (\xi - \eta)/i$, which replace $\partial^2 z / \partial \xi \partial \eta$ by
$\partial^2 z / \partial X^2 + \partial^2 z / \partial Y^2$. To sum up, every equation of the form (44)
whose coefficients A, B, C are real, can be reduced, by a suitable
choice of real variables, to one of the three following canonical
forms, each one of which belongs to a particular type:[10]

[10] We can get directly the canonical form which belongs to the elliptic
type without employing any imaginaries. Indeed, if we take as new variables
two functions $\xi(x, y)$, $\eta(x, y)$ satisfying the two equations

$$(E) \quad \frac{\partial \xi}{\partial x} = -\frac{B}{A} \frac{\partial \xi}{\partial y} - \frac{\sqrt{AC - B^2}}{A} \frac{\partial \eta}{\partial y}, \quad \frac{\partial \eta}{\partial x} = \frac{\sqrt{AC - B^2}}{A} \frac{\partial \xi}{\partial y} - \frac{B}{A} \frac{\partial \eta}{\partial y},$$

we find a transformed equation in which, it is easy to verify, we have $A_1 = C_1$,
$B_1 = 0$. But the integration of this system amounts basically to that of the
equation

$$\frac{\partial(\xi + i\eta)}{\partial x} = \left(\frac{-B + i\sqrt{AC - B^2}}{A}\right) \frac{\partial(\xi + i\eta)}{\partial y},$$

which is equivalent to equation (46).

$$(H) \qquad \frac{\partial^2 z}{\partial \xi \, \partial \eta} + f\left(\xi, \eta, z, \frac{\partial z}{\partial \xi}, \frac{\partial z}{\partial \eta}\right) = 0 \quad \text{(hyperbolic type)};$$

$$(E) \qquad \frac{\partial^2 z}{\partial \xi^2} + \frac{\partial^2 z}{\partial \eta^2} + f\left(\xi, \eta, z, \frac{\partial z}{\partial \xi}, \frac{\partial z}{\partial \eta}\right) = 0 \quad \text{(elliptic type)};$$

$$(P) \qquad \frac{\partial^2 z}{\partial \eta^2} + f\left(\xi, \eta, z, \frac{\partial z}{\partial \xi}, \frac{\partial z}{\partial \eta}\right) = 0 \quad \text{(parabolic type)}.$$

When equation (44) is *completely linear*, that is to say, linear with respect to z and all its derivatives, the same is true of the transformed equation (47), whatever the new variables ξ, η may be. The three canonical forms are therefore the following:

$$\frac{\partial^2 z}{\partial \xi \, \partial \eta} + a\frac{\partial z}{\partial \xi} + b\frac{\partial z}{\partial \eta} + cz + g = 0,$$

$$\frac{\partial^2 z}{\partial \xi^2} + \frac{\partial^2 z}{\partial \eta^2} + a\frac{\partial z}{\partial \xi} + b\frac{\partial z}{\partial \eta} + cz + g = 0,$$

$$\frac{\partial^2 z}{\partial \eta^2} + a\frac{\partial z}{\partial \xi} + b\frac{\partial z}{\partial \eta} + cz + g = 0,$$

a, b, c, g being functions of the variables ξ, η alone. The second form reduces to the first, if we introduce complex variables.

Examples: 1. The equation $rx^2 - ty^2 = 0$ is the hyperbolic type; the characteristics project on the xy-plane as the two families of curves $xy = C$, $y/x = C'$. Let us take for new variables $\xi = xy$, $\eta = y/x$; we have

$$p = y\frac{\partial z}{\partial \xi} - \frac{y}{x^2}\frac{\partial z}{\partial \eta}, \qquad q = x\frac{\partial z}{\partial \xi} + \frac{1}{x}\frac{\partial z}{\partial \eta},$$

$$r = y^2\frac{\partial^2 z}{\partial \xi^2} - 2\frac{y^2}{x^2}\frac{\partial^2 z}{\partial \xi \, \partial \eta} + \frac{y^2}{x^4}\frac{\partial^2 z}{\partial \eta^2} + \frac{2y}{x^3}\frac{\partial z}{\partial \eta},$$

$$t = x^2\frac{\partial^2 z}{\partial \xi^2} + 2\frac{\partial^2 z}{\partial \xi \, \partial \eta} + \frac{\partial^2 z}{\partial \eta^2}\frac{1}{x^2}.$$

The equation under consideration is changed into an equation where the two invariants h and k are zero (III, **21**), and whose integration is easy,

$$2\xi \frac{\partial^2 z}{\partial \xi \, \partial \eta} - \frac{\partial z}{\partial \eta} = 0.$$

2. The equation $ry^2 + tx^2 = 0$ belongs to the elliptic type; the integral curves of the equation $y^2 dy^2 + x^2 dx^2 = 0$ are imaginary. Setting $x^2 = \xi$, $y^2 = \eta$, the equation becomes

$$\frac{\partial^2 z}{\partial \xi^2} + \frac{\partial^2 z}{\partial \eta^2} + \frac{1}{2} \left(\frac{1}{\xi} \frac{\partial z}{\partial \xi} + \frac{1}{\eta} \frac{\partial z}{\partial \eta} \right) = 0.$$

24. Study of Cauchy's problem in a special case. The distinction between hyperbolic and elliptic equations can evidently be extended to equations of the second order of any form whatever, according to the nature of the characteristics. This distinction does not occur in the investigation of intermediate integrals; but, in the elliptic case, all the reasoning based on the theory of characteristics implicitly assumes that we are dealing with analytic integrals. It is to be observed, moreover, that the formulas, almost identical in appearance, can have entirely different interpretations, according to the type of equation to which they refer. In order to make this essential point very clear, we are going to study Cauchy's problem for the two equations $s = 0$, $r + t = 0$.

Let us take first of all the equation $s = 0$. Let M_1 be a manifold defined by the five *real* functions $x = f_1(\alpha)$, $y = f_2(\alpha)$, $z = f_3(\alpha)$, $p = \phi_1(\alpha)$, $q = \phi_2(\alpha)$ of the variable α, satisfying the relation $f'_3(\alpha) = \phi_1(\alpha) f'_1(\alpha) + \phi_2(\alpha) f'_2(\alpha)$. The equation $s = 0$ has two intermediate integrals $p = \psi(x)$, $q = \pi(y)$ and, in order to get the integral which includes all the elements of M_1, we must first determine the arbitrary functions ψ and π by the two conditions

$$\phi_1(\alpha) = \psi[f_1(\alpha)], \qquad \phi_2(\alpha) = \pi[f_2(\alpha)];$$

these functions being determined, the desired integral has for its expression

$$z = z_0 + \int_{x_0}^{x} \psi(x) \, dx - \int_{y_0}^{y} \pi(y) \, dy,$$

x_0, y_0, z_0 being the coordinates of a point on the given curve, corresponding to the value α_0 of the parameter. Let us make the change of variables

(49) $x = f_1(u), \qquad y = f_2(v);$

the expression for z becomes, in view of the relations which determine the functions ψ and π,

$$(50) \qquad z = z_0 + \int_{\alpha_0}^{u} \phi_1(u) f'_1(u)\,du + \int_{\alpha_0}^{v} \phi_2(v) f'_2(v)\,dv.$$

The coordinates x, y, z of a point of the surface sought for are thus expressed in terms of two parameters u and v by formulas (49) and (50). By assuming $v = u$, we indeed return to the given curve.

Let us set ourselves the same problem for Laplace's equation $r + t = 0$, the given data being the same. Taking as new variables $\xi = x + iy$, $\eta = x - iy$, we have $\partial z/\partial \xi = p_1 = (p - iq)/2$, $\partial z/\partial \eta = q_1 = (p + iq)/2$, and the equation becomes $\partial^2 z/\partial \xi \partial \eta = 0$. As to the manifold M_1, it is replaced by a new manifold M'_1, defined by the relations

$$\xi = f_1(\alpha) + i f_2(\alpha), \qquad \eta = f_1(\alpha) - i f_2(\alpha),$$

$$p_1 = \frac{\phi_1(\alpha) - i\,\phi_2(\alpha)}{2}, \quad q_1 = \frac{\phi_1(\alpha) + i\,\phi_2(\alpha)}{2}, \quad z = f_3(\alpha);$$

from the formulas just obtained we conclude that the integral of the equation $\partial^2 z/\partial \xi \partial \eta = 0$, containing all the elements of M'_1, is represented by the equations

$$\xi = f_1(u) + if_2(u), \qquad \eta = f_1(v) - if_2(v),$$

$$(51) \quad \begin{cases} z = z_0 + \dfrac{1}{2} \displaystyle\int_{\alpha_0}^{u} [\phi_1(u) - i\phi_2(u)]\,[f'_1(u) + if'_2(u)]\,du \\[2mm] \qquad + \dfrac{1}{2} \displaystyle\int_{\alpha_0}^{v} [\phi_1(v) + i\phi_2(v)]\,[f'_1(v) + if'_2(v)]\,dv. \end{cases}$$

Returning to the variables x, y, we obtain the following formulas to represent the integral of the equation $r + t = 0$, which has all the elements of the given manifold M_1:

$$(52) \quad \begin{cases} x = \dfrac{f_1(u) + f_1(v) + i[f_2(u) - f_2(v)]}{2}, \\[3mm] y = \dfrac{f_1(u) - f_1(v) + i[f_2(u) + f_2(v)]}{2i}, \end{cases}$$

the formula which gives z not being changed. For real values of the parameters u and v, x, y, and z have in general imaginary values; if we assign imaginary values to these parameters, formulas (51) and (52) have meaning only if the given functions f_1, f_2, ϕ_1, ϕ_2 are *analytic functions*. Let us suppose these functions holomorphic in a certain domain D of the plane of the complex variable α, containing a segment ab of the real axis, which corresponds to the given curve. These functions are represented, in the neighborhood of $\alpha = \alpha_0$, by a power series in $(\alpha - \alpha_0)$ with real coefficients, and therefore assume conjugate imaginary values for conjugate imaginary values of the variable in the domain D. In order that x, y, z be real, it will suffice to assign conjugate imaginary values to the parameters u and v, and the formulas which represent the integral can be written

$$
(53) \quad
\begin{cases}
x = \mathscr{R}[f_1(u) + if_2(u)], \qquad y = \mathscr{R}\left[\dfrac{f_1(u) + if_2(u)}{i}\right], \\[4mm]
z = z_0 + \mathscr{R}\left[\displaystyle\int_{\alpha_0}^{u} \{\phi_1(u) - i\phi_2(u)\}\{f'_1(u) + if'_2(u)\}\, du\right],
\end{cases}
$$

$\mathscr{R}(A)$ designating the real part of A, and the complex variable u describing the domain D. We see from this how many solutions of Cauchy's problems for the two equations which appear identical from the purely formal point of view, are in reality different. While formulas (49) and (50) simply suppose that the functions which are represented there are continuous and have continuous derivatives, formulas (51) and (52) have exact meaning only if the given functions f_i, ϕ_i are analytic functions, and in the final formulas (53), which represent the solution, the variable parameter u must assume complex values.

It is easy to be convinced that these conditions are not introduced by the mode of solution adopted, but that they stem from the very nature of the problem. Let C be a plane curve in the xy-plane, and D a domain containing this curve. If we are given the values of a function u and its partial derivatives $\partial u/\partial x$, $\partial u/\partial y$ along C, these values only being continuous and satisfying the relation

$$
du = \frac{\partial u}{\partial x}\, dx + \frac{\partial u}{\partial y}\, dy
$$

along this curve, there does not exist in general a solution of the Laplace equation $\Delta_2 u = 0$, continuous in D along with its derivatives of the first two orders, no matter how small this domain, and whose derivatives $\partial u/\partial x$, $\partial u/\partial y$ assume the given values on the curve C. Indeed, if such a solution existed, we should derive from it another function $v(x, y)$, satisfying the same conditions as $u(x, y)$ in D, and such that we have $\partial v/\partial x = -(\partial u/\partial y)$, $\partial v/\partial y = \partial u/\partial x$. The values of $\partial v/\partial x$, $\partial v/\partial y$ being known along C, this function $v(x, y)$ will itself be determined along C, with the exception of an additive constant; $u + iv$ will therefore be an analytic function holomorphic in the domain D of $x + iy$, the value of which will be known all along C. Now, we know that this function is completely determined if we know its value along an arc of C, however small. It then follows that the values of $\partial u/\partial x$ and of $\partial u/\partial y$ must be completely determined at any point whatever of C, if the values of these derivatives are known on a portion, however small, of this contour. It is clear that this condition will not be satisfied if the given functions for $\partial u/\partial x$, $\partial u/\partial y$ are only continuous. In reality, this is not the Cauchy problem set up for the equation $\Delta_2 u = 0$, but an entirely different problem, which will be studied later (Chap. V).

Exercises

1. Integrate the equations

$$x^2 r + 2xys + y^2 t = 0, \qquad \left(s + \frac{p - q}{x - y}\right)^2 = rt,$$

$$rt - s^2 + f'(x)pt = 0, \quad rt - s^2 = pqs, \quad qr + (zq - p)s - zpt = 0,$$

$$s = pq + e^z f(x, y), \qquad rxy + s(x^2 + y^2) + txy - py - qx = 0.$$

2. Find the surfaces whose lines of curvature of one of the systems are the plane curves whose planes pass through a fixed line (*Joachimsthal surfaces*), and the surfaces whose lines of curvature of one of the systems lie on concentric spheres (*Monge surfaces*).

3. Determine the functions $\lambda(x, y)$ such that the equation $r = \lambda^2 t$ is integrable by Monge's method.

4. Determine the Monge-Ampère equations for which the characteristics of one of the systems are asymptotic lines or lines of curvature of the integral surfaces (Lie).

Determine similarly the equations for which the two families of characteristics form a conjugate net on the integral surfaces.

5. *Minimal surfaces.* If we write the equation of the tangent plane to a surface in the form

$$(1 - \alpha\beta)X + i(1 + \alpha\beta)Y + (\alpha + \beta)Z + \xi(\alpha,\beta) = 0,$$

α and β being two variable parameters, in order that this surface have zero mean curvature, it is necessary and sufficient that we have (III, **22**)

$$(\alpha - \beta)\frac{\partial^2\xi}{\partial\alpha\,\partial\beta} + \frac{\partial\xi}{\partial\alpha} - \frac{\partial\xi}{\partial\beta} = 0.$$

Deduce from it the general equations of surfaces of zero mean curvature.

CHAPTER III

LINEAR EQUATIONS IN n VARIABLES

I. CLASSIFICATION OF EQUATIONS IN n VARIABLES

25. Characteristics of equations in n variables. The notion of characteristic can be extended to second order partial differential equations in any number of variables, and to equations of order higher than the second. We shall treat only the case of a second order equation in n variables, linear with respect to the second order derivatives

$$(1) \quad \sum a_{ik}p_{ik} + F(x_1, \ldots, x_n, z, p_1, \ldots, p_n) = 0, \qquad p_{ik} = \frac{\partial^2 z}{\partial x_i \partial x_k},$$

the coefficients a_{ik} depending only upon the variables $x_1, \ldots, x_n$. The Cauchy problem for this equation can be stated in the following manner: *Given in a space of* n *dimensions* $(x_1, x_2, \ldots, x_n)$ *a hypersurface* S *represented by the equation*

$$(2) \qquad \Phi(x_1, x_2, \ldots, x_n) = 0,$$

find an integral of equation (1), *knowing the values taken on by this integral and one of its first order partial derivatives along* S.

This problem is solved in general. Let us remark first of all that the values of the n partial derivatives p_i along S are not independent; if z and one of these derivatives are known at each point of S, we can derive from this the other first order partial derivatives by means of the identity $dz = \Sigma p_i \, dx_i$. Indeed, on the hypersurface S, x_1, $x_2, \ldots, x_n$ and z can be expressed in terms of the known functions of $n - 1$ parameters $u_1, u_2, \ldots, u_{n-1}$, and the preceding relation is equivalent to $n - 1$ distinct relations, which allow us to calculate the values of the n derivatives p_i if we know one of them.

Let us suppose for example that equation (2) for S can be solved for x_n; we can take for parameters

$$u_1 = x_1, \ldots, u_{n-1} = x_{n-1}.$$

Let $\pi(x_1, x_2, \ldots, x_{n-1})$ be the function to which z must reduce on this manifold. The $n - 1$ relations

$$\frac{\partial \pi}{\partial x_i} = p_i + p_n \frac{\partial x_n}{\partial x_i} \qquad (i = 1, 2, \ldots, n - 1)$$

permit us to express the $n - 1$ derivatives $p_1, p_2, \ldots, p_{n-1}$ in terms of the derivative p_n, which can be chosen arbitrarily along S.

When the functions a_{ik}, F, Φ are analytic functions of their arguments, we can take a new system of independent variables $(x'_1, \ldots, x'_n)$ in such a way that the equation of the hypersurface S become $x'_n = 0$ in this new system of variables. Equation (1) is replaced by an equation of the same form with analytical coefficients, and the proposed problem is reduced to the study of an integral of the new equation, which reduces for $x'_n = 0$ to a given function $f(x'_1, \ldots, x'_{n-1})$, while $\partial z / \partial x'_n$ reduces to another given function $\phi(x'_1, \ldots, x'_{n-1})$ of the same variables. These functions f and ϕ will also be analytic, if the data of the original problem are expressed by analytic conditions. If the coefficient of $\partial^2 z / \partial x'^2_n$ is not zero in the transformed equation, we can apply to this equation the general theorem (II, 2, **94**), and we conclude from it, returning to the first equation, that the Cauchy problem possesses an analytic solution holomorphic in the neighborhood of the hypersurface on which the given values lie. If, on the other hand, the coefficient a'_{nn} of $\partial^2 z / \partial x'^2_n$ is zero in the transformed equation, we can no longer apply the general existence theorem. Let us observe, without the necessity of making the calculation, that this coefficient a'_{nn} depends only upon the coefficients a_{ik} and the function Φ itself, but does not depend at all upon the given values on S. The hypersurfaces S, for which a'_{nn} is zero, are the *characteristics* of equation (1). These characteristic hypersurfaces are defined by a first order partial differential equation which we can form without making any changes of variables. Let us suppose, indeed, that we knew the values of z and its partial derivatives p_i at every point of the hypersurface (2), or, what amounts to the same thing, that we knew a system of $2n + 1$ functions x_i, p_k, z of $n - 1$ parameters, satisfying equation (2) and the relation $dz = \Sigma p_i \, dx_i$. In order to derive from this the values of the second order derivatives p_{ik}, at any point whatever of this manifold, we have the relations

$$(3) \qquad dp_i = p_{i1}dx_1 + \ldots + p_{ni}dx_n \qquad (i = 1, 2, \ldots, n)$$

and equation (1) itself. Let us suppose, for simplicity, that we have taken for parameters the $(n - 1)$ variables $x_1 \ldots, x_{n-1}$.

Relations (3) give us

$$\frac{\partial p_i}{\partial x_k} = p_{ik} + p_{in}\frac{\partial x_n}{\partial x_k}, \qquad \frac{\partial p_n}{\partial x_i} = p_{ni} + p_{nn}\frac{\partial x_n}{\partial x_i},$$

and consequently

$$p_{ik} = p_{nn}\frac{\partial x_n}{\partial x_i}\frac{\partial x_n}{\partial x_k} + \frac{\partial p_i}{\partial x_k} - \frac{\partial p_n}{\partial x_i}\frac{\partial x_n}{\partial x_k} \qquad (i, k = 1, 2, \ldots, n - 1).$$

Putting the values of the derivatives p_{ik}, p_{ni}, taken from these formulas, into equation (1), we obtain an equation of the first degree to determine p_{nn}

$$(4) \qquad\qquad Ap_{nn} + B = 0,$$

where the coefficient A has the expression

$$(5) \qquad A = \sum a_{ik}\frac{\partial x_n}{\partial x_i}\frac{\partial x_n}{\partial x_k} \qquad (i, k = 1, 2, \ldots, n),$$

on condition that we replace $\partial x_n/\partial x_n$ by (-1).

If A is not zero for the hypersurface considered, we obtain the values of the derivatives p_{ik} at each point of S, and, by passing on to derivatives of higher order, we verify step by step that all these derivatives can be calculated without ambiguity. We have the general case where Cauchy's problem has one and only one solution.

The situation is no longer the same if the hypersurface S satisfies the relation $A = 0$, which we can write in a more symmetric form

$$(6) \qquad \sum a_{ik}\frac{\partial \Phi}{\partial x_i}\frac{\partial \Phi}{\partial x_k} = 0 \qquad (i, k = 1, 2, \ldots, n),$$

supposing this manifold defined by equation (2). The hypersurface S is then a characteristic of the equation (1), and we can no longer apply the reasonings of the general case. When we have $A = 0$, $B = 0$ at the same time, the value of the derivative p_{nn} is indeterminate, and the Cauchy problem presents an indeterminate situation.

We have proved that this indeterminateness was variable when the functions a_{ik}, F, Φ, and the given values are analytic.[1]

Let us suppose the variables real, as well as the functions a_{ik}, F; in order that *real* characteristics exist, it is necessary that the first order equation (6) have real integrals. Now the first member is a quadratic form with respect to the derivatives of A, and therefore can be written in the form of a sum of n squares of linear functions of these derivatives multiplied by constant factors, when the discriminant Δ of the form $\Sigma a_{ik} u_i u_k$ is not zero. This leads to a classification of equations (1) based on the nature of the characteristics.

If the discriminant Δ of the quadratic form is not zero, and if all the coefficients of the squares are of the same sign, equation (6) possesses no real integral, other than $f = C$, and therefore there are no real characteristics for equation (1). We say that it belongs to the *elliptic* type.

If the discriminant Δ is not zero without all the coefficients of the squares having the same sign, equation (6) has real integrals, and there exist real characteristics for equation (1), which is said to be of the *hyperbolic* type.

If the discriminant Δ is zero, equation (6) can be decomposed into a sum of $n - p$ squares ($p > 0$), and equation (1) belongs to the *parabolic* type. An equation of this type can have real characteristics, or not have any, according to the case. If for example $n = 3$, the equation $(\partial \phi / \partial x)^2 = (\partial \phi / \partial y)^2$ has real integrals, while the equation

$$\left(\frac{\partial \phi}{\partial x} + a \frac{\partial \phi}{\partial z} \right)^2 + \left(\frac{\partial \phi}{\partial y} + b \frac{\partial \phi}{\partial z} \right)^2 = 0$$

possesses real integrals only if the two equations

$$\frac{\partial \phi}{\partial x} + a \frac{\partial \phi}{\partial z} = 0, \qquad \frac{\partial \phi}{\partial y} + b \frac{\partial \phi}{\partial z} = 0$$

form a Jacobian system. Every equation which has real characteristics is therefore of the hyperbolic type or of the parabolic type.

26. Wave propagation. Equations with real characteristics occur, to the exclusion of equations of the elliptic type, in all phenomena where there is *wave* propagation. It is easy to get a clear

---

[1] The theorem has not yet been proven in an absolutely general fashion for a non-analytic equation, but it has been verified in all the cases which have been considered.

idea of this *a priori*. Let us consider first of all a disturbance propagated along a straight line of indefinite length, taken as the x-axis. Let us suppose, for example, that we have a cylinder of indefinite length, of very small cross section, filled with a gas whose state at each instant is the same at every point of each slice perpendicular to the generatrices. This state is characterized by a variable z, which depends upon the abscissa x of the slice considered and upon the time t. In the most usual problems, z is an integral of a second order equation linear in the second order derivatives

$$(7) \qquad H\frac{\partial^2 z}{\partial x^2} + 2K\frac{\partial^2 z}{\partial x\, \partial t} + L\frac{\partial^2 z}{\partial t^2} + M = 0,$$

which has the solution $z = 0$, corresponding to the state of rest.

We suppose that if we have just produced a disturbance in one portion of the cylinder, this disturbance is propagated by waves, that is to say that a slice with abscissa x, lying outside of the disturbed portion at the beginning remains at rest until a certain moment $t = \phi(x)$ from which moment on it begins to vibrate. Let us consider x and t as the rectangular coordinates of a point; let C be the curve having $t = \phi(x)$ as its equation, and let $z = f(x, t)$ be the integral of equation (7) which is in accord with the phenomenon studied. The curve C decomposes the xt-plane into two regions; in the region situated below C, we have $t \lessgtr \phi(x)$ and $z = 0$; on the other hand, in the region lying above C, z is different from zero. Along the curve C, we shall accept as true that z and its partial derivatives $\partial z/\partial x$, $\partial z/\partial t$ are zero, which amounts to assuming that z and its partial derivatives vary continuously when we pass from the part not yet disturbed to the part already disturbed. The integral surface $z = f(x, t)$ is therefore tangent to the plane $z = 0$ all along the curve C, which is consequently a characteristic of this particular integral (III, **17**); in other words, *the equation* t $= \phi$(x), *which corresponds to the front of the wave, is that of a characteristic curve on the plane* z $= 0$.

These characteristic curves are the integral curves of the differential equation $H_0 dt^2 - 2K_0 dt\, dx + L_0 dx^2 = 0$, H_0, K_0, L_0 designating what the coefficients H, K, L become when we have replaced in it z, $\partial z/\partial x$, $\partial z/\partial t$ by zero. In particular, when H, K, L do not contain x and t, H_0, K_0, L_0 are constants, and the two systems of characteristics consist of parallel lines. The equation of the wave front $t = \phi(x)$ is of the form $t = ax + b$, and we deduce from it that the disturbance is propagated with a constant velocity $1/a$.

Let us consider moreover the equation of the propagation of sound in space. The components of the velocity of a gaseous molecule located, at the instant t, at the point with coordinates (x, y, z) are the partial derivatives of a function $u(x, y, z, t)$, which satisfies the partial differential equation

$$(8) \qquad \frac{\partial^2 u}{\partial x^2} + \frac{\partial^2 u}{\partial y^2} + \frac{\partial^2 u}{\partial z^2} - \frac{1}{a^2}\frac{\partial^2 u}{\partial t^2} = 0,$$

a being a constant.

If, for $t = 0$, we introduce a disturbance restricted to a region of space, the molecule located at a point (x, y, z) outside this region remains at rest until the instant $t = \phi(x, y, z)$, from which time on u ceases being zero. The equation $\phi(x, y, z) = t$, where t has a fixed value, separates the region not yet disturbed from the region already disturbed. If we allow u and its partial derivatives to vary continuously as we pass from one region to the other, the equation $\phi(x, y, z) - t = 0$ represents, in four-dimensional space (x, y, z, t), a characteristic hypersurface of equation (8), since there must exist an integral of this equation which is tangent to the particular integral $u = 0$ all along this hypersurface. Relation (6), which defines the characteristic hypersurfaces of equation (8), becomes in the present case, assuming the equation of this hypersurface solved for t,

$$(9) \qquad \left(\frac{\partial \phi}{\partial x}\right)^2 + \left(\frac{\partial \phi}{\partial y}\right)^2 + \left(\frac{\partial \phi}{\partial z}\right)^2 = \frac{1}{a^2};$$

according to a known result[2], the equation

$$\phi(x, y, z) = C$$

[2] We can also verify this result by showing that the orthogonal trajectories of the family of surfaces $\phi(x, y, z) = C$ are lines. If u, v, w are the direction cosines of the normal to the surface of this family which passes through a point (x, y, z), we have, from equation (9),

$$u = a\frac{\partial \phi}{\partial x}, \qquad v = a\frac{\partial \phi}{\partial y}, \qquad w = a\frac{\partial \phi}{\partial z},$$

and it is sufficient to prove that u, v, w do not change when we pass from a point m of space to an infinitesimally nearby point m' along a line of direction (u, v, w) coming from this point. Then we have, within a factor,

$$du = \frac{\partial^2 \phi}{\partial x^2}\frac{\partial \phi}{\partial x} + \frac{\partial^2 \phi}{\partial x\, \partial y}\frac{\partial \phi}{\partial y} + \frac{\partial^2 \phi}{\partial x\, \partial z}\frac{\partial \phi}{\partial z} = \frac{1}{2}\frac{\partial}{\partial x}\left[\left(\frac{\partial \phi}{\partial x}\right)^2 + \left(\frac{\partial \phi}{\partial y}\right)^2 + \left(\frac{\partial \phi}{\partial z}\right)^2\right] = 0.$$

then represents a family of parallel surfaces, and therefore *the successive positions of the wave front form a family of parallel surfaces.* We can state a more exact result. For $t = 0$, the equation $\phi(x, y, z) = 0$ ought to represent the surface Σ_0 which separates the region of space already vibrating from the region at rest at the instant $t = 0$. We obtain the integral of equation (9) satisfying this condition by taking the envelop of the complete integral

$$at = \sqrt{(x - \alpha)^2 + (y - \beta)^2 + (z - \gamma)^2},$$

when the point (α, β, γ) describes the surface Σ_0. Let $t = F(x, y, z)$ be the equation of this envelop; from the theory of variation of parameters (II, 2, **90**), $F(x, y, z)$ is an integral of equation (9), and it is clear that, for $t = 0$, the envelop reduces to the surface Σ_0 itself. We therefore obtain the position of the wave front at time t by taking the envelop of the spheres of radius at whose center describes the surface Σ_0; it is evident that the portion of this envelop which is exterior to Σ_0 is alone involved in the question. All these results, which have been deduced solely from the theory of characteristics, will be proven later (III, **28**).

27. Generalities on completely linear equations. A large number of problems in mathematical physics lead to partial differential equations, which are *linear* and homogeneous with respect to the unknown function and its derivatives; the desired integral must, besides, satisfy conditions which can be very diverse in nature. From the linear form of these equations it follows that if p particular integrals are known, every linear combination with constant coefficients of these p integrals is also an integral. If an integral depending upon one or several arbitrary parameters is known, we can derive from it new integrals by differentiations or quadratures. For example, let $\phi(x, y, z, \ldots; a)$ be an integral depending on a parameter a, not occurring in the coefficients of the equation under consideration. We verify immediately that $\partial\phi/\partial a$ is also an integral, a fact we explain because we can consider this derivative as the limit of a linear combination of the two integrals

$$\phi(x, y, z, \ldots; a + h), \qquad \phi(x, y, z, \ldots; a).$$

The reasoning is general; if an integral depends upon a certain number of parameters $a, b, c, \ldots, l$, not occurring in the coefficients of the equation, every partial derivative, of any order whatever, of the integral with respect to these parameters, is a new integral, if, however, these derivatives exist. It may happen also that the derivatives of the integral with respect to one of the independent variables are also integrals; this is what will happen, for example, if one of the variables does not occur in the coefficients of the equation and if we take the derivatives with respect to this variable. In particular, in the case of a linear equation with *constant* coefficients, all the partial derivatives of an integral are also integrals, assuming, of course, that these derivatives exist and have themselves derivatives of an order equal to the order of the equation being considered.

From an integral depending upon *arbitrary parameters* we can also derive by quadratures integrals depending upon *arbitrary functions*. Let us suppose, for example, that for a given linear equation in four independent variables x, y, z, t, an integral $u = \phi(x, y, z, t; a, b, c)$ is known, depending upon the three arbitrary parameters. If we multiply this particular solution by an arbitrary function $f(a, b, c)$ of these parameters, the integral of the product of $f(a, b, c)$ by $\phi(x, y, z, t; a, b, c)$, taken over a *fixed* domain of one, two, or three dimensions of (a, b, c)-space, will also be a solution of the partial differential equation considered, whatever be the function $f(a, b, c)$. This results immediately from the customary formulas for differentiation under the integral sign, but we can simply observe with Fourier that an integral of this type is basically only the sum of an infinity of particular solutions. When we know several distinct particular integrals depending upon arbitrary parameters, we can form in this manner other integrals depending upon arbitrary functions. When we express the fact that the integrals thus obtained satisfy desired conditions, we are led in general to *integral equations* for the determination of the arbitrary functions.

It happens also, for certain particular integrals depending on arbitrary parameters, that we can derive from them new integrals by quadratures taken over domains which are themselves variable with x, y, z, t. It is precisely these integrals which in general play the most important role.[3]

If an infinity of linearly distinct integrals, $\phi_1, \phi_2, \ldots, \phi_n, \ldots$, is known, it is evident that the series

$$\sum_{n=1}^{+\infty} C_i \phi_i,$$

[3] J. Le Roux has studied these integrals, which he calls *principal*, in several papers (*Annales de l'École Normale*, 3rd series, Vol. XII, 1895; *Journal de Mathématiques*, 5th series, Vol. IV, 1898; Vol. VI, 1900; Vol. IX, 1903). We shall see an interesting example a little later (III, **28**).

where the coefficients C_i are constants, is also an integral, provided that this series, and those that can be derived from it by differentiation up to the order of the equation, are uniformly convergent. It is even possible that all these conditions are not necessary. From every integral depending upon one or several arbitrary parameters, we can evidently derive—and in an infinity of ways—an infinity of linearly distinct particular integrals by assigning to these parameters a set of particular values and, therefore, construct an infinity of integrals with series representations. In general we choose the particular values of these parameters to satisfy certain boundary conditions. Let us suppose, for example, that an integral $\phi(x, y, z; \alpha)$, depending on a parameter α, is zero all along certain manifolds for an infinite set of values of this parameter, $\alpha_1, \ldots, \alpha_n, \ldots$ Every series $\Sigma C_n \phi(x, y, z; \alpha_n)$ formally satisfies the equation under consideration and vanishes along the same manifolds. If we can determine the coefficients C_n so that this integral satisfies the other conditions imposed on the desired solution, the problem will be solved. It is clear that in each particular case the question of convergence will have to be examined.

Most often, particular integrals containing arbitrary parameters are suggested by the very nature of the problem, or by the analytic form of the coefficients. For example, given an equation with *constant coefficients*, analogy with linear differential equations of the same type leads us to look for particular integrals expressed in terms of the exponential function. Writing that $e^{\alpha x + \beta y}$ is an integral of an equation of this type in two variables, we obtain *one* equation of condition between the constants α and β, from which we derive one or several integrals depending upon an arbitrary parameter.

All the preceding applies to the three types of linear equations—elliptic, hyperbolic, or parabolic. These three types occur in mathematical physics; the propagation of sound, for example, is governed by an equation of hyperbolic type; and the dispersion of heat by an equation of parabolic type. The distribution of electricity on one or several conductors, or the distribution of temperatures in the interior of a body in temperature equilibrium, lead to equations of elliptic type. It is to be noticed that the problems to which one is led are different according to the type of equation which governs the phenomenon; but, in each case, the problem is well defined, that is, the data are precisely those which completely determine the solution for the corresponding type of equation.

For equations of hyperbolic or parabolic type, the problem to be solved is *Cauchy's problem*,[4] or a *mixed problem*, which is obtained by combining the Cauchy problem with certain boundary conditions, whose significance will be made exact in each particular case. For an equation of the elliptic type, the problem is entirely different; it is concerned with finding a regular integral on the interior of a *closed* variety S_{n-1} in $n - 1$ dimensions, knowing the value of this integral at every point of S_{n-1}, or a relation between the integral and some of its first derivatives along this variety. The most celebrated type of this kind of question is *Dirichlet's problem*, which we shall study in detail. Let us remark once and for all that in these different problems, the hypotheses are not necessarily analytic, so that, even in Cauchy's problem, the general existence theorem (II, 2, **94**) is indeed far from furnishing the solution of every question which can be raised. In the case where it does apply, it does not yield solutions except in the neighborhood of the manifold determined by the initial conditions; this is insufficient for our purposes.

II. APPLICATIONS TO A FEW EXAMPLES

Before studying in a systematic fashion equations of the different types, we shall give several examples of synthetic solutions, which provide an application of the preceding generalities.

28. The sound equation. The Cauchy problem for the equation of the propagation of sound (III, **26**)

$$(10) \qquad \frac{\partial^2 u}{\partial x^2} + \frac{\partial^2 u}{\partial y^2} + \frac{\partial^2 u}{\partial z^2} = \frac{1}{a^2} \frac{\partial^2 u}{\partial t^2}$$

consists of finding an integral $u(x, y, z, t)$ reducing for $t = 0$ to a given function $f(x, y, z)$, while $\partial u/\partial t$ reduces to another given function $\phi(x, y, z)$. These two functions f and ϕ, as well as their partial derivatives, are assumed continuous everywhere, and zero outside a certain region R, which is the location of the initial disturbance. The problem was first solved by Poisson and Cauchy; the following method, due to Boussinesq, allows an easy discussion of all the circumstances of the phenomenon.

The function $u = 1/r$, where r is the distance of a variable point

---

[4] The value of the integral alone, along a characteristic, must be considered as equivalent to the hypothesis of Cauchy. The Cauchy problem and the mixed problem occur in general in this fashion for an equation of *parabolic* type. For all these generalities, one may read with interest an article by Hadamard in the *Bulletin de la Société de Physique* (1906).

(x, y, z) from a fixed point (α, β, γ), is an integral of equation (10) depending upon three parameters α, β, γ. The double integral

$$(11) \qquad u(x, y, z, t) = \int \int \frac{\mu(\alpha, \beta, \gamma) d\sigma}{r},$$

where $\mu(\alpha, \beta, \gamma)$ is an arbitrary function of α, β, γ, taken over the surface of the sphere Σ of radius at, with the point (x, y, z) as center, is also an integral, as we are going to show; it is to this integral that Boussinesq has given the name *spherical potential* (see Chap.VI). Let us observe that the particular integral $1/r$ does not depend upon t; the domain of integration depends only upon t in the formula (11), so that $1/r$ can be considered as a *principal* integral, in the sense of Le Roux (III, 27).[5]

[5] The method of Boussinesq can be connected to a general theorem of Weierstrass on linear equations with constant coefficients (see Volterra, *Leçons professées à Stockholm*, 1906, p. 58). Let $\theta(x, y, z)$ be a homogeneous function of the first degree in x, y, z such that the equation $\theta(x, y, z) = t$ represents a closed surface Σ, surrounding the origin, which is intersected in only one point by a half-ray emanating from the origin. Let us consider an integral

$$I = \int \int \int \phi(u, v, w) f(x + u, y + v, z + w)\, du\, dv\, dw$$

taken over a domain contained between the two surfaces Σ_{t_0}, Σ_t, t_0 being any constant. The derivative

$$\frac{\partial I}{\partial t} = F(x, y, z, t)$$

is a function of the four variables x, y, z, t which is an integral of the linear equation with constant coefficients

$$(E) \qquad \Sigma A_{h_1 h_2 h_3 h_4} \frac{\partial^n V}{\partial x^{h_1}\, \partial y^{h_2}\, \partial z^{h_3}\, \partial t^{h_4}} = 0,$$

whatever the arbitrary function f, provided that the equation

$$(E') \qquad \Sigma (-1)^{n-h_4} A_{h_1 h_2 h_3 h_4} \frac{\partial^n V}{\partial x^{h_1}\, \partial y^{h_2}\, \partial z^{h_3}\, \partial t^{h_4}} = 0$$

has the integral $\phi(x, y, z)\ \Phi[t - \theta(x, y, z)]$, Φ being an arbitrary function. In the case of equation (10), the two equations (E), (E') are identical and have the integral $(1/r) \cdot \Phi(at - r)$, where

$$r = \sqrt{x^2 + y^2 + z^2}.$$

We can therefore in this case take

$$\phi = 1/r, \qquad \theta = \sqrt{x^2 + y^2 + z^2};$$

the surfaces Σ_t are spheres, and we see easily that $\partial I/\partial t$ is identical with the surface integral of Boussinesq.

The method of Kirchhoff is also based on the use of the integrals $(1/r) \cdot \Phi(at - r)$.

To calculate the second derivatives $d^2u/\partial x^2$, $\partial^2u/\partial y^2$, $\partial^2u/\partial z^2$, it is convenient to make the change of variables

$$\alpha = x + at\xi, \qquad \beta = y + at\eta, \qquad \gamma = z + at\zeta;$$

when the point α, β, γ, describes the sphere Σ, the point ξ, η, ζ, describes the sphere S of *unit* radius, having the origin as center, and we have between the corresponding elements of area ds and $d\sigma$ of the two spheres the relation $d\sigma = a^2t^2ds = r^2ds$. Formula (11) becomes

$$(12) \qquad u(x, y, z, t) = \int \int \mu(x + at\xi, y + at\eta, z + at\zeta)atds,$$

the new integral being taken over the surface of the sphere S. The domain of integration being independent of x, y, z, we have immediately

$$\Delta_2 u = \frac{\partial^2 u}{\partial x^2} + \frac{\partial^2 u}{\partial y^2} + \frac{\partial^2 u}{\partial z^2}$$

$$= \int \int_{(S)} \Delta_2\mu(x + at\xi, y + at\eta, z + at\zeta)at\,ds,$$

or, returning to the original domain of integration,

$$(13) \qquad \Delta_2 u = \int \int_{(\Sigma)} \frac{1}{r}\left(\frac{\partial^2 \mu}{\partial \alpha^2} + \frac{\partial^2 \mu}{\partial \beta^2} + \frac{\partial^2 \mu}{\partial \gamma^2}\right) d\sigma,$$

the double integral being taken over the surface of the sphere Σ.

The expression for $\partial u/\partial t$, derived from formula (12), is composed of two terms and can be written

$$\frac{\partial u}{\partial t} = \frac{u}{t} + at \int \int_S \left[a\xi\frac{\partial \mu}{\partial x} + a\eta\frac{\partial \mu}{\partial y} + a\zeta\frac{\partial \mu}{\partial z}\right] ds,$$

or, reverting to the sphere Σ,

$$\frac{\partial u}{\partial t} = \frac{u}{t} + \frac{1}{t} \int \int_\Sigma \left[\frac{\alpha - x}{at}\frac{\partial \mu}{\partial \alpha} + \frac{\beta - y}{at}\frac{\partial \mu}{\partial \beta} + \frac{\gamma - z}{at}\frac{\partial \mu}{\partial \gamma}\right] d\sigma.$$

But $(\alpha - x)/at$, $(\beta - y)/at$, $(\gamma - z)/at$ are the direction cosines of the exterior normal to Σ, and the double integral of the second member is identical with the surface integral

$$J = \int \int \frac{\partial \mu}{\partial \alpha} d\beta \, d\gamma + \frac{\partial \mu}{\partial \beta} d\gamma \, d\alpha + \frac{\partial \mu}{\partial \gamma} d\alpha \, d\beta,$$

taken over the exterior surface of Σ, or again, according to Green's theorem, with the triple integral (I, **151**)

$$(14) \qquad J = \int \int \int \left(\frac{\partial^2 \mu}{\partial \alpha^2} + \frac{\partial^2 \mu}{\partial \beta^2} + \frac{\partial^2 \mu}{\partial \gamma^2} \right) dv,$$

taken over the interior of Σ. From the formula which gives $\partial u / \partial t$,

$$\frac{\partial u}{\partial t} = \frac{u}{t} + \frac{1}{t} J,$$

we derive, by differentiating again with respect to t,

$$(15) \qquad \frac{\partial^2 u}{\partial t^2} = - \frac{u}{t^2} + \frac{1}{t} \left(\frac{u}{t} + \frac{1}{t} J \right) - \frac{1}{t^2} J + \frac{1}{t} \frac{\partial J}{\partial t} = \frac{1}{t} \frac{\partial J}{\partial t},$$

which we can write $(a^2/r)(\partial J / \partial r)$, r being the radius of Σ. It would be easy to calculate $\partial J / \partial r$ by replacing the rectangular coordinates α, β, γ by the polar coordinates (ρ, θ, ψ) in the triple integral (14), but we can also observe that when r increases by dr, the increment ΔJ is represented by a triple integral taken over the portion of space contained between the two concentric spheres of radius r and $r + dr$. The principal part of this increment is evidently equal to the product of dr by the double integral of

$$\left(\frac{\partial^2 \mu}{\partial \alpha^2} + \frac{\partial^2 \mu}{\partial \beta^2} + \frac{\partial^2 \mu}{\partial \gamma^2} \right)$$

taken over the surface of the sphere of radius r. We therefore have

$$(16) \qquad \frac{\partial^2 u}{\partial t^2} = \frac{a^2}{r} \frac{\partial J}{\partial r} = \frac{a^2}{r} \int \int_{(\Sigma)} \left(\frac{\partial^2 \mu}{\partial \alpha^2} + \frac{\partial^2 \mu}{\partial \beta^2} + \frac{\partial^2 \mu}{\partial \gamma^2} \right) d\sigma;$$

comparing this with formula (13), we see that $u(x, y, z, t)$ is indeed an integral of equation (10), whatever the function $\mu(\alpha, \beta, \gamma)$, provided that the derivatives which enter into the calculation are continuous. Formula (12) shows immediately that $u(x, y, z, 0) = 0$, while the limit of u/t, when t approaches zero, is equal to $4\pi a\mu(x, y, z)$. Therefore integral (11) satisfies the initial conditions

$$u(x, y, z, 0) = 0, \qquad \frac{\partial u}{\partial t} = 4\pi a\mu(x, y, z) \qquad \text{(for } t = 0\text{).}$$

Besides, $u_1(x, y, z, t) = \partial u/\partial t$ is also an integral of equation (10) (III, 27) and formula (16) shows that $\partial u_1/\partial t$ is zero for $t = 0$. This new integral therefore satisfies the initial conditions

$$u_1(x, y, z, 0) = 4\pi a\mu(x, y, z), \qquad \partial u/\partial t = 0 \qquad \text{(for } t = 0\text{).}$$

This being so, let us set

$$(17) \qquad \begin{cases} F(x, y, z, t) = \dfrac{1}{4\pi a} \displaystyle\int\int_{(\Sigma)} \dfrac{f(\alpha, \beta, \gamma)}{r}\, d\sigma, \\[3mm] \Phi(x, y, z, t) = \dfrac{1}{4\pi a} \displaystyle\int\int_{(\Sigma)} \dfrac{\phi(\alpha, \beta, \gamma)}{r}\, d\sigma: \end{cases}$$

it is clear that the function

$$(18) \qquad u(x, y, z, t) = \frac{\partial F}{\partial t} + \Phi(x, y, z, t)$$

gives the solution of Cauchy's problem for equation (10), for from the preceding formulas it reduces to $f(x, y, z)$ for $t = 0$, while $\partial u/\partial t$ is equal to $\phi(x, y, z)$. From the formula which gives $\partial F/\partial t$, we see that this function u is expressed by a double integral taken over the surface of the sphere of radius at and with center (x, y, z), and therefore the value of u at time t at a point (x, y, z) depends only upon the values of f and of ϕ on the portion of the sphere of radius at lying in the region R where the initial disturbance is produced.

It is easy, according to this, to take account of the various circumstances of the phenomenon. Let us suppose that the region R is bounded by a closed surface S; let M be a point of space exterior to R, d and D the least and the greatest distance of this point from a point of S.

As long as t is less than d/a, the sphere with radius at and center at M does not reach the region R, $u(x, y, z, t)$ is zero, and the molecule situated at M remains at rest until the instant $t_1 = d/a$, when it begins to vibrate. But, from the moment when t exceeds the value

D/a, the surface of the sphere of radius at and center M has no point in common with the region R, and the molecule at M returns to a state of rest.

The locus of points which are reached by the vibration in time t is the surface parallel to S obtained by measuring off a length at in the direction of the exterior normal; the various positions of the wave front are therefore surfaces parallel to S (III, **26**), and a gives the speed of propagation. Two wave fronts pass through the point M, the forward wave front which we have just defined, and a backward wave front, the locus of points obtained by laying off on the normal to S a length equal to D.

When the region R is infinite, there is certainly always a forward wave front for a point M located exterior to R, but there is not, in general, a backward wave front, for $u(x, y, z, t)$ remains different from zero (or from a constant) as soon as t exceeds the value d/a.

29. Cylindrical waves. If the given functions $f(x, y, z)$ and $\phi(x, y, z)$ do not depend upon z, that is to say if the initial state is the same all along a parallel to the z-axis, it is clear that the integral (18) is itself independent of z. In fact, when z varies, with x, y, t remaining fixed, the sphere Σ can only be displaced parallel to Oz, but the double integrals taken over the surface of this sphere do not change value. The state is therefore the same at each instant along a parallel to Oz, and we can restrict ourselves to studying what takes place in the xy-plane. Formula (18) then represents the integral of the equation

$$(19) \qquad \frac{\partial^2 u}{\partial x^2} + \frac{\partial^2 u}{\partial y^2} = \frac{1}{a^2}\frac{\partial^2 u}{\partial t^2},$$

which reduces to $f(x, y)$, whereas $\partial u/\partial t = \phi(x, y)$, for $t = 0$. The double integrals (17) are taken over the surface of the sphere Σ with radius $r = at$, having for its center the point with coordinates $(x, y, 0)$. We can replace these integrals by the double integrals taken over the great circle of this sphere lying in the xy-plane, by noticing that the element of area $d\sigma$ has

$$d\sigma = \frac{r\,d\alpha\,d\beta}{\sqrt{r^2 - (x - \alpha)^2 - (y - \beta)^2}}$$

as its expression, and that each element of the great circle is the projection of two symmetric elements of the sphere. Formula (18) then becomes

$$(20) \begin{cases} u(x, y, t) = \dfrac{1}{2\pi a} \displaystyle\int \int_\Gamma \dfrac{\phi(\alpha, \beta)\, d\alpha\, d\beta}{\sqrt{a^2t^2 - (x - \alpha)^2 - (y - \beta)^2}} \\[4mm] \qquad + \dfrac{1}{2\pi a}\dfrac{\partial}{\partial t}\left[\displaystyle\int \int_\Gamma \dfrac{f(\alpha, \beta)\, d\alpha\, d\beta}{\sqrt{a^2t^2 - (x - \alpha)^2 - (y - \beta)^2}} \right], \end{cases}$$

the two double integrals being taken over the circle Γ with radius at and center at the point (x, y).

Let us assume that the functions $f(x, y)$ and $\phi(x, y)$ are zero out-side the region R' bounded by a closed curve C, which corresponds to the case where the region R, location of the initial disturbance, is the interior of a cylinder with generatrices parallel to the z-axis, this disturbance being the same at all the points of a parallel to the generatrices. If the point (x, y) is outside the region R', $u(x, y, t)$ will be zero as long as at is less than the shortest distance d of this point from C, but as soon as t exceeds d/a, the circle Γ always con-tains a part at least of R' and $u(x, y, t)$ does not become zero (or constant) again in general. There is, therefore, always a forward wave front, whose successive positions are parallel cylindrical surfaces, but *there is no backward wave front.* In other terms, there is an infinite *diffusion* of sound behind the wave front. An ear located at a point of space will receive indefinitely an impression from the moment when the front reaches it, but this impression becomes more attenuated with the time. Indeed, as t increases indefinitely, we see readily that the two double integrals which figure in formula (20) approach zero, and we can prove with complete rigor that the same is true of the partial derivatives $\partial u/\partial x$, $\partial u/\partial y$, $\partial u/\partial z$.

Plane waves. Let us again take the more special case where the two functions $f(x, y, z)$ and $\phi(x, y, z)$ depend only upon x. Physically, this hypothesis corresponds to the case where R is the region con-tained between two planes P_1 and P_2 normal to Ox, the initial disturbance being the same at all points of any plane parallel to these. We discover, as above, that the function $u(x, y, z, t)$ is itself independent of y and of z, and that formula (18) represents the integral of the equation

$$(21) \qquad \frac{\partial^2 u}{\partial x^2} = \frac{1}{a^2}\frac{\partial^2 u}{\partial t^2},$$

so that, for $t = 0$, u and $\partial u/\partial t$ reduce to $f(x)$ and to $\phi(x)$, respectively.

The two double integrals which occur in this formula are taken over the surface of the sphere of radius $r = at$ and center at $(x, 0, 0)$. Noticing that the area of the zone contained between two planes perpendicular to Ox, with abscissas α and $\alpha + d\alpha$, can be expressed as $2\pi at\, d\alpha$, we see at once that these double integrals reduce to simple integrals, and that formula (18) becomes

$$
(22) \quad
\begin{cases}
u(x, t) = \dfrac{1}{2a}\left[\displaystyle\int_{x-at}^{x+at} \phi(\alpha)\, d\alpha + \dfrac{\partial}{\partial t} \int_{x-at}^{x+at} f(\alpha)\, d\alpha \right] \\[3mm]
\qquad = \dfrac{1}{2a} \displaystyle\int_{x-at}^{x+at} \phi(\alpha)\, d\alpha + \dfrac{f(x + at) + f(x - at)}{2}.
\end{cases}
$$

In the case we are studying, the two functions $f(x)$ and $\phi(x)$ are zero outside an interval (x_0, x_1). Let us assume $x_0 < x_1 < x$. As long as t is less than $(x - x_1)/a$, the two functions $f(\alpha)$ and $\phi(\alpha)$ are zero in the interval of integration and we have $u = 0$. When t is greater than $(x - x_0)/a$, we can replace the limits of integration by x_0 and x_1, *and* u(x, t) *will remain constant*. Since the impression perceived by the ear depends only upon the derivatives of u, we see that there is always a forward wave front and a backward wave front. These results will be verified later (III, 36) by a direct study of equation (21).

30. Propagation of heat in an unbounded medium. Analytically, the problem is presented thus:[6] Find an integral of the equation

$$
(23) \quad \frac{\partial^2 u}{\partial x^2} + \frac{\partial^2 u}{\partial y^2} + \frac{\partial^2 u}{\partial z^2} = \frac{1}{a^2}\frac{\partial u}{\partial t},
$$

regular for every set of values of x, y, z, and for $t > 0$, which reduces to a given function $f(x, y, z)$ for $t = 0$. In order that a product of the

---

[6] This is in reality a particular case of Cauchy's problem (Footnote 4, this chapter) since the hypersurface $t = 0$ of the (x, y, z, t)-space is a characteristic manifold. From the physical point of view, this problem corresponds to the following problem. Assuming space filled with a homogeneous fluid whose temperature at each point is known at time $t = 0$, we wish to determine the temperature at any instant whatever. We can further assume that we have introduced, in the space at 0°, a hot body having the same properties, from the caloric point of view, as the exterior fluid. The problem would be entirely different if we plunged into an enclosure at 0° a heated body of different character, which we then permitted to cool without restraint, while maintaining the temperature of the enclosure at 0°. We treat two particular cases in sections **31** and **32**.

form $XYZT$, where X, Y, Z, T depend, respectively, only upon x, y, z, t, be an integral of equation (23), it is necessary and sufficient that we have

$$\frac{X''}{X} + \frac{Y''}{Y} + \frac{Z''}{Z} = \frac{1}{a^2}\frac{T'}{T},$$

and consequently each of the ratios which occur in this relation must reduce to a constant. If we wish the variables x, y, z to occur as trigonometric arguments, the ratios must be so taken that, for example, X''/X has a negative value, and we thus obtain a particular integral

$$(24) \qquad v = e^{-(\alpha^2+\beta^2+\gamma^2)a^2} \cos\alpha(x-\lambda)\cos\beta(y-\mu)\cos\gamma(z-\nu),$$

depending upon *six* arbitrary constants $\alpha, \beta, \gamma, \lambda, \mu, \nu$. The expression

$$(25) \qquad w = \int_0^{+\infty}\int_0^{+\infty}\int_0^{+\infty} v\,d\alpha\,d\beta\,d\gamma$$

will also be a particular integral of (23); now, w is the product of three simple integrals such as

$$(26) \qquad \int_0^{+\infty} e^{-a^2\alpha^2 t}\cos\alpha(x-\lambda)\,d\alpha.$$

The value of this integral is easily derived from an earlier formula which we can write as

$$\int_0^{+\infty} e^{-y^2}\cos 2by\,dy = \frac{1}{2}\sqrt{\pi}e^{-b^2},$$

replacing y by $\alpha a\sqrt{t}$ (α being the new variable of integration) and b by $(x-\lambda)/2a\sqrt{t}$. We thus obtain

$$\int_0^{+\infty} e^{-a^2\alpha^2 t}\cos\alpha(x-\lambda)\,d\alpha = \frac{\sqrt{\pi}}{2a\sqrt{t}}e^{-\frac{(x-\lambda)^2}{4a^2 t}},$$

and two entirely similar formulas giving the values of the integrals analogous to (26), which gives, finally,

$$(27) \qquad w = \pi^{\frac{3}{2}}\frac{e^{-[(x-\lambda)^2+(y-\mu)^2+(z-\nu)^2]/(4a^2 t)}}{(2a\sqrt{t})^3}.$$

The new integral w depends upon only three arbitrary constants λ, μ, ν. The expression

$$(28) \qquad u = \frac{1}{\pi^3} \int_{-\infty}^{+\infty} \int_{-\infty}^{+\infty} \int_{-\infty}^{+\infty} wf(\lambda, \mu, \nu) \, d\lambda \, d\mu \, d\nu$$

is another integral. To prove that this is the required integral, let us make the change of variables

$$\lambda = x + 2a\sqrt{t}\xi, \qquad \mu = y + 2a\sqrt{t}\eta, \qquad \nu = z + 2a\sqrt{t}\zeta;$$

replacing w by its value, formula (28) becomes

$$(29) \qquad \begin{cases} u = \pi^{-\frac{3}{2}} \int_{-\infty}^{+\infty} \int_{-\infty}^{+\infty} \int_{-\infty}^{+\infty} e^{-\xi^2-\mu^2-\zeta^2} \\ \qquad \times f(x + 2a\sqrt{t}\xi, y + 2a\sqrt{t}\eta, z + 2a\sqrt{t}\zeta) \, d\xi \, d\eta \, d\zeta. \end{cases}$$

For $t = 0$, this integral reduces to

$$\pi^{-(3/2)}f(x, y, z) \int_{-\infty}^{+\infty} e^{-\xi^2} \, d\xi \int_{-\infty}^{+\infty} e^{-\eta^2} \, d\eta \int_{-\infty}^{+\infty} e^{-\zeta^2} \, d\zeta,$$

that is, to $f(x, y, z)$, since each of the simple integrals is equal to $\sqrt{\pi}$.

Let us assume that the function $f(x, y, z)$ is zero, except for a bounded region R of space where it is *positive*. This hypothesis corresponds to the case where we have introduced into our space at $0°$ a body occupying the region R, with a temperature of more than $0°$. We can then in formula (28) take for the region of integration the region R itself, since $f(\lambda, \mu, \nu)$ is zero outside this region. This formula shows us that however small t may be, u has a positive value at each point of space. It follows that the propagation of heat, starting with a hot body, in a space at $0°$, occurs in an instantaneous manner, that is, at the very instant following the introduction of the hot body, the temperature at any point whatever of space begins to rise. There is therefore no heat wave, which we could have foreseen *a priori*, since equation (23) is the parabolic type and does not possess any other real characteristics apart from the hypersurfaces $t = C$.

Formula (28) likewise shows that every hot body influences the calculation of the temperature at point (x, y, z) at any instant whatever, since the second member is a triple integral taken over the region in space occupied by this body. Consequently, an observer situated at this point would experience at an instant t a sensation of heat which depends upon the initial state of *the entire hot body*; we have seen, on the contrary, in the study of the propagation of sound that the auditory sensation at time t depends only upon the initial state of points located on a sphere of radius at, having its center at the point (x, y, z). According to Boussinesq, this analytic fact explains why sight and hearing provide us with a rather precise knowledge of the external world, while heat phenomena supply only confused and indistinct impressions. This is related to the fact that optical and acoustical phenomena are governed by equations whose solutions involve double integrals, while heat phenomena are governed by equations whose solutions involve triple integrals.

31. The problem of the loop. We shall call a wire of very small cross section, forming a closed circuit, a *loop*. We are given the initial distribution of temperature in the loop, and we are required to find this distribution when the loop has been freely allowed to cool during a certain time. The equation of the problem is the following:

$$(30) \qquad \frac{\partial u}{\partial t} + au = k\frac{\partial^2 u}{\partial x^2},$$

a and k being positive constants, t representing the time, x the length of the wire taken along its axis starting from a certain origin, and u the temperature at time t of the cross section with abscissa x. We shall assume that we have chosen the unit of length so that the total length of the wire will be 2π. Setting $u = ve^{-at}$, equation (30) reduces to

$$(31) \qquad \frac{\partial v}{\partial t} = k\frac{\partial^2 v}{\partial x^2}.$$

The question is to find an integral of this equation, defined for all positive values of t, and which reduces for $t = 0$ to a given function $f(x)$, which necessarily has a period of 2π. It is clear that the function v must also have the same period.

To solve this problem, Fourier observed at first that equation (31) possessed an infinity of simple solutions, which are obtained by taking the product of a function of t by a periodic function, with period 2π, of x. All these solutions are of the form

$$e^{-kn^2t}(A \cos nx + B \sin nx),$$

n being any integer whatever, and A and B arbitrary constants.

By means of these simple solutions, we can form the required integral, in the very general case where the function $f(x)$ can be expanded in a Fourier series:

$$(32) \qquad f(x) = \frac{a_0}{2} + \sum_{n=1}^{+\infty} (a_n \cos nx + b_n \sin nx);$$

it is clear, indeed, that the function represented by the series

$$(33) \qquad v = \frac{a_0}{2} + \sum_{n=1}^{+\infty} e^{-n^2 kt}(a_n \cos nx + b_n \sin nx)$$

satisfies equation (31) *formally*, and, for $t = 0$, this series reduces to the expansion of $f(x)$.

The reasoning is clearly lacking in rigor, but it is easy to make up for it. Let us observe first of all that $|a_n|$ and $|b_n|$ have an upper bound M; the series (33) and the series obtained for $\partial v/\partial t$ and $\partial^2 v/\partial x^2$ are uniformly convergent for every value of t greater than a positive number τ; it is sufficient, to see this, to compare the general term to the term of same degree of the convergent series $2M \sum n^2 e^{-n^2 k \tau}$. Relation (31) therefore holds for every value of $t > \tau$, and consequently for every positive value of t, since τ is an arbitrary positive number. It remains to prove that when t approaches zero, x remaining constant, the sum of the series (33) has as a limit the sum of the series (32), which is assumed convergent. Now, if we set $q = e^{-kt}$, series (33) is a power series in q

$$(33') \qquad v = \frac{a_0}{2} + \sum_{n=1}^{+\infty} q^{n^2}(a_n \cos nx + b_n \sin nx),$$

all of whose exponents are perfect squares. When t approaches zero through positive values, q approaches unity and, from Abel's theorem, the sum of series (33') has for its limit the sum of that series where we have set $q = 1$, that is, series (32).

It is to be noticed that relation (31) is not necessarily satisfied for $t = 0$; this is the case, for example, if the given function $f(x)$ does not have a second derivative.[7]

---

[7] Whatever the continuous function $f(x)$, it follows from Weierstrass's theorem that the sum of the series (33), where a_n and b_n are the coefficients of the Fourier series coming from $f(x)$, has the limit $f(x)$ when t approaches zero through positive values (see É. Picard, *Traité d'Analyse*, 2nd edition, Vol. I, p. 283).

Remark. Each term of series (33′) can be expanded in a power series in powers of x. Replacing each term by its expansion, v is represented by the sum of a double series each term of which is a power of x. This double series is *absolutely convergent* for every positive value of t. Indeed, let M be the upper bound of the absolute values $|a_n|$ and $|b_n|$. The sum of the absolute values of the terms in the nth line of the table is clearly less than $Mq^{n^2} e^{n\rho}$, ρ being equal to $|x|$. Now the series whose general term is $q^{n^2} e^{n\rho}$ is convergent, for any ρ, when $q < 1$. It follows from this that *for every positive value of* t, the function $v = F(x, t)$, which represents the heat state of the loop at the instant t, is *an entire function of* x. An arbitrarily chosen continuous function of x cannot therefore represent the heat state of the loop at a time subsequent to that when we permit it to cool off without restraint.

32. Cooling of a sphere. Let us assume that a sphere of radius R is immersed in an enclosure at $0°$, and that the initial temperature of any point of this sphere is a function of the distance r from the center, alone; from symmetry, the same will be true at any instant whatever. The temperature u of a point of the sphere at time t is a function of the variables r and t, which satisfies the equation

$$(34) \qquad \frac{1}{k} \frac{\partial u}{\partial t} = \frac{\partial^2 u}{\partial r^2} + \frac{2}{r} \frac{\partial u}{\partial r}.$$

This function is defined for every positive value of t, and for every value of r taken between 0 and R, and must reduce to a known function $f(r)$, defined from 0 to R, when t becomes zero. Moreover, if we admit Newton's law of cooling, this function u must satisfy a condition at the surface, which is as follows: for $r = R$, we must have $\partial u/\partial r + hu = 0$, h being a positive constant; and this regardless of the value of t.

Equation (34) is simplified if we set $u = v/r$ and becomes

$$(35) \qquad \frac{\partial^2 v}{\partial r^2} = \frac{1}{k} \frac{\partial v}{\partial t},$$

while the condition relative to the surface becomes

$$(36) \qquad \frac{\partial v}{\partial r} = \frac{1 - hR}{R} v \qquad \text{(for } r = R)$$

and the new initial condition is $v = r \cdot f(r)$ for $t = 0$.

Equation (35) is identical with equation (31') of the loop problem, but the desired integral must satisfy an entirely different boundary condition. In order that a solution of the form

$$v = e^{-\mu^2 kt}(A \cos \mu r + B \sin \mu r)$$

suit the new problem, it is necessary first of all that $v/r = u$ remain finite in value for $r = 0$, and consequently that A be zero. For this integral to satisfy condition (36), it is necessary moreover that μ be a root of the transcendental equation

$$(37) \qquad \tan(\mu R) = \frac{\mu R}{1 - hR}.$$

We can easily show that this equation has an infinity of positive roots $\mu_1, \mu_2, \ldots \mu_n, \ldots$ Indeed, if we set $\mu R = x$, the problem is reduced to the search for the points of intersection of the curve $y = \tan x$ with the line $(1 - hR)y = x$. If, for example, $1 - hR$ is positive, equation (37) has one and only one root between $[(2n - 1)\pi]/2R$ and $[(2n + 1)\pi]/2R$, this root is greater than $n\pi/R$, and the difference of two consecutive roots is greater than $\pi/2R$. That being the case, let us assume that the function $rf(r)$ can be expanded in the interval $(0, R)$ in a series of the form

$$(38) \quad rf(r) = A \sin(\mu_1 r) + A_2 \sin(\mu_2 r) + \ldots + A_n \sin(\mu_n r) + \ldots,$$

the coefficients A_n being constants. The series

$$(39) \qquad v = A_1 e^{-\mu_1^2 kt} \sin(\mu_1 r) + A_2 e^{-\mu_2^2 kt} \sin(\mu_2 r) + \ldots$$

gives the solution of the problem. In fact, this series is uniformly convergent for $t \geq 0$, and if we set $e^{-kt} = q$, we can repeat for the series $\Sigma A_n q^{\mu^2} \sin(\mu_n r)$ the reasoning by which one establishes Abel's theorem, and we conclude from it that v has $rf(r)$ as its limit when t approaches zero. To prove that the series derived from v by differentiating term by term are uniformly convergent, we have only to repeat the calculations in the loop problem. The only difference is that the set of integral numbers is replaced by the set of increasing numbers $\mu_1, \mu_2, \ldots$ in which $\mu_n - \mu_{n-1}$ lies between $\pi/2R$ and $3\pi/2R$. The possibility of expanding $rf(r)$ in a series of form (38), when this function satisfies the Dirichlet conditions, has been rigorously established by Cauchy[8] (see Exercise 2).

[8] *Oeuvres complètes*, 1st series, Vol. VII. See also: É. Picard, *Traité d'Analyse*, Vol. II, p. 179–195.—H. Poincaré, *Théorie analytique de la propagation de la chaleur* [*Leçons rédigées* par Rouyer & Baire, Chap. XI and following].

Comments and Exercises

1. *Problem treated by Fourier.* We consider the unbounded solid
included between two parallel planes B and C, and a plane A which
is perpendicular to them. We assume each point M of plane A to be
maintained at a constant temperature which is a given function
$\phi(x)$ of the single distance x from this point to plane B, and that
each point of the faces B and C is kept at $0°$. In the end an equilibrium of temperature is established. Required to find the final
temperature $u(x, y)$ at a point P whose distances from planes B
and A are x and y, respectively.

The function $u(x, y)$ must satisfy Laplace's equation $\Delta u = 0$;
must reduce to $\phi(x)$ for $y = 0$; must be zero, for any y, when $x = 0$
and $x = 1$; and must be very small for large y. We start with the
simple solution

$$e^{-\frac{m\pi v}{l}} \sin \frac{m\pi x}{l}$$

which satisfies the last conditions, and we develop $\phi(x)$ in a series
of sines of multiples of $\pi x/l$.

2. Let μ, μ' be two distinct roots of equation (37). Required to
prove that

$$\int_0^R \sin(\mu r) \sin(\mu' r)\, dr = 0.$$

It follows from this that we can determine the coefficients of series
(38) in the same way as the coefficients of a Fourier series, assuming
this series to be uniformly convergent.

CHAPTER IV

LINEAR EQUATIONS OF THE HYPERBOLIC TYPE

I. STUDY OF SOME PROBLEMS RELATING TO THE EQUATION $s = f(x, y)$

33. Determination of an integral from Cauchy's data. We shall begin by studying in detail a certain number of problems relating to the elementary equation

(1) $$\frac{\partial^2 z}{\partial x\, dy} = f(x, y);$$

an integral is called *regular* in a domain if it is continuous and has continuous partial derivatives of the first order in this domain. The function $f(x, y)$ is itself assumed continuous.[1] Let us propose first of all to determine an integral, knowing the values which it assumes on two characteristics of different systems, or more precisely, let us seek an integral reducing, for $y = y_0$, to a given function $\phi(x)$ and, for $x = x_0$, to another known function $\psi(y)$, the two functions satisfying the condition $\phi(x_0) = \psi(y_0)$. If the two functions $\phi(x)$ and $\psi(x)$ are determined respectively in the intervals $(x_0, x_0 + \alpha)$ and $(y_0, y_0 + \beta)$, the integral sought for is itself determined in the interior of a rectangle bounded by the lines $x = x_0, x = x_0 + \alpha,$ $y = y_0, y = y_0 + \beta$, and we shall be able to write it at once, by observing that the double integral

$$\int_{x_0}^{x} d\xi \int_{y_0}^{y} f(\xi, \eta)\, d\eta$$

---

[1] We assume for simplicity that the Ox and Oy axes are rectangular, but it is clear that the results are independent of this hypothesis, if the double integrals which occur in the formulas are written to show plainly the limits of the successive integrations which are to be carried out.

is an integral of equation (1) which is zero for $y = y_0$, whatever the value of x, and for $x = x_0$, whatever the value of y. But we shall treat the problem by a uniform procedure, applicable to all the problems which are to follow.

Let us suppose, for the sake of definiteness, $\alpha > 0$, $\beta > 0$, and let $ABCD$ be the rectangle whose vertices have the coordinates (x_0, y_0), $(x_0 + \alpha, y_0)$, $(x_0 + \alpha, y_0 + \beta)$, $(z_0, y_0 + \beta)$. From a point M taken in the interior or on the perimeter of this rectangle let us drop the perpendiculars MP and MQ on the sides AB and AD. Every integral $z(x, y)$ of equation (1) also satisfies the relation

$$(2) \qquad \int \int \frac{\partial^2 z(\xi, \eta)}{\partial \xi \, \partial \eta} d\xi \, d\eta = \int \int f(\xi, \eta) \, d\xi \, d\eta,$$

the two double integrals being taken over the area of rectangle $APMQ$. Now, the first member has for its value $z(x, y) + z(x_0, y_0) - z(x_0, y_0) - z(x, y_0)$; for the desired integral, $z(x, y_0)$, $z(y, x_0)$ are precisely the given functions $\phi(x)$ and $\psi(y)$, and this integral has the expression

$$(3) \qquad z(x, y) = \phi(x) + \psi(y) - \phi(x_0) + \int_{x_0}^{x} d\xi \int_{y_0}^{y} f(\xi, \eta) \, d\eta.$$

It is clear that the function so obtained satisfies the conditions imposed; in order that it be regular in the rectangle $ABCD$, it is necessary, in addition, that the functions $\phi(x)$ and $\psi(y)$ have continuous derivatives.

If the functions $\phi(x)$ and $\psi(y)$ are continuous, as well as $\phi'(x)$ and $\psi'(y)$, except for a *finite* number of values of x taken between x_0 and $x_0 + \alpha$, and for a finite number of values of y between y_0 and $y_0 + \beta$, then $z(x, y)$ is regular in the rectangle $ABCD$, except along a finite number of segments of characteristics. We see, from this, that every discontinuity of the integral or of its derivatives at a boundary point of the domain appears in the entire domain. If the functions $\phi(x)$ and $\psi(y)$ have no derivative, $z(x, y)$ is not properly speaking an integral of equation (1) unless we adopt for the derivative $\partial^2 z/\partial x \partial y$ the generalized definition (I, **14**).

Let us now consider an arc of the curve AB (Fig. 1a) which is met in only one point by a parallel to each of the axes. Cauchy's problem can be posed thus: *Determine an integral of equation* (1), *knowing the values of the partial derivatives* $\partial z/\partial x$, $\partial z/\partial y$ *at an arbitrary point of the arc* AB, *and the value of the integral itself at a point of this arc.*

From the hypotheses made about arc AB, we can assume that the two partial derivatives $\partial z/\partial x$, $\partial z/\partial y$ are given functions of x and y, respectively, along AB, $\partial z/\partial x = \pi(x)$, $\partial z/\partial y = \chi(y)$. Let us assume

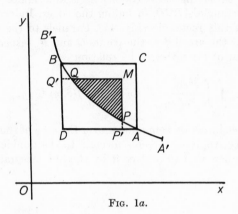

Fig. 1a.

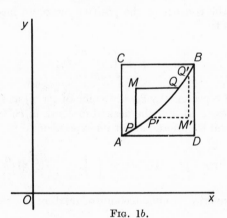

Fig. 1b.

further, for the sake of definiteness, that we know the value z_0 of the integral at a point A with coordinates (x_0, y_0); the value of this integral at any point whatever of the arc AB with coordinates (x, y) is given by the formula

$$(4) \qquad z(x, y) = z_0 + \int_{x_0}^{x} \pi(\xi)\,d\xi + \int_{y_0}^{y} \chi(\eta)\,d\eta.$$

We can therefore say that we assume as known the values of the
integral and its two partial derivatives $\partial z/\partial x$, $\partial z/\partial y$ at an arbitrary
point of AB, these three functions being connected by relation (4).
The integral satisfying these conditions is determined throughout
the entire rectangle $ABCD$, including the edges. Indeed, let M be
any point of this rectangle (Fig. 1*a*). Parallels to the axes drawn
from M meet the arc AB in the points Q and P, respectively, and
every integral of (1) satisfies the relation

(5)
$$\int \int \frac{\partial^2 z(\xi, \eta)}{\partial \xi \, \partial \eta} d\xi \, d\eta = \int \int f(\xi, \eta) \, d\xi \, d\eta,$$

the two double integrals being taken over the area of the curvilinear
triangle PMQ. Applying Green's formula to the double integral of
the first member, we can replace it by the line integral

$$\int \frac{\partial z}{\partial \eta} d\eta$$

taken around the contour in the positive sense, an integral which
clearly reduces to

$$z_M - z_P + \int_{(QP)} \frac{\partial z}{\partial \eta} d\eta;$$

for brevity, we represent by z_M the value of $z(x, y)$ at the point M
with coordinates (x, y). For the desired integral, $\partial z/\partial \eta = \chi(\eta)$ along
AB. This integral therefore has for its expression

$$z_M = z_P - \int_{(QP)} \chi(\eta) \, d\eta + \int \int_{(PMQ)} f(\xi, \eta) \, d\xi \, d\eta,$$

which we can rewrite, taking account of relation (4), as

(6)
$$z(x, y) = z_0 + \int_{x_0}^{x} \pi(\xi) \, d\xi + \int_{y_0}^{y} \chi(\eta) \, d\eta + \int \int_{(PMQ)} f(\xi, \eta) \, d\xi \, d\eta.$$

We verify that this function $z(x, y)$ is an integral of equation (1)
satisfying Cauchy's conditions, by observing that the double integral
of the second member is a particular integral of (1) which is zero,
as well as its partial derivatives of the first order for every point

of arc AB (I, **130**). We can again write formula (1) in the equivalent forms

$$(6') \qquad z_M = z_P + \int_{(PO)} \chi(\eta) \, d\eta + \int \int_{(PMQ)} f(\xi, \eta) \, d\xi \, d\eta,$$

$$(6'') \qquad z_M = z_Q + \int_{(QP)} \pi(\xi) \, d\xi + \int \int_{(PMQ)} f(\xi, \eta) \, d\xi \, d\eta,$$

in which only the values of the integral and of one of its derivatives along the arc AB are involved. We verify without difficulty that these formulas apply also in the case where arc AB has the position shown in Figure 1*b*, as long as the sign of the double integral is changed.

Integral (6) will be regular in the entire rectangle, provided that the functions $\pi(x)$ and $\chi(y)$ are continuous in this domain. If these functions have a finite number of points of discontinuities, the derivatives $\partial z/\partial x$, $\partial z/\partial y$ will be discontinuous along certain segments of characteristics. Similarly, if we are given the value of the integral $z = \Phi$ at any point whatever of AB, and the partial derivative $\partial z/\partial x = \pi(x)$, then in order that the function $z(x, y)$ represented by (6'') be regular, it is necessary that the difference

$$\Phi - \int_{x_0}^{x} \pi(\xi) \, d\xi$$

be a function of y possessing a continuous derivative along the arc AB.

The formulas which solve the problem give rise to several important remarks:

1. It is clear from these formulas that the value of the integral at the point M depends only upon the values assumed along arc PQ by the function and its derivatives of the first order, and consequently the value of $z(x, y)$ at an infinitely nearby point of arc AB depends only upon the values of z and its derivatives on that portion of arc AB *infinitely nearby* point M. These formulas (6), (6'), (6'') give z only in the interior of the rectangle $ABCD$, but the Cauchy data along AB determine an integral only in this domain. There exists in fact an infinity of integrals of (1), regular in a domain $\mathscr{D}$ containing the rectangle $ABCD$ and which coincide with the preceding integral in this rectangle. To comprehend clearly this essential point, let us prolong the arc AB in both

directions, in such a way as to obtain an arc $A'B'$ satisfying the same conditions as AB, and let us give along $A'B'$ two continuous functions of x and of y, respectively, which coincide with $\pi(x)$ and $\chi(y)$ in the portion AB. The integral of (1) which assumes the value z_0 at the point A and whose partial derivatives $\partial z/\partial x$, $\partial z/\partial y$ are equal to these functions along $A'B'$ is regular in the new rectangle $A'B'C'D'$, and it coincides with the integral (6) in the interior and on the sides of the rectangle $ABCD$. If the first integral has continuous partial derivatives up to the nth order, we can always choose new given values in such a way as to preserve the continuity of these derivatives when we leave the rectangle $ABCD$.

2. Let us consider in particular the equation $s = 0$ and the integral $Z(x, y)$ of this equation which, along the arc AB, reduces to a continuous function Φ of the parameter which fixes the position of a point on this arc, while $\partial z/\partial x$ is equal along AB to a continuous function $\Pi(x)$. This integral is represented by formula (6″), where we are assuming $f = 0$ and $\pi(\xi)$ replaced by $\Pi(\xi)$. Let us suppose that, along AB, the two functions Φ and $\Pi(x)$ can be expanded in the series

$$\Phi = \phi_1 + \phi_2 + \ldots + \phi_i + \ldots,$$

$$\Pi(x) = \pi_1(x) + \pi_2(x) + \ldots + \pi_i(x) + \ldots,$$

the second being *uniformly convergent*. The formula which gives $Z(x, y)$ can then be written as

$$(7) \qquad Z(x, y) = \sum_{i=1}^{\infty} \left[(\phi_i)_Q + \int_{(QP)} \pi_i(\xi)\, d\xi \right] = \sum_{i=1}^{+\infty} z_i(x, y),$$

where $z_i(x, y)$ is the integral which reduces to ϕ_i, while $\partial z_i/\partial x$ is equal to $\pi_i(x)$, along AB. This remark applies also to problems which we are going to treat in the following sections.

3. The first problem treated can be considered as a limiting case of Cauchy's problem. In fact, when we are given the function $\phi(x)$ to which an integral $z(x, y)$ reduces for $y = y_0$, we know thereby the derivative $\partial z/\partial x = \phi'(x)$ along this characteristic as well. The derivative $\partial z/\partial y$ also depends upon an arbitrary constant, but if we know in addition the function $\psi(y)$ to which $z(x, y)$ reduces for $x = x_0$, $\partial z/\partial y$ is known for $x = x_0$, $y = y_0$, and therefore its value is determined at every point of the characteristic $y = y_0$ (III, **18**). We are going to treat other problems where one is given the value

of the integral on certain arcs of the curve, which are not characteristics, along with the Cauchy data furnished for other portions of
the curves.

34. Mixed problems. Let $OABC$ be the rectangle bounded by
the lines $x = 0$, $x = a > 0$, $y = 0$, $y = b > 0$, and OD an arc of
the curve emanating from the origin and lying in this rectangle,
such that the parallel to the x-axis drawn from any point M of
this rectangle meets OD in one and only one point N. This arc
OD is represented by an equation $x = \pi(y)$, the function $\pi(y)$ being
continuous in the interval $(0, b)$. Let us propose finding an integral
$z(x, y)$ of (1) which reduces to a function $\phi(x)$ for $y = 0$, and to
another function $\psi(y)$ when the point M occurs on arc OD, the
two functions ϕ and ψ satisfying the condition $\phi(0) = \psi(0)$. If the
two functions $\phi(x)$ and $\psi(y)$ are determined in the intervals $(0, a)$ and

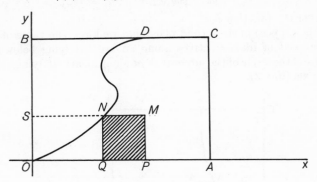

Fig. 2.

$(0, b)$, respectively, the desired integral is determined in the rectangle
$OACB$. We have indeed for any integral whatever of equation (1)

$$(8) \qquad \int\int_{(R)} \frac{\partial^2 z(\xi, \eta)}{d\xi \, d\eta} d\xi \, d\eta = \int\int_{(R)} f(\xi, \eta) \, d\xi \, d\eta,$$

the two double integrals being taken over the rectangle $MNQP$.
But the double integral of the first member is equal to
$z_M + z_Q - z_N - z_P$, and z_Q, z_N, z_P are known from the conditions
satisfied by the integral $z(x, y)$ under consideration; we therefore
have for the value of this integral at the point M with coordinates
(x, y) the following expression:

$$(9) \qquad z(x, y) = \phi(x) + \psi(y) - \phi[\eta(y)] + \int\int_{(R)} f(\xi, \eta) \, d\xi \, d\eta,$$

and we readily see that the sign of the double integral must be changed when the point M lies between arc OD and the y-axis. Conversely, the function $z(x, y)$ represented by this formula satisfies all the desired conditions. On the one hand, it is evident that it reduces to $\phi(x)$ when the point M lies on OA and to $\psi(y)$ when M lies on the arc OD. On the other hand, it is an integral of (1), for the double integral which is in the second member is the difference of two double integrals, one of which is taken over the rectangle $OPMS$ and the other of which over the rectangle $OQNS$, and this last integral depends only upon y. This integral $z(x, y)$ is regular in the rectangle $OACB$ provided that the functions ϕ, ψ, π have continuous derivatives in the corresponding intervals. We shall observe that at the origin the partial derivatives p_0 and q_0 satisfy the relation

$$(10) \qquad q_0 + p_0\pi'(0) = \psi'(0),$$

whatever the function $\phi(x)$.

Let us suppose in the second place that we know the value of the integral and of its derivatives along an arc OA lying below the x-axis and the value of the integral alone along an arc OE lying above the x-axis (Fig. 3).

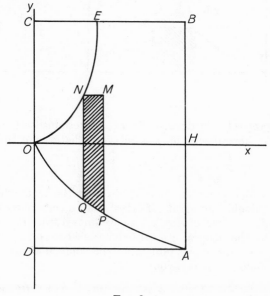

FIG. 3.

Arc OA is intersected in only one point by a parallel to each axis in the rectangle $ODAH$, while in the rectangle $OHBC$ arc OE is intersected in one and only one point by every parallel to the x-axis. We have the Cauchy data along arc OA, and consequently the integral is determined in the entire rectangle $ODAH$ and in particular on OH. Knowing the values of the integral on OH and on OE, we are led back to the preceding problem, assuming, of course, that the given values for the integral approach the same limit at the point O, on the two arcs OA and OE. But there is occasion to make an essential remark. Let us call $z_1(x, y)$ the integral which is determined in the rectangle $ODAH$ by the Cauchy data, along OA, and $z_2(x, y)$ the integral determined in the rectangle $OHBC$ which coincides with $z_1(x, y)$ along OH, and which reduces to a known function $z = \psi(y)$ along arc OE, the latter having for its equation $x = \pi(y)$. These two integrals are equal at all points of OH, and therefore the same is true of their derivatives $\partial z_1/\partial x$, $\partial z_2/\partial x$ but nothing shows that the same will be true of the derivatives $\partial z_1/\partial y$, $\partial z_2/\partial y$ and this will not occur if the given values are arbitrary. In order for it to be so, it is sufficient that these derivatives be equal at the origin (III, **17**). Let us call

$$(p_1)_0, \qquad (q_1)_0, \qquad (p_2)_0, \qquad (q_2)_0$$

the values of the derivatives of z_1 and z_2 at the origin; $(p_1)_0$ and $(q_1)_0$ are known from the Cauchy conditions relative to the arc OA. We have in addition $(p_2)_0 = (p_1)_0$; in order to have $(q_2)_0 = (q_1)_0$ also, it is necessary and sufficient, from the remark just now made, that we have

$$(q_1)_0 + (p_1)_0 \, \pi'(0) = \psi'(0).$$

When this condition is satisfied, the integral which coincides with $z_1(x, y)$ in the rectangle $ODAH$ and with $z_2(x, y)$ in the rectangle $OHBC$ is regular in the entire rectangle $ABCD$. Its value at a point of rectangle $ODAH$ is furnished by formula (6). We can directly obtain its value at a point of the rectangle $OHBC$ by starting with the relation

$$\int \int \frac{\partial^2 z(\xi, \eta)}{\partial \xi \, \partial \eta} \, \partial \xi \, d\eta = \int \int f(\xi, \eta) \, d\xi \, d\eta,$$

the two double integrals being taken over the curvilinear quadrilateral $MNQP$, and by applying Green's formula to the first member.

We thus find

(11)

$$z_M = z_P + z_N - z_Q + \int_{(PQ)} \chi(\eta)\,d\eta + \int\int_{(MNQP)} f(\xi,\eta)\,d\xi\,d\eta$$

by assuming that along OA the derivative $\partial z/\partial y$ reduces to $\chi(y)$. The double integral which is in the second member must be changed in sign when the point M is between arc OE and OC.

We could imagine many other combinations to determine an integral, for example by assuming the Cauchy data known along an arc AB, and the values of the integral along the two arcs of the curve AC, BD coming from the points A and B. The problem of the vibrating string (III, **37**) will provide us with an example of this type.

35. Determination of an integral from its values along two curves. The last problem treated will not be determinate if we have been given only the values of the integral along two arcs OA and OE, since we can again choose arbitrarily the function to which one of the partial derivatives of z reduces along OA. But it is no longer the same when the two arcs lie in the same angle of the characteristics. Let us consider in the rectangle $OABC$ two arcs OD, OE of a curve passing through the origin, of which the lower arc OD is met in only one point by a parallel to the y-axis, while the arc OE is met in only one point by a parallel to the x-axis. Let $y = \pi(x)$, $x = \chi(y)$ be the equations of these two arcs of the curve which we have represented by dotted lines for convenience in drawing (Fig. 4). There exists one and only one integral of equation (1) which reduces to a given function $\phi(x)$ along OD, and to another given function $\psi(y)$ along OE; we can obviously assume that these two functions are zero at the origin.

We shall first consider the case where $\phi(x)$ and $\psi(y)$ are identically zero.

Beginning from any point M whatever of the rectangle $OABC$, we draw two broken lines. One of them, L, drawn in the heavy line, is obtained by drawing through M the line Mm_1 parallel to the y-axis up to its intersection at m_1 with OD; then the parallel m_1p_1 to the x-axis, the parallel p_1m_2 to the y-axis, and so on alternately. The second broken line, L', the dotted line, is obtained by an analogous construction, beginning with the parallel Mn_1 to the x-axis. It is clear that these two broken lines have an infinite number of vertices and that they approach the origin more and more.

This granted, let I and I' be the double integrals $\iint f(\xi, \eta)\, d\xi\, d\eta$ taken, respectively, over the portions of the plane comprised, on the one hand, between the x-axis, the line L, and the ordinate MP, and on the other hand, between the y-axis, the line L' and the line MQ. It is clear that these integrals depend, respectively, only upon x

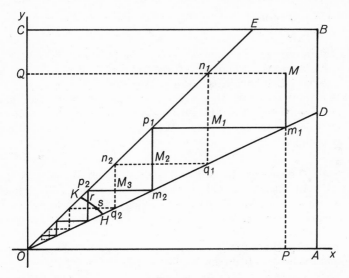

FIG. 4.

and upon y, and that the two lines L and L' coincide when point M lies on one of the lines OD, OE. The function

$$z(x, y) = \int_0^x \int_0^y f(\xi, \eta)\, d\xi\, d\eta - I - I'$$

is therefore an integral of the equation $\partial^2 z/\partial x \partial y = f(x, y)$ which becomes zero when the point M lies on OD or on OE.

To treat the case when the functions $\phi(x)$ and $\psi(y)$ are arbitrary, let us designate by $F(x, y)$ the double integral

$$\int_0^x \int_0^y f(\xi, \eta)\, d\xi\, d\eta$$

which is a regular function in the rectangle $OABC$. If $Z(x, y)$ is another regular integral of equation (1), we have $\partial^2(Z - F)/\partial x \partial y = 0$, and, consequently, by considering successively all the rectangles

$Mn_1M_1m_1$, $M_1p_1M_2q_1$, $M_2n_2M_3m_2$, ... we can write the series of equalities (I, 130):

$$(12) \quad \begin{cases} Z_M + Z_{M_1} - Z_{m_1} - Z_{n_1} = F_M + F_{M_1} - F_{n_1} - F_{m_1}, \\ Z_{M_1} + Z_{M_2} - Z_{p_1} - Z_{q_1} = F_{M_1} + F_{M_2} - F_{p_1} - F_{q_1}, \\ Z_{M_2} + Z_{M_3} - Z_{m_2} - Z_{n_2} = F_{M_2} + F_{M_3} - F_{m_2} - F_{n_2}, \\ \dots\dots\dots\dots\dots\dots\dots\dots\dots\dots\dots\dots\dots \end{cases}$$

In this sequence of equalities, everything is known except Z_M, Z_{M_1}, ... In order to eliminate these unknowns, it is sufficient to add the preceding equalities, after having multiplied them by $+1$ and -1 alternately. We thus obtain Z_M expressed in a series, and we prove conversely that this series is convergent and represents a regular function in the rectangle $OABC$, satisfying the conditions of the problem.[2]

Remark. Let us cut the two arcs OD, OE by an arc such as HK (Fig. 4). An integral would be determined in an easily defined domain if we knew the Cauchy data along KH and the values of the integral along HD and KE. In the case of the figure, the value of the integral at M would be obtained by adding to the three equalities (12) the formula obtained by the application of Green's theorem to the double integral

$$\int \int \frac{\partial^2 (Z - F)}{\partial \xi\, d\eta} d\xi\, d\eta$$

taken over the area of the curvilinear pentagon $M_3p_2rsq_3$, and then eliminating the unknowns Z_{M_1}, Z_{M_2}, Z_{M_3}.

36. Rectilinear motion of a gas. Let us consider a cylindrical tube filled with gas, closed at one end O, and open at the other; if we impart to the plane cross section at O a certain motion by means of the inner surface or of a moving piston, there occur for the column of air contained in the cylinder certain modifications which are studied in acoustics. Let MN be a cross section of gas located at the distance x from O, let z be its displacement at time t; z is a function of x and of t, and physical considerations show that

---

[2] E. Goursat, *Annales de la Faculté des Sciences de Toulouse*, 2nd series, Vol. VI, 1904, p. 117.

z satisfies the partial differential equation

(13)
$$\frac{\partial^2 z}{\partial t^2} = a^2 \frac{\partial^2 z}{\partial x^2}$$

a being a constant. This equation reduces to the form $\partial^2 z/\partial \xi \partial \eta = 0$ by taking as new variables $\xi = x + at$, $\eta = x - at$, provided that we assume the second partial derivatives of z to be continuous (I, **41**), and consequently the characteristics are represented in the xt-plane by the two families of lines $x \pm at = C$.

The integral sought for must satisfy the following conditions: at the beginning instant $t = 0$, the inner walls and the column of air are at rest, that is, we have $z = 0$, $\partial z/\partial t = 0$ for $t = 0$, $x \geq 0$; these are the Cauchy data along the positive part of the x-axis; we impart to the initial cross section a motion whose law is known, that is, for $x = 0$, $t \geq 0$, z must reduce to a function $f(t)$ which, with its derivative, vanishes for $t = 0$. The problem to be solved is therefore a *mixed problem* and the solution is easily arrived at from the general theory of III, **34**. Let us draw through the origin the two characteristics $x = \pm at$ (Fig. 5). Since z and $\partial z/\partial t$ are zero along the

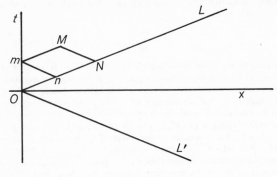

Fig. 5.

x-axis, z is also zero in the entire angle LOL' formed by the characteristics, and in particular along OL. To get the value of z at a point $M(x, t)$ lying above OL, let us draw Mm parallel to OL, and the parallels MN, mn to the second characteristic. From what we have seen much earlier, we must have

$$Z_M + Z_n = Z_N + Z_m;$$

and therefore $Z_M = Z_m$. Now, the ordinate of the point m is $t - x/a$, and consequently

$$Z_M = f\left(t - \frac{x}{a}\right).$$

To sum up, the desired integral has for its expression

$$z = 0 \quad \left(\text{for } t \leq \frac{x}{a}\right), \quad z = f\left(t - \frac{x}{a}\right) \quad \left(\text{for } t \geq \frac{x}{a}\right).$$

We see that the cross section, at a distance x from the initial cross section, remains at rest as long as $t \leq x/a$; the constant a therefore represents the speed of propagation of the wave. If we cease to have an effect on the initial cross section at the end of a time T, the function $f(t)$ remains constant for $t \geq T$; the cross section of abscissa x which gets in motion at the instant x/a returns to rest from the instant $(x/a) + T$ on. Since the integral depends only upon $t - (x/a)$, we see that the wave is propagated completely with no interior change; we say that such a wave is *regular*.[3]

---

[3] In reality, equation (13) is suitable only for *small movements* in the gas. The precise equation is

$$(13') \quad \frac{\partial^2 z}{\partial t^2} = [\psi'(p)]^2 \frac{\partial^2 z}{\partial x^2}, \quad p = \frac{\partial z}{\partial x}, \quad \psi(p) = -\frac{1}{k}(1 + p)^{\frac{1-m}{2}},$$

k and m being two constants of which the second, m, is greater than unity. We pass from (13') to the simplified equation of the text by assuming that the variations of $\psi'(p)$ during the motion are infinitely small, and by replacing $\psi'(p)$ by a constant a. But we can also solve the proposed problem for equation (13'), that is, find an integral $z(x, t)$ of this equation, which together with its first order derivatives $p = \partial x/\partial z$, $q = \partial z/\partial t$ is continuous for $x > 0$, $t \geq 0$, which vanishes for $t = 0$ whatever the value of x, and which reduces for $x = 0$ to a function $f(t)$, which, as well as its derivative $f'(t)$, is zero for $t = 0$. From the physical significance of this problem, a point on the positive half of the x-axis remains at rest until a certain moment $t = \phi(x)$, $\phi(x)$ being a positive and increasing function; that is, there is a propagation by waves. The surface which represents the integral sought after therefore coincides with the plane $z = 0$ in the region comprised between the x-axis and the curve $t = \phi(x)$. Above this curve C, the desired solution is represented by a surface tangent to the xy-plane along C, and we are brought back to the problem of Hugoniot (III, **20**).

We have seen above that this integral surface S is a developable surface tangent to the xy-plane along the curve C, which is a characteristic for the solution $z = 0$. In the present case, the characteristics lying in the xy-plane are the two systems of lines $t = t_0 \pm \dfrac{x}{\psi'(0)}$. Since the curve C must pass through the origin and lie in the angle xOt, if the initial cross section begins

continued on page 127

Let us consider in the second place a cylinder infinite in both directions. We shall assume that the initial disturbance has been produced in a bounded portion of the tube; analytically, this is tantamount to saying that for $t = 0$, z and $\partial z/\partial t$ must reduce to given functions $f(x)$ and $\phi(x)$ which are zero outside an interval $(0, 1)$. This is the Cauchy problem itself, the data being valid along the entire x-axis, and we can foresee without any calculation the nature of the solution. Through the origin and through the point A of abscissa l on the x-axis let us draw the characteristics; these lines divide the plane into a certain number of regions (Fig. 6). Let MP, MQ be the two characteristics which pass through a point

---

continued from page 126

its motion at the instant $t = 0$, this curve C necessarily coincides with line D, $x = t\psi'(0)$, and we have already seen that the wave is propagated with constant velocity $\psi'(0)$.

To effect the determination of the surface S, we notice that it must satisfy one of the two equations $\psi(p) \pm q = \psi(0)$, for the differential equations of the two systems of characteristics of equation (13′) possess the two integral combinations

$$d[q + \psi(p)] = 0, \qquad d[q - \psi(p)] = 0.$$

The first is proper for the characteristics of the system to which the line D does not belong, and, consequently, we must take the $+$ sign before q. This first order equation is also written

$$(e) \qquad \frac{\partial z}{\partial x} = \left(1 + k\frac{\partial z}{\partial t}\right)^{\frac{2}{1-m}} - 1,$$

and we are led to look for an integral of this first order equation passing through the plane curve Γ of the zt-plane, represented by the equation $z = f(t)$. Now, equation (e) has the complete integral composed of planes (II, 2, **82**),

$$z = [(1 + ka)^{2/(1-m)} - 1]x + at + b,$$

and the integral sought for is the envelop of this plane when we establish a relation between a and b such that it includes a tangent to Γ (II, 2, **83**). The equation of the plane P passing through the tangent to L at the point with coordinates $[0, \lambda, f(\lambda)]$ is, as is readily seen,

$$z = f(\lambda) + f'(\lambda)(t - \lambda) + \{[1 + kf'(\lambda)]^{2/(1-m)} - 1\}x.$$

Between the line D and the t-axis, the desired function $z(x, t)$ is therefore represented on the developable surface, the envelop of plane P, depending upon the variable parameter λ.

If a portion of the edge of regression of this surface projects into the angle xOt, the second derivatives r, s, t become infinite at these points. This discontinuity corresponds to the *Riemann-Hugoniot phenomenon*. (For the complete study of the rectilinear motion of a gas, see Hadamard, *Leçons sur la propagation des ondes*, Chap. IV.)

M; we have seen that the value of the integral at M is expressed by an integral taken along PQ, which depends only upon the given functions $f(x)$ and $\phi(x)$. These functions being zero to the right of A and to the left of O, the desired integral is zero in the regions (I) and (I′), it is equal to a constant K in the region (II), and to the same constant with its sign changed, $-K$, in region (II′). In one of the regions marked by horizontal hatchings only, it preserves a constant value when M is displaced parallel to the characteristic OB; it is therefore a function of $x - at$; similarly, in one, of the regions marked only by vertical hatchings, it is a function of $x + at$. Finally, in the parallelogram $OCAB$, it depends simultaneously upon $x + at$ and upon $x - at$.

It is easy to verify these conclusions by the calculus. The general integral of equation (13) is $z = F(x + at) + \Phi(x - at)$, the functions F and Φ being determined within an additive constant. These functions must satisfy the initial conditions

$$F(x) + \Phi(x) = f(x), \quad F'(x) - \Phi'(x) = \frac{1}{a}\phi(x);$$

we may assume $F(0) = \Phi(0)$, and consequently set

$$F(x) - \Phi(x) = \frac{1}{a}\int_0^x \phi(x)\,dx = \psi(x);$$

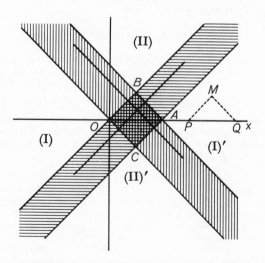

Fɪɢ. 6.

the desired integral therefore has for its expression [cf. III, **29,** formula (22)]

(14) $z = \frac{1}{2}[f(x + at) + \psi(x + at)] + \frac{1}{2}[f(x - at) - \psi(x - at)].$

Let us recall that $f(x)$ is zero outside the interval $(0, l)$, that $\psi(x)$ is zero for $x \leq 0$, and preserves a constant value H for $x \geq l$. Applying formula (14) to each of the regions of the plane successively, it is easy to reach again the preceding conclusions. Let us give, for example, to x a constant value $x_1 > l$. When t varies from 0 to $(x_1 - l)/a$, $f(x_1 + at)$ and $f(x_1 - at)$ are zero, $\psi(x_1 + at)$ and $\psi(x_1 - at)$ have the same constant value H; we therefore have $z = 0$. When t varies from $(x_1 - l)/a$ to x_1/a, $f(x_1 + at) = 0$, $\psi(x_1 + at) = H$, and z has the expression $H/2 + \frac{1}{2}[f(x_1 - at) - \psi(x_1 - at)]$. Finally, for $t \geq x_1/a, f(x_1 + at), f(x_1 - at)$ and $\psi(x_1 - at)$ are zero, and $z = H/2$. The wave reaches the cross section with abscissa x_1 at the instant $(x_1 - l)/a$, and this cross section remains at rest, with a constant displacement $H/2$, at the instant x_1/a. We would see in the same way that there exists a regular wave which is propagated to the left. Everything happens to sum up, as though the initial disturbance arose from the superposition of two regular waves which break up to be propagated, one to the right, the other to the left, with a velocity a.

We can also come up again with formula (22) (Chap. III) by making the change of variable $x + at = \xi$, $x - at = \eta$, and applying the general formula (6) to the transformed equation (see Exercise 2).

37. Vibrating strings. Suppose an elastic string OA of length l is fixed at its two extremities, and that we displace it from its position of equilibrium. The displacement z normal to the string at a point with abscissa x and at time t, is a function of the variables x and t which also satisfies equation (13). This unknown function z must also satisfy other conditions: 1. *the initial conditions*, which express the fact that at the initial instant $t = 0$ we know, for each value of x, z and $\partial z/\partial t$, say $z = f(x)$, $\partial z/\partial t = \phi(x)$, these functions being zero for $x = 0$ and for $x = l$; 2. *the boundary conditions*, which express the fact that the extremities of the string are fixed, that is to say, that z is zero, for any t, at $x = 0$ and $x = l$; we encounter again a mixed problem. Through the point A of abscissa l on the x-axis, let us draw the characteristic $x + at = l$, and At', parallel to the t-axis, and through the origin the characteristic $x - at = 0$

(Fig. 7). The data are those of Cauchy on OA, and we must have $z = 0$ on the lines Ot and At'.

The Cauchy data determine the integral in the triangle OAB. Having the values of the integral along OO_1 and OB, it is determined in triangle OBO_1; in the same way, the integral is determined in the

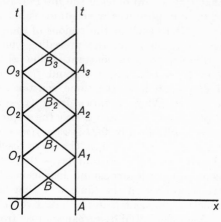

FIG. 7.

triangle ABA_1 by its value along AB and AA_1.[4] Knowing the values of the integral along BO_1 and BA_1, it is determined in the parallelogram $O_1BA_1A_1$; continuing thus, we see step by step that it is determined in the entire region comprised between the parallels Ot, At', above the x-axis.

Let $z = F(x + at) + \Phi(x - at)$ be the integral sought; from the initial conditions we must have

$$F(x) + \Phi(x) = f(x), \qquad F'(x) - \Phi'(x) = \frac{\phi(x)}{a}.$$

From this we deduce, as just above,

$$F(x) = \frac{f(x) + \psi(x)}{2}, \qquad \Phi(x) = \frac{f(x) - \psi(x)}{2},$$

setting

$$\psi(x) = \frac{1}{a} \int_0^x \phi(x)\, dx.$$

---

[4] These integrals agree with each other along AB and OB, for as a result of the data, $\partial z/\partial x$ and $\partial z/\partial t$ are zero at the points O and A (see III, **34**).

These formulas define the two functions $F(u)$, $\Phi(u)$ only for the values of u taken between 0 and 1. In order that the solution have a meaning, it is necessary that $F(u)$ be defined for all positive values of the argument, and $\Phi(u)$ for all negative values. The end conditions give the relations

$$F(at) + \Phi(-at) = 0, \qquad F(l + at) + \Phi(l - at) = 0,$$

whatever the value of t, so that we can write, replacing at by u,

$$F(u) + \Phi(-u) = 0, \qquad F(l + u) + \Phi(l - u) = 0, \quad u > 0.$$

From the first we deduce that $\Phi(-u) = -F(u)$, which shows that the function Φ will be determined for all negative values of u if $F(u)$ is known for the positive values of u. When u varies from 0 to l, $l - u$ decreases from l to 0, $\Phi(l - u)$ is known; the same is therefore true of $F(l + u)$, and consequently $F(u)$ is determined from 0 to $2l$. On the other hand, replacing u by $u + l$ in the second of the preceding relations, we have

$$F(2l + u) + \Phi(-u) = 0,$$

and therefore

$$F(2l + u) = F(u).$$

The function $F(u)$ having the period $2l$, it is therefore determined for every positive value of u, and therefore the same is true of $\Phi(u)$ for $u < 0$.

Bernoulli's method. Let us seek first of all the particular integrals of equation (13) of the form $U(x)V(t)$, the function $U(x)$ being zero for $x = 0$ and for $x = l$. We must have

$$\frac{U''(x)}{U(x)} = \frac{1}{a^2} \frac{V''(t)}{V(t)},$$

and therefore the common value of these ratios must reduce to a constant K. In order for the equation $U''(x) = KU(x)$ to have a particular integral vanishing for $x = 0$ and $x = l$, K must be of the form $-(n^2\pi^2/l^2)$, n being an integer, and we then obtain an infinity of integrals of (13) of the wanted form

$$z = \sin\frac{n\pi x}{l}\left(C\cos\frac{an\pi t}{l} + C'\sin\frac{an\pi t}{l}\right),$$

each of which defines a vibratory motion of period $2l/na$. For $t = 0$, this integral reduces to $C \sin n\pi x/l$, while $\partial z/\partial t$ is equal to

$$\frac{an\pi}{l} C' \sin \frac{n\pi x}{l}.$$

This being the case, let us suppose that the two functions $f(x)$ and $\phi(x)$ can be expanded in a sine series in the interval $(0, l)$,

$$(15) \qquad f(x) = \sum_{n=1}^{+\infty} A_n \sin \frac{n\pi x}{l}, \quad \phi(x) = \sum_{n=1}^{+\infty} B_n \sin \frac{n\pi x}{l}.$$

It is clear that the series

$$(16) \quad z = \sum_{n=1}^{+\infty} A_n \sin \frac{n\pi x}{l} \cos \frac{an\pi t}{l} + \sum_{n=1}^{+\infty} B_n \frac{l}{an\pi} \sin \frac{n\pi x}{l} \sin \frac{an\pi t}{l}$$

satisfies equation (13) formally, and that it reduces to $f(x)$, while the series obtained by differentiating it term by term with respect to t reduces to $\phi(x)$, for $t = 0$. This is Bernoulli's solution. It clearly lacks rigor, but it is possible to justify it by means of several hypotheses of a very general nature. Indeed we are able to represent the desired solution, in the interior of triangle OAB, by formula (22) (Chap. III); it then results that if the series $\phi(x)$ is uniformly convergent, the desired integral is represented in this triangle by the sum of the series Σz_n obtained by taking as terms the integrals which correspond to the initial conditions

$$z_n = A_n \sin \frac{n\pi x}{l}, \quad \frac{dz_n}{\partial t} = B_n \sin \frac{n\pi x}{l} \quad \text{(for } t = 0\text{)};$$

it is therefore represented by Bernoulli's series (16). From the manner in which the values of the integral at any point whatever were deduced from the values which it assumes in the triangle OAB, it is evident that the formula is valid in the entire domain. Now, from a general proposition on Fourier series, series (15) are uniformly convergent, if the functions $f(x)$ and $\phi(x)$, satisfying Dirichlet's conditions, are continuous.[5] (Cf. III, **33**, Remark 1.)

---

[5] See, for example, the *Traité d'Analyse* by Picard, (Vol. I, 2nd edition, p. 256.)

II. SUCCESSIVE APPROXIMATIONS.
RIEMANN'S METHOD

38. Determinations of an integral from its values along two characteristics. We are going to take up again, for a linear equation of the general form of the hyperbolic type

(17) $$\frac{\partial^2 z}{\partial x \, \partial y} = a \, \frac{\partial x}{\partial z} + b \, \frac{\partial z}{\partial y} + cz + f(x, y),$$

the problems already solved for the elementary equation $s = f(x, y)$; the functions $a(x, y)$, $b(x, y)$, $c(x, y)$, $f(x, y)$ are assumed continuous. Let us propose first of all to find an integral which reduces for $y = y_0$ to a given function $\phi(x)$ and, for $x = x_0$, to another function $\psi(y)$, satisfying the condition $\psi(y_0) = \phi(x_0)$. We may evidently assume $x_0 = y_0 = 0$; we shall further admit, for the sake of definiteness, that $\phi(x)$ is defined in an interval $(0, \alpha)$ and $\psi(y)$ in an interval $(0, \beta)$, α and β being two positive numbers, and we shall try to determine the integral in the rectangle R bounded by the lines $x = 0$, $x = \alpha$, $y = 0$, $y = \beta$. The method we are going to follow is due to Picard.[6] Let us write equation (17) in the somewhat more general form

(18) $$\frac{\partial^2 z}{\partial x \, \partial y} = \lambda \left[a(x, y) \, \frac{\partial z}{\partial x} + b(x, y) \, \frac{\partial z}{\partial y} + c(x, y)z \right] + f(x, y),$$

λ being a parameter which we shall then take as unity in the result, and let us first of all look for a power series in λ,

(19) $$z = z_0(x, y) + \lambda z_1(x, y) + \ldots + \lambda^n z_n(x, y) + \ldots$$

formally satisfying equation (18) and the initial conditions. For $\lambda = 0$, equation (18) reduces to the equation already studied, $s = f(x, y)$, and consequently we shall take for the first term of series (19) the function

$$z_0(x, y) = \phi(x) + \psi(y) - \phi(0) + \int_0^x d\zeta \int_0^y f(\zeta, \eta) \, d\eta,$$

which reduces to $\phi(x)$ for $y = 0$ and to $\psi(y)$ for $x = 0$; the other coefficients $z_1, z_2, \ldots$ must all be zero for $x = 0$, whatever y may be,

---

[6] *Journal de Mathématiques* (1890). Note I of Vol. IV of the *Leçons sur la Théorie des surfaces* by Darboux.

and for $y = 0$, whatever x. Equating the two coefficients of λ in the two members of equation (18), after the substitution, we get

$$z_1(x, y) = \int_0^x d\xi \int_0^y \left[a(\xi, \eta)\frac{dz_0}{\partial \xi} + b(\xi, \eta)\frac{\partial z_0}{\partial \eta} + c(\xi, \eta)z_0 \right] d\eta,$$

and in a general way $z_n(x, y)$ is derived from $z_{n-1}(x, y)$ by the recurrence formula

$$(20) \qquad z_n(x, y) = \int_0^x d\xi \int_0^y \left[a(\xi, \eta)\frac{\partial z_{n-1}}{\partial \xi} \right. $$

$$\left. + b(\xi, \eta)\frac{\partial z_{n-1}}{\partial \eta} + c(\xi, \eta)z_{n-1} \right] d\eta.$$

The result obtained in this manner does not differ from that which we should have obtained by the application of the method of successive approximations, the first approximate value being $z_0(x, y)$. The second approximation will evidently be $z_0 + \lambda z_1$, the third $z_0 + \lambda z_1 + \lambda^2 z_2$, and, generally, the nth approximation will be precisely the sum of the first n terms of series (19). If the functions $\phi(x)$ and $\psi(y)$ are continuous and have a continuous derivative in the intervals $(0, \alpha)$ and $(0, \beta)$, every function $z_n(x, y)$ will be regular in the rectangle R.

To prove the convergence of series (19), we shall rely upon the following remark: let $z(x, y)$ be a regular function in R, and $Z(x, y)$ the double integral

$$Z(x, y) = \int_0^x d\xi \int_0^y \left[a(\xi, \eta)\frac{\partial z}{\partial \xi} + b(\xi, \eta)\frac{\partial z}{\partial \eta} + c(\xi, \eta)z \right] d\eta;$$

if we replace the coefficients a, b, c by other positive coefficients A, B, C, constants or variables, but greater in absolute value than the coefficients a, b, c; and if similarly we replace $z(x, y)$ by another function $u(x, y)$, such that u, $\partial u/\partial x$, $\partial u/\partial y$ are dominant functions in R for z, $\partial z/\partial x$, $\partial z/\partial y$, it is clear that $Z(x, y)$ will be replaced by another function $U(x, y)$ which will be positive along with its derivatives in R, and that we shall have at every point of this domain

$$|Z| < U, \qquad \left| \frac{\partial Z}{\partial x} \right| < \frac{\partial U}{\partial x}, \qquad \left| \frac{\partial Z}{\partial y} \right| < \frac{\partial U}{\partial y}.$$

This being so, let us assume that we have, at every point of R,

$$(21)\begin{cases} |z_{n-1}(x, y)| < H\,\dfrac{(x + y)^n}{n!}, & \left|\dfrac{\partial z_{n-1}}{\partial x}\right| < H\,\dfrac{(x + y)^{n-1}}{(n - 1)!} \\[3mm] \left|\dfrac{\partial z_{n-1}}{\partial y}\right| < H\,\dfrac{(x + y)^{n-1}}{(n - 1)!}, \end{cases}$$

H being a positive number. Let M be the upper bound of the absolute values of the coefficients a, b, c in R; from the preceding remark, we shall have

$$|z_n(x, y)| < \int_0^x \int_0^y MH\left[\,2\,\frac{(x + y)^{n-1}}{(n - 1)!} + \frac{(x + y)^n}{n!}\,\right] dx\,dy,$$

and *a fortiori*

$$|z_n(x, y)| < H\,\frac{(x + y)^{n+1}}{(n + 1)!}\left[\,2M + \frac{M(x + y)}{n + 2}\,\right],$$

and we see similarly that $|\partial z_n/\partial x|$ and $|\partial z_n/\partial y|$ are less than

$$H\,\frac{(x + y)^n}{n!}\left[\,2M + \frac{M(x + y)}{n + 1}\,\right].$$

Therefore inequalities (21) imply the following

$$(21)\begin{cases} |z_n(x, y)| < HK\,\dfrac{(x + y)^{n+1}}{(n + 1)!}, & \left|\dfrac{\partial z_n}{\partial x}\right| < HK\,\dfrac{(x + y)^n}{n!}, \\[3mm] \left|\dfrac{\partial z_n}{\partial y}\right| < HK\,\dfrac{(x + y)^n}{n!}, \end{cases}$$

K being a positive number which depends only upon M and the dimensions of rectangle R. If L is an upper bound of

$$|z_0|,\quad \left|\frac{\partial z_0}{\partial x}\right|,\quad \left|\frac{\partial z_0}{\partial y}\right|,$$

we have at first

$$|z_1(x, y)| < 3\,MLxy,\quad \left|\frac{\partial z_1}{\partial x}\right| < 3\,MLy,\quad \left|\frac{\partial z_1}{\partial y}\right| < 3\,MLx,$$

and *a fortiori*

$$|z_1(x, y)| < 3 \, ML \, \frac{(x + y)^2}{1 \cdot 2}, \quad \left| \frac{\partial z_1}{\partial x} \right| < 3 \, ML \, (x + y),$$

$$\left| \frac{\partial z_1}{\partial y} \right| < 3 \, ML \, (x + y).$$

We deduce from these, reasoning step by step, the inequalities

$$|z_n(x, y)| < 3 \, MLK^{n-1} \, \frac{(x + y)^{n+1}}{(n + 1)!}, \quad \left| \frac{\partial z_n}{\partial x} \right| < 3 \, MLK^{n-1} \, \frac{(x + y)^n}{n!}, \ldots,$$

which prove that series (19) and the two series obtained from it by differentiation are uniformly convergent in the domain R. Let $z(x, y)$ be the sum of series (19), which is a regular function in R. To prove that it is indeed an integral of equation (18), it is sufficient to observe that, in the manner in which we have determined the successive coefficients z_n, we have

$$S_n(x, y) = \phi(x) + \psi(y) - \phi(0) + \int_0^x \int_0^y f(\xi, \eta) \, d\xi \, d\eta$$

$$+ \lambda \int_0^x d\xi \int_0^y \left[a(\xi, \eta) \, \frac{\partial S_{n-1}}{\partial \xi} + \ldots + c(\xi, \eta) \, S_{n-1} \right] d\eta,$$

$S_n(x, p)$ being the sum of the first n terms of series (19). When n increases indefinitely, S_{n-1}, $\partial S_{n-1}/\partial x$, $\partial S_{n-1}/\partial y$, approach $z(x, y)$, $\partial z/\partial x$, $\partial z/\partial y$ uniformly, and we have in the limit

$$(22) \quad z(x, y) = \phi(x) + \psi(y) - \phi(0) + \int_0^x \int_0^y f(\xi, \eta) \, d\xi \, d\eta$$

$$+ \lambda \int_0^x d\xi \int_0^y \left[a(\xi, \eta) \, \frac{\partial z}{\partial \xi} + b(\xi, \eta) \, \frac{\partial z}{\partial \eta} + c(\xi, \eta)z \right] d\eta.$$

The function $z(x, y)$ is therefore indeed an integral of (18) and it is clear that it also satisfies the initial conditions.

It is the only integral regular in R *satisfying these conditions.* Indeed, let $Z(x, y)$ be an integral satisfying these conditions; let us set

$$Z - S_n = U_n(x, y),$$

S_n having always the same meaning. Comparing the expression for

S_n written above with the formula

$$Z(x, y) = \phi(x) + \psi(y) - \phi(0) + \int_0^x \int_0^y f(\xi, \eta) \, d\xi \, d\eta$$

$$+ \lambda \int_0^x \int_0^y \left[a(\xi, \eta) \frac{\partial Z}{\partial \xi} + b(\xi, \eta) \frac{\partial Z}{\partial \eta} + c(\xi, \eta)Z \right] d\xi \, d\eta,$$

we get

$$U_n(x, y) = \lambda \int_0^x d\xi \int_0^y \left[a(\xi, \eta) \frac{\partial U_{n-1}}{\partial \xi} \right.$$

$$\left. + b(\xi, \eta) \frac{\partial U_{n-1}}{\partial \eta} + c(\xi, \eta) \, U_{n-1}(\xi, \eta) \right] d\eta.$$

It follows from the calculation just made that $U_n(x, y)$ approaches zero when n increases indefinitely, whatever may be the function $U_0(x, y)$ with which we have started defining the sequence of functions $U_1, U_2, \ldots, U_n, \ldots$ The integral $Z(x, y)$ is therefore the limit of $S_n(x, y)$, that is, it is identical with $z(x, y)$.

If the functions $\phi(x)$, $\psi(y)$ or their derivatives $\phi'(x)$, $\psi'(y)$ have a finite number of discontinuities in the intervals $(0, \alpha)$ and $(0, \beta)$, while remaining bounded, the functions $z_1, z_2, \ldots$ are still regular in the domain R, and the integral $z(x, y)$ represented by series (19) is itself regular in R, except along a finite number of segments of characteristics (*cf.* III, 33).

39. Riemann's function. The problem which has just been treated can always be reduced to the particular case where the two functions $\phi(x)$ and $\psi(y)$ are identically zero, by taking for the unknown $z - \phi(x) - \psi(y) + \phi(0)$ in place of z. This transformation only modifies the expression for $f(x, y)$ without changing the coefficients a, b, c. The first term $z_0(x, y)$ of the series (19) is then equal to the double integral

$$z_0(x, y) = \int_0^x d\xi \int_0^y f(\xi, \eta) \, d\eta.$$

In a general way, let us assume that z_{n-1} has the form

$$(23) \qquad z_{n-1}(x, y) = \int_0^x d\xi \int_0^y f(\xi, \eta) \, g_{n-1}(x, y; \xi, \eta) \, d\eta,$$

$g_{n-1}(x, y; \xi, \eta)$ being a continuous function of the two pairs of variables (x, y), (ξ, η) which possesses partial derivatives continuous with respect to x and to y. We are going to prove that $z_n(x, y)$ can be put in an analogous form. To apply the recurrence formula (20), let us calculate first of all $z_{n-1}(\xi, \eta)$, $\partial z_{n-1}/\partial \xi$, $\partial z_{n-1}/\partial \eta$. By hypothesis, we have, after replacing x, y, ξ, η in (23) by ξ, η, u, v,

$$z_{n-1}(\xi, \eta) = \int_0^\xi du \int_0^\eta f(u, v) g_{n-1}(\xi, \eta; u, v)\, dv$$

and, consequently,

$$\frac{dz_{n-1}(\xi, \eta)}{\partial \xi} = \int_0^\xi \int_0^\eta f(u, v) \frac{\partial g_{n-1}}{\partial \xi}\, du\, dv$$

$$+ \int_0^\eta f(\xi, v) g_{n-1}(\xi, \eta; \xi, v)\, dv,$$

$$\frac{\partial z_{n-1}(\xi, \eta)}{\partial \eta} = \int_0^\xi \int_0^\eta f(r, v) \frac{\partial g_{n-1}}{\partial \eta}\, du\, dv$$

$$+ \int_0^\xi f(u, \eta) g_{n-1}(\xi, \eta; u, \eta)\, du.$$

The expression for $z_n(x, y)$ will be composed of three terms:

$$(24) \quad z_n(x, y) = \left[\int_0^x d\xi \int_0^y d\eta \int_0^\xi du \right] \int_0^\eta f(u, v) \left[a(\xi, \eta) \frac{\partial g_{n-1}}{\partial \xi} \right.$$

$$\left. + b(\xi, \eta) \frac{\partial g_{n-1}}{\partial \eta} + c(\xi, \eta) g_{n-1} \right] dv$$

$$+ \int_0^x d\xi \int_0^y d\eta \int_0^\eta a(\xi, \eta) f(\xi, v) g_{n-1}(\xi, \eta; \xi, v)\, dv$$

$$+ \int_0^x d\xi \int_0^y d\eta \int_0^\xi b(\xi, \eta) f(u, \eta) g_{n-1}(\xi, \eta; u, \eta)\, du.$$

Let us invert the order of the first two integrations in the first triple integral of the second member by applying Dirichlet's formula (I, **124**); it can again be written

$$\int_0^x d\xi \int_0^y dv \int_0^y a(\xi, \eta) f(\xi, v) g_{n-1}(\xi, \eta; \xi, v)\, d\eta,$$

or, permuting the letters η and v,

$$(25) \quad \int_0^x d\xi \int_0^y d\eta \int_0^y a(\xi, v) f(\xi, \eta) g_{n-1}(\xi, v; \xi, \eta) \, dv$$

$$= \int_0^x d\xi \int_0^y f(\xi, \eta) \, d\eta \left[\int_\eta^y a(\xi, v) g_{n-1}(\xi, v; \xi, \eta) \, dv \right].$$

The second triple integral of formula (24) can be similarly written

$$\int_0^x d\xi \int_0^y f(\xi, \eta) \, d\eta \left[\int_\xi^x b(u, \eta) g_{n-1}(u, \eta; \xi, \eta) \, du \right].$$

As to the quadruple integral which forms the first term of $z_n(x, y)$, it is taken over a domain of four-dimensional space which is defined by the inequalities

$$0 \leq u \leq \xi \leq x, \quad 0 \leq v \leq \eta \leq y.$$

If we integrate first with respect to the variables ξ, η, the limits will be u and x for ξ, v and y for η, and the limits will then be 0 and x for u, 0 and y for v. This quadruple integral can therefore be written in the equivalent form

$$\int_0^x du \int_0^y dv \int_u^x d\xi \int_v^y f(u, v) \left[a(\xi, \eta) \frac{\partial g_{n-1}(\xi, \eta; u, v)}{\partial \xi} + \ldots \right] d\eta,$$

or, again by permuting the two pairs of variables (u, v) and (ξ, η),

$$\int_0^x d\xi \int_0^y d\eta f(\xi, \eta)$$

$$\left\{ \int_\xi^y du \int_\eta^y \left[a(u, v) \frac{dg_{n-1}(u, v; \xi, \eta)}{\partial u} + \ldots \right] dv \right\}.$$

We see therefore that after all these transformations the expression for $z_n(x, y)$ takes the form

$$(26) \quad z_n(x, y) = \int_0^x d\xi \int_0^y f(\xi, \eta) g_n(x, y; \xi, \eta) \, d\eta$$

by setting

$$(27) \quad g_n(x, y; \xi, \eta) = \int_{\xi}^{x} du \int_{\eta}^{y} \left[a(u\,v) \frac{\partial g_{n-1}(u, v; \xi, \eta)}{\partial u} + \ldots \right] dv$$

$$+ \int_{\xi}^{x} b(u, \eta)\, g_{n-1}(u, \eta; \xi, \eta)\, du$$

$$+ \int_{\eta}^{y} a(\xi, v)\, g_{n-1}(\xi, v; \xi, \eta)\, dv.$$

Starting from $g_0 = 1$, we shall calculate step by step by this formula $g_1(x, y; \xi, \eta)$, $g_2(x, y; \xi, \eta)$, ... The result obtained can be stated thus: *The integral of equation* (18), *which is zero for* x = 0, *whatever the value of* y, *and for* y = 0, *whatever the value of* x, *is represented in the rectangle* R *by the double integral*

$$(28) \quad z(x, y) = \int_{0}^{x} d\xi \int_{0}^{y} f(\xi, \eta)\, G\,(x, y; \xi, \eta; \lambda)\, d\eta,$$

$G(\mathrm{x}, \mathrm{y}; \xi, \eta; \lambda)$ *designating the sum of the series*

$$(29) \quad G(x, y; \xi, \eta; \lambda) = 1 + \lambda\, g_1\,(x, y; \xi, \eta) + \ldots$$

$$+ \lambda^n\, g_n\,(x, y; \xi, \eta) + \ldots.$$

This function G was introduced by Riemann in an entirely different manner which will be explained later on.

We could study this series (29) directly as we did series (19), but it is easy to derive its properties from what precedes. Let us observe first of all that it formally satisfies the homogeneous equation

$$(30) \quad \frac{\partial^2 G}{\partial x\ \partial y} = \lambda \left(a\, \frac{\partial G}{\partial x} + b\, \frac{\partial G}{\partial y} + c G \right);$$

we can indeed write, according to the recurrence formula (27), and since the series (29) is uniformly convergent, as well as those which we derive from it differentiating with respect to x and with respect to y,

$$G(x, y; \xi, \eta; \lambda) = \lambda \int_{\xi}^{x} du \int_{\eta}^{y} \left[a(u, v) \frac{\partial F(u, v; \xi, \eta; \lambda)}{\partial u} + \ldots \right] dv$$

$$+ X(x; \xi, \eta, \lambda) + Y(y; \xi, \eta, \lambda).$$

We therefore also have

$$\frac{\partial^2 G}{\partial x\,\partial y} = \lambda \left[a(x, y)\,\frac{\partial G}{\partial x} + b(x, y)\,\frac{\partial G}{\partial y} + c(x, y)G \right].$$

On the other hand, for $x = \xi$, it also reduces to the series

(31) $1 + g_1(\xi, y; \xi, \eta)\,\lambda + \ldots + g_n(\xi, y; \xi, \eta)\,\lambda^n + \ldots$

and the recurrence relation (27) here becomes

$$g_n(\xi, y; \xi, \eta) = \int_\eta^y a(\xi, v)\,g_{n-1}(\xi, v; \xi, \eta)\,dv.$$

The series (31) is precisely the series which we should obtain by developing in powers of λ the integral of the linear equation

$$\frac{dw}{dy} = \lambda a(\xi, y)\,w,$$

which reduces to *one* for $y = \eta$, an integral which has

$$e^{\lambda \int_\eta^y a(\xi,\,\eta)dv}$$

for its expression. We should see in the same way that for $y = \eta$, G reduces to

$$e^{\lambda \int_\xi^x b(u,\,\eta)du}.$$

We have demonstrated in the preceding paragraph that there exists an integral of equation (30) which reduces to

$$e^{\lambda \int_\eta^y a(\xi,\,v)dv}$$

for $x = \xi$ and to

$$e^{\lambda \int_\xi^x b(u,\,\eta)du}$$

for $y = \eta$. This integral is represented by a uniformly convergent series all of whose terms, from the very way in which they were obtained, are holomorphic functions of λ. It is therefore itself an entire function of the parameter λ, and its expansion in powers of λ necessarily coincides with series (29). To sum up, *the function* G(x, y; ξ, η, λ) *is an integral of equation* (30) *which satisfies the limiting conditions below*:

(32) $G = e^{\lambda \int_\xi^x b(u,\,\eta)du}$ (for $y = \eta$),

            $G = e^{\lambda \int_\eta^y a(\xi,\,v)dv}$ (for $x = \xi$).

40. First solution of Cauchy's problem. Let us take up again in the same way Cauchy's problem for the general equation (18), and let us propose to expand in powers of the parameter λ the integral satisfying the same conditions as in III, **28**. We shall take for the first term of the series the integral $z_0(x, y)$ of the equation $s = f(x, y)$ satisfying the given conditions, and we shall determine the successive coefficients $z_1(x, y)$, $z_2(x, y)$, ..., by means of the recurrence law

$$(33) \qquad z_n(x, y) = \pm \int\!\!\int_{(PMQ)} \left[a(\xi, \eta)\, \frac{dz_{n-1}}{\partial \xi} + b(\xi, \eta)\, \frac{dz_{n-1}}{\partial \eta} \right.$$

$$\left. + \; c(\xi, \eta) z_{n-1}(\xi, \eta) \right] d\xi \, d\eta,$$

where we take the $+$ sign or the $-$ sign before the integral according as the arc AB on which the given data lie has the disposition of Figure 1a or of Figure 1b. The domain of integration, which is the curvilinear triangle PMQ, is chosen in such a fashion that $z_n(x, y)$, as well as its partial derivatives of the first order, is zero along the arc AB. Let us consider for the sake of definiteness, the case of Figure 1a, and let us suppose the point M is above the arc AB. A very simple device suffices to reduce formula (33) to a recurrence formula of the form (20). Let us suppose, in fact, three functions $\alpha(x, y)$, $\beta(x, y)$, $\gamma(x, y)$, zero in the curvilinear triangle ABD, below AB, and equal respectively to the coefficients $a(x, y)$, $b(x, y)$, $c(x, y)$ above AB. It is clear that if we have $u_{n-1}(x, y) = z_{n-1}(x, y)$, the double integral

$$(33') \qquad u_n(x, y) = \int\!\!\int_{(P'MQ'D)} \left[\alpha(\xi, \eta)\, \frac{\partial u_{n-1}}{\partial \xi} + \beta(\xi, \eta)\, \frac{\partial u_{n-1}}{\partial \eta} \right.$$

$$\left. + \; \gamma(\xi, \eta)\, u_{n-1}(\xi, \eta) \right] d\xi \, d\eta,$$

taken over the rectangle $P'MQ'D$, will be zero if the point M is below the arc AB and equal to $z_n(x, y)$ if the point M is above AB. Despite the discontinuity of the functions $\alpha(x, y)$, $\beta(x, y)$, $\gamma(x, y)$ along AB, this function, as well as its partial derivatives $\partial u_n/\partial x$, $\partial u_n/\partial y$, is continuous in rectangle R. This being the case, let us suppose that we wish to develop in powers of λ the integral of the auxiliary equation

$$(34) \quad \frac{\partial^2 u}{\partial x \, \partial y} = \lambda \left[\alpha(x, y) \frac{\partial u}{\partial x} + \beta(x, y) \frac{\partial u}{\partial y} + \gamma(x, y)u \right] + f(x, y),$$

which takes on the same values as $z_0(x, y)$ along the sides AD and BD of R.

$$(35) \quad u(x, y) = u_0(x, y) + \lambda u_1(x, y) + \ldots + \lambda^n u_n(x, y) + \ldots.$$

We clearly have $u_0(x, y) = z_0(x, y)$, and the coefficients $u_1, u_2, \ldots$ are obtained step by step by means of formula (33′). Despite the discontinuity of the coefficients α, β, γ along the arc AB, the reasoning of III, **38** applies without modification, and this series is uniformly convergent, as are those derived from it by differentiating term by term with respect to x or y. If the point $M(x, y)$ is below arc AB, we evidently have $u_n(x, y) = 0$, $n \geq 1$, and series (35) is reduced to its first term $u_0(x, y)$. But if the point M is above AB, we see step by step, by virtue of the preceding remark, that we have $u_1(x, y) = z_1(x, y), \ldots, u_n(x, y) = z_n(x, y)$, and series (35) represents precisely, in the curvilinear triangle ACB, an integral $z(x, y)$ of equation (18) such that

$$\delta = z(x, y) = z_0(x, y),$$

is zero, as well as $\partial\delta/\partial x$, $\partial\delta/\partial y$, along AB. The series obtained by the method of successive approximations therefore represents an integral satisfying the Cauchy conditions above AB, and we would see in a similar fashion that this series is also uniformly convergent below AB. The reasoning is completed as above.

In the particular case where the desired integral, as well as its two partial derivatives, must be zero along AB, the first term of the series has for its expression

$$z_0(x, y) = \int \int_{(PMQ)} f(\xi, \eta) \, d\xi \, d\eta,$$

and, by a sequence of transformations of multiple integrals, entirely analogous to those which were carried out in Section **39**, we prove step by step that $z_n(x, y)$ can be put in the form

$$z_n(x, y) = \int \int_{(PMQ)} f(\xi, \eta) \, g_n(x, y; \xi, \eta) \, d\xi \, d\eta,$$

the functions $g_1(x, y; \xi, \eta)$, $g_2(x, y; \xi, \eta)$, . . . being derived from

$$g_0(x, y; \xi, \eta) = 1,$$

by means of the recurrence formula (27). The value of the integral satisfying these conditions is therefore represented, at a point $M(x, y)$ of rectangle R, by the double integral

$$(36) \qquad z(x, y) = \int \int_{(PMQ)} f(\xi, \eta) \; G \; (x, y; \xi, \eta; \lambda) \; d\xi \, d\eta,$$

G being the Riemann function defined above; in the case of Figure 1b, the double integral must be preceded by the minus sign.

Let us suppose, in the second place, that the Cauchy data along AB are arbitrary. Let $\zeta(x, y)$ be any function whatever satisfying these conditions, for example, the integral of the equation $s = 0$. Setting $z = \zeta + u$, we are led to the equation

$$(37) \qquad \frac{\partial^2 u}{\partial x \, dy} = \lambda \left(a \frac{\partial u}{\partial x} + b \frac{\partial u}{\partial y} + cu \right) + f(x, y)$$

$$+ \lambda \left(a \frac{\partial \zeta}{\partial x} + b \frac{\partial \zeta}{\partial y} + c\zeta \right) - \frac{\partial^2 \zeta}{\partial x \, \partial y},$$

and the function $u(x, y)$ must be zero, as well as $\partial u/\partial x$, $\partial u/\partial y$, along AB. The coefficients a, b, c being fixed, the Riemann function G is the same for the two equations (18) and (37). The desired integral therefore has the expression

$$(38) \quad z(x, y) = \zeta(x, y) + \int \int_{(PMQ)} f(\xi, \eta) \; G \; (x, y; \xi, \eta; \lambda) \; d\xi \, d\eta$$

$$+ \int \int_{(PMQ)} \left\{ \lambda \left[a(\xi, \eta) \frac{\partial \zeta}{\partial \xi} + b(\xi, \eta) \frac{\partial \zeta}{\partial \eta} + c(\xi, \eta)\zeta \right] - \frac{\partial^2 \zeta}{\partial \xi \, \partial \eta} \right\} G \; d\xi \, d\eta.$$

We would similarly have the integral assuming the same values as a given function $\zeta(x, y)$ along AD and BD by taking the rectangle $MQ'DP'$ as the domain of integration of the double integral.

We can arrive at formula (36) very easily by a synthetic method. We have seen that the integral of a linear differential equation with second member $F(y) = f(x)$, which, with its first $n - 1$

derivatives is zero for $x = x_0$, is represented by a definite integral

$$\int_{x_0}^{x} \phi(x, \alpha) f(\alpha) \, d\alpha,$$

$\phi(x, \alpha)$ being a fixed function of x and of α. By analogy, let us seek to determine *a priori* a function $\phi(x, y; \xi, \eta)$ such that the double integral

$$(39) \qquad z(x, y) = \int\int_{(PMQ)} f(\xi, \eta) \, \phi \, (x, y; \xi, \eta) \, d\xi \, d\eta$$

taken over the triangle *PMQ* is an integral of equation (18); we shall suppose for the calculation that the function ϕ is continuous and possesses continuous derivatives $\partial\phi/\partial x$, $\partial\phi/\partial y$, $\partial^2\phi/\partial x \partial y$. The derivative $\partial z/\partial x$ will be composed of two terms, one of which is obtained by the usual formula for differentiation under the integral sign, and the other of which comes from the variation of the field of integration. To calculate this last term, let us observe that when one gives to x an increment $\Delta x > 0$, the field of integration is increased by a band of width Δx, having *MP* for its height (Fig. 1) and the principal part of the value of the double integral taken over this band is evidently

$$\Delta x \int_{(PM)} f(x, \eta) \, \phi \, (x, y; x, \eta) \, d\eta.$$

We therefore have

$$\frac{\partial z}{\partial x} - \int\int_{(PMQ)} f(\xi, \eta) \, \frac{\partial\phi}{\partial x} \, d\xi \, d\eta + \int_{(PM)} f(x, \eta) \, \phi \, (x, y; x, \eta) \, d\eta,$$

a formula which could also be established by an elementary calculation, when the variable limits in the double integral (39) are written explicitly. We find in the same way

$$\frac{\partial z}{\partial y} = \int\int_{(PMQ)} f(\xi, \eta) \, \frac{\partial\phi}{\partial y} \, d\xi \, d\eta + \int_{(QM)} f(\xi, y) \, \phi \, (x, y; \xi, y) \, d\xi,$$

$$\frac{\partial^2 z}{\partial x \, \partial y} = \int\int_{(PMQ)} f(\xi, \eta) \, \frac{\partial^2\phi}{\partial x \, \partial y} \, d\xi \, d\eta$$

$$+ \int_{(PM)} f(x, \eta) \, \frac{\partial}{\partial y} \, [\phi(x, y; x, \eta)]l$$

$$+ \int_{(QM)} f(\xi, y) \, \frac{\partial}{\partial x} \, [\phi(x, y; \xi, y) \,] \, d\xi + \phi(x, y; x, y) f(x, y).$$

In order that the function $z(x, y)$, represented by formula (39), be an integral of equation (18), for an arbitrary function $f(x, y)$, it is necessary and sufficient that after the substitution the terms under the different integral signs be identical, as well as the terms outside of every integral sign, that is, that we have

$$\frac{\partial^2 \phi}{\partial x \, \partial y} = \lambda \left[a(x, y) \frac{\partial \phi}{\partial x} + b(x, y) \frac{\partial \phi}{\partial y} + c(x, y) \phi \right],$$

$$\frac{\partial}{\partial y}[\phi(x, y; x, \eta)] = \lambda \, a(x, y) \, \phi \, (x, y; x, \eta),$$

$$\frac{\partial}{\partial x}[\phi(x, y; \xi, y)] = \lambda \, b(x, y) \, \phi \, (x, y; \xi, y),$$

$$\phi(x, y; x, y) = 1.$$

These conditions are identical with those which determine the function

$$G(x, y; \xi, \eta; \lambda).$$

Indeed, the first condition expresses the fact that $\phi(x, y; \xi, \eta)$ is an integral of the homogeneous equation (30). As to the other three, we derive from them that

$$\phi(x, y; x, \eta) = e^{\lambda \int_\eta^\lambda a(x, v) \, dv},$$

$$\phi(x, y; \xi, y) = e^{\lambda \int_\xi^x b(u, y) \, du}.$$

It is sufficient to replace x by ξ in the first of these relations and y by η in the second to regain conditions (32).

41. The adjoint equation. Riemann has solved the same problem by an entirely different method, which rests on the theory of the adjoint equation.[7] Given a linear homogeneous equation of

---

[7] *Göttingen Abhandlungen*, Vol. VIII, 1860; *Œuvres*, p. 145. See also Chap. IV of Vol. II of the *Théorie des surfaces* by G. Darboux (see Exercise 5). The method which Riemann had applied to only one particular equation has been extended by G. Darboux to the general equation of form (18).

the second order

$$(40) \quad \mathscr{F}(z) = A \frac{\partial^2 z}{\partial x^2} + B \frac{\partial^2 z}{\partial x \, \partial y} + C \frac{\partial^2 z}{\partial y^2} + D \frac{\partial z}{\partial x} + E \frac{\partial z}{\partial y} + Fz,$$

if we multiply each term by the same function $u(x, y)$ and integrate by parts as many times as possible, we obtain a sequence of identities

$$Au \frac{\partial^2 z}{\partial x^2} = \frac{\partial}{\partial x} \left[Au \frac{\partial z}{\partial x} - \frac{\partial (Au)}{\partial x} z \right] + z \frac{\partial^2 (Au)}{\partial x^2},$$

$$Bu \frac{\partial^2 z}{\partial x \, \partial y} = \frac{\partial}{\partial y} \left(Bu \frac{\partial z}{\partial x} \right) - \frac{\partial}{\partial x} \left[z \frac{\partial Bu)}{\partial y} \right] + z \frac{\partial^2 (Bu)}{\partial x \, \partial y},$$

$$Cu \frac{\partial^2 z}{\partial y^2} = \frac{\partial}{\partial y} \left[Cu \frac{\partial z}{\partial y} - \frac{\partial (Cu)}{\partial y} z \right] + z \frac{\partial^2 (Cu)}{\partial y^2},$$

$$Du \frac{\partial z}{\partial x} = \frac{\partial}{\partial x} (Duz) - z \frac{\partial (Du)}{\partial x},$$

$$Eu \frac{\partial z}{\partial y} = \frac{\partial}{\partial y} (Euz) - z \frac{\partial (Eu)}{\partial y},$$

$$Fuz = zF(u),$$

and we derive from them the following relation, which holds good for all possible forms of the functions u and z,

$$(41) \quad\quad\quad u\mathscr{F}(z) - z\mathscr{G}(u) = \frac{\partial H}{\partial x} + \frac{\partial K}{\partial y}.$$

We have set

$$(42) \quad \mathscr{G}(u) = \frac{\partial^2 (Au)}{\partial x^2} + \frac{\partial^2 (Bu)}{\partial x \, \partial y} + \frac{\partial^2 (Cu)}{\partial y^2} - \frac{\partial (Du)}{\partial x} - \frac{\partial (Eu)}{\partial y} + Fu,$$

$$(43) \quad \begin{cases} H = Au \dfrac{\partial z}{\partial x} - z \dfrac{\partial (Au)}{\partial x} - z \dfrac{\partial (Bu)}{\partial y} + Duz, \\[2ex] K = Bu \dfrac{\partial z}{\partial x} + Cu \dfrac{\partial z}{\partial y} - z \dfrac{\partial (Cu)}{\partial y} + Euz. \end{cases}$$

The equation $\mathscr{G}(u) = 0$ is the *adjoint* equation of equation (40). We could verify by a direct calculation that there is a reciprocity between these two equations, which is also a consequence of identity

(41). Let us remark that in this identity we can replace H by $H + (\partial\theta/\partial y)$, and K by $K - (\partial\theta/\partial x)$, $\theta(x, y)$ being an arbitrary function.[8]

The double integral $\iint[u\mathscr{F}(z) - z\mathscr{G}(u)]\, dx\, dy$, taken over a domain where the functions z and u are continuous, as well as their derivatives up to the second order, can, from identity (41) be replaced by the line integral

$$(44) \qquad\qquad \int_{(\Gamma)} H\, dy - K\, dx,$$

taken in the positive sense around the contour Γ which bounds this domain. In particular, if z and u are respectively the integrals of equation (40) and of its adjoint, regular in any domain at all, the line integral (44), taken around the contour of this domain, is always zero.

42. Riemann's method.

Let us apply this result to a linear equation of the hyperbolic type, which we shall now write

$$(45) \qquad \mathscr{F}(z) = \frac{\partial^2 z}{\partial x\, \partial y} + a\,\frac{\partial z}{\partial x} + b\,\frac{\partial z}{\partial y} + cz = 0,$$

----

[8] We can extend the definition of the adjoint equation to a linear equation in any number of variables. For the equation in n variables

$$\mathscr{F}(z) = \sum a_{ik}\,\frac{\partial^2 z}{\partial x_i \partial x_k} + \sum b_i\,\frac{\partial z}{\partial x_i} + cz = 0,$$

the adjoint equation is

$$\mathscr{G}(u) = \sum \frac{\partial^2 (a_{ik}u)}{\partial x \partial x_k} - \sum \frac{\partial(bu)}{\partial x} + cu = 0$$

and we have the identity

$$u\mathscr{F}(z) - z\mathscr{G}(u) = \frac{\partial M_1}{\partial x_1} + \frac{\partial M_2}{\partial x_2} - \ldots - \frac{\partial M_n}{\partial x_n},$$

$M_1, M_2, \ldots, M_n$ being bilinear functions with respect to z, u, and their derivatives of the first order, the expression for which we would have by means of the identities

$$U\frac{\partial^2 V}{\partial x_i \partial x_k} - V\frac{\partial^2 U}{\partial x_i \partial x_k} = \frac{\partial}{\partial x_i}\left(U\frac{\partial V}{\partial x_k}\right) - \frac{\partial}{\partial x_k}\left(V\frac{\partial U}{\partial x}\right),$$

$$U\frac{\partial V}{\partial x_i} + V\frac{\partial U}{\partial x_i} = \frac{\partial(UV)}{\partial x_i}.$$

We shall see examples later (sections **45, 72, 78**).

we have, in this particular case,

$$
(46) \quad \begin{cases} \mathscr{G}(u) = \dfrac{\partial^2 u}{\partial x\, y} - a\,\dfrac{\partial a}{\partial x} - b\,\dfrac{\partial u}{\partial y} + \left(c - \dfrac{\partial a}{\partial x} - \dfrac{\partial b}{\partial y} \right) u = 0, \\[2ex] \qquad H = auz - z\,\dfrac{\partial u}{\partial y}, \quad K = buz + u\,\dfrac{\partial z}{\partial x}. \end{cases}
$$

Let $z(x, y)$ be an integral of equation (45)[9] satisfying the Cauchy conditions along an arc AB (Fig. 1a), and let $u(x, y)$ be any integral whatever of the adjoint equation regular in the rectangle $ACBD$. Replacing under the $\int$ sign the letters x and y by the letter ξ, η, we have, from the general proposition,

$$
(47) \quad \int_{(QP)} H\, d\eta - K\, d\xi + \int_{(PM)} H\, d\eta - \int_{(MQ)} K\, d\xi = 0,
$$

the same substitution having been made in H and K; the point M is a point of the rectangle $ACBD$, with coordinates x, y. By hypothesis, we know the value of the desired integral $z(\xi, \eta)$ and of its partial derivatives along arc AB, $u(\xi, \eta)$ is a fixed solution of the adjoint equation. Therefore, the first line integral, taken along arc QP, is a known function of the coordinates x and y of the point M. It appears on the contrary that the line integrals along PM and along MQ cannot be calculated without knowing the values of z along these lines. Riemann's device consists precisely in choosing the function u in such a way as to eliminate these integrals. We have

$$
\int_{MQ} K\, d\xi = \int_{MQ} \left(buz + u\,\frac{\partial z}{\partial \xi} \right) d\xi,
$$

which an integration by parts immediately allows us to write as

$$
\int_{MQ} C\, d\xi = (uz)_M^Q + \int_{MQ} z\left(bu - \frac{\partial u}{\partial \xi} \right) d\xi,
$$

and the general formula (47) gives us

$$
(48) \quad (uz)_M = (uz)_Q + \int_{MQ} z\left(bu - \frac{\partial u}{\partial \xi} \right) d\xi
$$

$$
- \int_{PM} z\left(au - \frac{\partial u}{\partial \eta} \right) d\eta + \int_{PQ} H\, d\eta - K\, d\xi.
$$

[9] We assume, for simplicity, $f(x, y) = 0$. If f were not zero, there would be an additional term, easy to include in the expression for the integral.

In order to make those integrals disappear in which the unknown values of z along PM and MQ occur, it is sufficient to take for $u(\xi, \eta)$ an integral of the adjoint equation (where x and y have been replaced by ξ, η), satisfying the following conditions

$$\frac{\partial}{\partial \xi}u(\xi, y) = b(\xi, y)u(\xi, y), \quad \frac{\partial}{\partial \eta}u(x, \eta) = a(x, \eta)u(x, \eta).$$

Now $u(\xi, y)$ and $u(x, \eta)$ represent respectively the functions of ξ and of η to which this integral reduces along MQ and MP. Designating by u_m the value of this integral when the point (ξ, η) is at M, it is necessary and sufficient that we have

$$u(\xi, y) = u_M\, e^{\int_x^\xi b(t, y)dt}, \ u(x, \eta) = u_M\, e^{\int_y^\eta a(x, v)dv},$$

in order for the integrals along MP and MQ to disappear in formula (48). Assuming $u_M = 1$, we shall designate by $u(x, y; \xi, \eta)$ the function of the two pairs of variables (x, y), (ξ, η) thus determined. Considered as a function of the variables (ξ, η), it is a solution of the adjoint equation

$$\frac{\partial^2 u}{\partial \xi\, \partial \eta} - a(\xi, \eta)\frac{\partial u}{\partial \xi} - b(\xi, \eta)\frac{\partial u}{\partial \eta} + \left[c(\xi, \eta) - \frac{\partial a}{\partial \xi} - \frac{\partial b}{\partial \eta}\right]u(\xi, \eta) = 0;$$

for $\xi = x$, it reduces to

$$e^{\int_y^\eta a(x, v)dv}$$

and, for $\eta = y$, it reduces to

$$e^{\int_x^\xi b(t,y)dt};$$

it is therefore equal to one, for $\xi = x$, $\eta = y$. If we assume that we have determined this integral of the adjoint equation, formula (48) gives us the value at the point (x, y) of the integral which satisfies the Cauchy conditions along arc AB

$$(49)\quad z_M = (uz)_Q + \int_{(QP)} uz(b\, d\xi - a\, d\eta) + \int_{(QP)} u\frac{\partial z}{\partial \xi}d\xi + z\frac{\partial u}{\partial \eta}d\eta.$$

In this formula only the values of z and of $\partial z/\partial \xi$ along AB occur. Taking account of the identity

$$(uz)_Q - (uz)_P = \int_{(PQ)} \frac{\partial(uz)}{\partial \xi}d\xi + \frac{\partial(uz)}{\partial \eta}d\eta,$$

we can replace formula (49) by one or the other of the formulas

$$(49')\quad z_M = (uz)_P + \int_{PQ} uz(a\,d\eta - b\,d\xi) + \int_{PQ} u\frac{\partial z}{\partial \eta}\,d\eta + z\frac{\partial u}{\partial \xi}\,d\xi,$$

$$(49'')\quad z_M = \frac{(uz)_P + (uz)_Q}{2} + \int_{PQ} uz(a\,d\eta - b\,d\xi)$$

$$+ \frac{1}{2}\int_{(PQ)} u\left(\frac{\partial z}{\partial \eta}\,d\eta - \frac{\partial z}{\partial \xi}\right) + \frac{1}{2}\int_{PQ} z\left(\frac{\partial u}{\partial \xi}\,d\xi - \frac{\partial u}{\partial \eta}\,d\eta\right),$$

of which the last is the most symmetric, but depends upon the values of z and its two derivatives along AB.

In all these formulas, the point (x, y) is considered fixed, and the variables of integration are ξ, η so that the variables x and y occur under the $\int$ sign only in u and its derivatives. We can repeat for these formulas all the remarks which had been made in connection with the equation $s = 0$ (III, **33**); Riemann's function $u(x, y; \xi, \eta)$ reduces to unity in this particular case.

These formulas are applied again when the arc AB coincides with the broken line ADB; the points P and Q then become P' and Q' and formula (49'), for example, gives

$$z_M = (uz)_{P'} + \int_{(P'D)} \left(z\frac{\partial u}{\partial \xi} - buz\right)d\xi + \int_{(DQ')} \left(\frac{\partial z}{\partial \eta} + az\right)d\eta,$$

which can be rewritten, integrating $z(\partial u/\partial z)$ by parts, as

$$(50)\quad z_M = (uz)_D - \int_{(P'D)} u\left(\frac{\partial z}{\partial \xi} + bz\right)d\xi + \int_{(DQ')} u\left(\frac{\partial z}{\partial \eta} + az\right)d\eta.$$

To calculate z_M, it is sufficient, conforming to the general theory, to know the values of z along the broken line ADB. Indeed, if $z(x, y)$ is any known function of x along AD, $\partial z/\partial x$ is known along AD, and, for the same reason, $\partial z/\partial y$ is a known function of y along DB.

Let x_1, y_1 be the coordinates of point D; let us designate by

$$z(x, y; x_1, y_1)$$

the integral of the equation $\mathscr{F}(z) = 0$ which satisfies the following conditions

$$z(x, y_1; x_1, y_1) = e^{-\int_{x_1}^{x} b(t, y_1)\, dt},$$

$$z(x_1, y; x_1, y_1) = e^{-\int_{y_1}^{y} a(x_1, v)\, dv}.$$

This integral is equal to one at the point D and, when we replace x, y by ξ, η, it satisfies the two relations

$$bz + \frac{\partial z}{\partial \xi} = 0, \quad az + \frac{\partial z}{\partial \eta} = 0$$

along AD and BD, respectively. If we have taken this integral for z, formula (50) reduces to $z_M = u_D$, that is, we have

(51) $z(x, y; x_1, y_1) = u(x, y; x_1, y_1).$

Replacing x_1, y_1 by ξ, η, respectively, we see that the function $u(x, y; \xi, \eta)$, considered as a function of x, y, is an integral of the proposed equation which satisfies conditions entirely the same as those which determine it when we consider it as a function of (ξ, η), since a and b must be replaced by $-a$ and $-b$ when we pass from an equation to its adjoint. The knowledge of this function $u(x, y; \xi, \eta)$ will therefore also permit us to solve the Cauchy problem for the adjoint equation, and we can say that *the integration of a linear equation and the integration of its adjoint equation are two equivalent problems.*

The last conditions which determine $u(x, y; \xi, \eta)$ are identical with those which determine the function $G(x, y; \xi, \eta)$ when we put $\lambda = -1$. It is easy from this to verify the identity of the two solutions. Formula (38), indeed, can be written, by supposing $f(x, y)$ zero, and replacing G by $-u$,

(38′) $z(x, y) = \zeta(x, y) + \displaystyle\int\!\!\int_{(PMQ)} \mathscr{F}[\zeta(\xi, \eta)] u(x, y; \xi, \eta)\, d\xi\, d\eta.$

This being the case, it is sufficient to apply to this double integral the general formula (44) which leads to a line integral, and the transformations which have just been carried out lead precisely to Riemann's solution. The values of ζ, $\partial\zeta/\partial y$, $\partial\zeta/\partial x$, along arc AB, are indeed equal by hypothesis to the values of the desired integral and its derivatives $\partial z/\partial x$, $\partial z/\partial y$, along the same arc. One can only note that the solution of Cauchy's problem given by formula (38) in the form of a double integral does not assume the existence of the adjoint equation, that is, the existence of the derivatives $\partial a/\partial x$, $\partial b/\partial y$.

43. Equations with constant coefficients. Every linear equation of the hyperbolic type with constant coefficients has for characteristics two families of lines (III, **26**); if we refer it to its characteristics, the coefficients a, b, c which occur in the reduced form (45) can also be assumed constant. If we then set $z = ue^{-bx-ay}$, we reduce it to an equation not containing first order derivatives, and in which the coefficient of u is again constant. Every equation of the type considered can therefore be reduced to the simple form

$$(52) \qquad \frac{\partial^2 z}{\partial x \partial y} + cz = 0,$$

c being a constant coefficient. If c is not zero, the change of x into kx again permits us to give this coefficient an arbitrary value, ± 1 for example. Equation (52) is, after the elementary equation $s = 0$, one of the simplest types to which Riemann's method applies. We know indeed how to find the function $u(x, y; \xi, \eta)$ for this equation, for it is sufficient to find an integral reducing to unity for $x = \xi$, for any y, and for $y = \eta$, for any x. Let us set $v = (x - \xi)(y - \eta)$ and let us seek a particular integral of (52) depending only upon v, say $z = \phi(v)$; we are led to the second order equation

$$v\phi''(v) + \phi'(v) + c\phi(v) = 0,$$

which is one of the forms of the Bessel equation (II, 2, **52**).

We have seen that this equation has as an integral an entire function of v reducing to *one* for $v = 0$, and this integral can be expressed as $J(-cv)$ where $J(t)$ is the power series

$$J(t) = 1 + \frac{t}{1} + \frac{t^2}{(1.2)^2} + \ldots + \frac{t^n}{(n!)^2} + \ldots.$$

We can therefore also solve the Cauchy problem for an equation of hyperbolic type with constant coefficients.

Let us consider for example the *telegrapher's equation*,[10] which

[10] The method set forth here is due to É. Picard (*Bulletin de la Société Mathématique de France*, Vol. 22, 1894, p. 2–8).

is written, with a suitable choice of units,

$$(53) \qquad \frac{\partial^2 V}{\partial x^2} - \frac{\partial^2 V}{\partial t^2} - 2\frac{\partial V}{\partial t} = 0;$$

V designates the potential at time t at a point of abscissa x on an indefinite rectilinear wire, lying along the x-axis, which transmits an electrical impulse. The characteristics here are the two families of lines $x \pm t = C$; taking as two new variables $x' = (x - t)/\sqrt{2}$, $y' = (x + t)/\sqrt{2}$ and at the same time setting $V = ze^{-t}$, equation (53) becomes

$$(54) \qquad \frac{\partial^2 z}{\partial x'\, \partial y'} + \frac{1}{2}z = 0.$$

We assume that an initial electrical impulse has been produced on the wire between the two points $x = 0$ and $x = a(a > 0)$, and we seek the value of V at time t at the point with abscissa x. Analytically, the problem to be solved is the following: We know the values at time $t = 0$ of z and of $\partial z/\partial t$,

$$z = f(x), \qquad \frac{\partial z}{\partial t} = g(x),$$

these functions being zero outside the interval $(0, a)$; to derive from this $z(x, t)$ for any x and t $(t > 0)$.

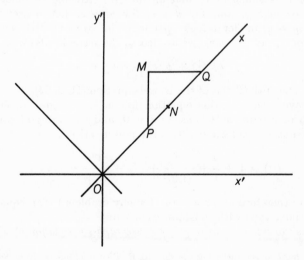

FIG. 8.

This is precisely the Cauchy problem, and the curve along which the values are given is the line $t = 0$ in the xt-axes, and the line $y' = x'$ in the x', y' system of axes. The values of z and of its partial derivatives $\partial z/\partial x'$, $\partial z/\partial y'$, along this line are the consequences of the given values.

Let M be a point with coordinates (x, t), t being positive, in the x, t system. The value of the desired integral at the point M is given by the general formula (49″) which here becomes

$$(55) \quad z_M = \frac{(u\,z)_P + (u\,z)_Q}{2}$$

$$+ \frac{1}{2} \int_{(PQ)} u\left(\frac{\partial z}{\partial \eta}\,d\eta - \frac{\partial z}{\partial \xi}\,d\xi\right) - z\left(\frac{\partial u}{\partial \eta}\,d\eta - \frac{\partial u}{\partial \xi}\,\partial\xi\right),$$

Riemann's function u being equal to $J(-\frac{1}{2}v)$, where $v = (x' - \xi)(y' - \eta)$; we shall designate it by $\phi(v)$. Let N be a point of the segment PQ with coordinates $(\lambda, 0)$ in the x, t system; its coordinates in the x', y' system are $\xi = \eta = \lambda/\sqrt{2}$, and λ varies from $x - t$ to $x + t$ along the segment PQ. In order to apply formula (55), it is necessary to know $u, z, \partial u/\partial \xi, \partial u/\partial \eta, \partial z/\partial \xi, \partial z/\partial \eta$, at every point N of PQ.

We have first of all

$$v = \left(x' - \frac{\lambda}{\sqrt{2}}\right)\left(y' - \frac{\lambda}{\sqrt{2}}\right) = \left(\frac{x + t - \lambda}{\sqrt{2}}\right)\left(\frac{x - t - \lambda}{\sqrt{2}}\right)$$

$$= \frac{(x - \lambda)^2 - t^2}{2},$$

$$u = \phi\left[\frac{(x - \lambda)^2 - t^2}{2}\right];$$

$$\frac{\partial u}{\partial \xi} = \phi'(v)\,(\eta - y') = \phi'\left[\frac{(x - \lambda)^2 - t^2}{2}\right]\left(\frac{\lambda - x - t}{\sqrt{2}}\right),$$

$$\frac{\partial u}{\partial \eta} = \phi'(v)\,(\xi - x') = \phi'\left[\frac{(x - \lambda)^2 - t^2}{2}\right]\left(\frac{\lambda - x + t}{\sqrt{2}}\right).$$

We see in the same way, taking account of the initial conditions that at every point N of PQ we have

$$\frac{\partial z}{\partial \xi} = \frac{1}{\sqrt{2}}[f'(\lambda) - g(\lambda)] \qquad \frac{\partial z}{\partial \eta} = \frac{1}{\sqrt{2}}[f'(\lambda) + g(\lambda)].$$

At the points P, Q, we have $u = 1$, z reduces respectively to $f(x - t)$ and to $f(x + t)$, and formula (55) becomes

$$(56) \quad z = \frac{f(x - t) + f(x + t)}{2}$$

$$+ \frac{1}{2} \int_{x-t}^{x+t} \left\{ \phi \left[\frac{(x - \lambda)^2 - t^2}{2} \right] g(\lambda) - tf(\lambda)\phi' \left[\frac{(x - \lambda)^2 - t^2}{2} \right] \right\} d\lambda.$$

The variables x' and y' do not occur in the final formula (56), which expresses the solution directly in terms of the given values. In order to discuss this solution, let us recall that the functions $f(x)$ and $g(x)$ are zero outside the interval $(0, a)$. Let us assume $x' > a$; as long as we have $t < x - a$, $x - t$ and $x + t$ will be greater than a, and the second member of formula (56) will be zero. The electric impulse will therefore reach the point with abscissa x only at the end of time $t - a$. If t is greater than $x - a$ and less than x, $x - t$ is less than a and positive, $x + t$ is always greater than a, $f(x + t)$ is zero and we can replace the upper limit $x + t$ of the integral by a. Formula (56) can be written

$$(56') \quad z = \frac{f(x - t)}{2} + \frac{1}{2} \int_{x-t}^{a} F(x, t, \lambda) \, d\lambda \qquad (x - a < t < x)$$

by designating the function under the $\int$ sign by $F(x, t, \lambda)$. Finally, if t is $> x$, $x - t$ is negative, $x + t$ is greater than a, $f(x + t)$ and $f(x - t)$ are zero; we can take 0 and a for the limits of integration, and the formula which gives z becomes

$$(56'') \quad z = \frac{1}{2} \int_{0}^{a} F(x, t, \lambda) \, d\lambda \qquad (t > x).$$

We see therefore that the value of z, for a given value of $x > a$, ceases being zero only when t reaches the value $x - a$, but from this value of t on, it does not become zero again. There is indeed for the disturbance a forward wave front which advances with a velocity equal to one, but there is no *backward front*. We can say again that between the times $t = x - a$ and $t = x$, there passes through the point x a wave represented by formula (56'); but this wave leaves behind it a sort of *residue*, represented by (56''). When t increases indefinitely, this residue approaches a limit independent of x. The discussion would be analogous for negative x. Let us observe that the potential V is equal to ze^{-t}, and the presence of the exponential factor produces a very rapid abatement.

44. Other problems. The Cauchy problem is not the only one which can be solved by linear equations of hyperbolic type. We can also have mixed problems to solve, as in the case of the equation $s = 0$. The method of successive approximations applies again to these problems. Let us suppose, for example, that we wish to obtain an integral of the equation

$$s = \lambda(ap + bq + cz) + f(x,y)$$

assuming the given values along the characteristic $y = 0$ and along the arc of the curve OND (Fig. 2) which is intersected in only one point by a parallel to the x-axis. Designating by $z_0(x, y)$ the integral of the equation $s = f(x, y)$ which satisfies these conditions (III, **34**), we shall define step by step the functions z_n by the relation

$$z_n(x, y) = \int\int_{(MNQP)}$$

$$\left[a(\xi, \eta)\,\frac{\partial z_{n-1}}{\partial \xi} + b(\xi, \eta)\,\frac{\partial z_{n-1}}{\partial \eta} + c(\xi, \eta)z_{n-1}\right] d\xi\,d\eta,$$

the integral being taken over the rectangle $MNQP$; by considerations analogous to those of III, **38**, we show that the series

$$z_0(x, y) + \lambda z_1(x, y) + \ldots + \lambda^n z_n(x,y) + \ldots$$

is uniformly convergent, as well as the two series formed by the first order partial derivatives. We can equally employ the method of successive approximations to determine an integral taking on the given values along the two arcs of the curve lying in the same angle of the characteristics. Hadamard showed also that we could extend Riemann's method to these problems; the function $u(x, y; \xi, \eta)$ must be replaced by a solution of the adjoint equation, which introduces lines of discontinuity.[11]

The method of successive approximations also permits us to treat the same problems for an equation of the more general form

$$(57) \qquad\qquad s = F(x, y, z, p, q).$$

---

[11] É. Picard, Note 1 of Vol. IV of *Leçons sur la théorie des surfaces* by Darboux, p. 353 and ff. — É. Goursat, *Annales de la Faculté des Sciences de Toulouse*, 2nd series, Vol. VI, 1904, p. 117. — *Bulletin de la Société mathématique* (Meeting of May 24, 1911). — J. Hadamard, *Bulletin de la Société mathématique*, Vol. XXXI, p. 208, and Vol. XXXII, p. 242.

We shall restrict ourselves to the simplest of these problems, one which consists of determining an integral, knowing the values which it assumes along the two characteristics of different systems. In order to simplify the exposition a little, we shall suppose that we are seeking an integral of (57) which vanishes for $x = 0$, for any y, and for $y = 0$, for any x; it is clear that simple transformations permit the reduction of the general case to this particular case. On the function $F(x, y, z, p, q)$ we shall make the following hypotheses: this function is continuous in the domain D defined by the inequalities

$$0 \leq x \leq \alpha, \quad 0 \leq y \leq \beta, \quad |z| \leq H, \quad |p| \leq P, \quad |q| \leq Q,$$

α, β, H, P, Q being positive numbers. Moreover, in this domain, it satisfies the Lipschitz condition with respect to z, p, q, that is, being given the values of x, y, z, p, p', q, q' taken in the preceding intervals, we have

$$(58) \qquad |F(x, y, z', p', q') - F(x, y, z, p, q)|$$
$$< K_1|z' - z| + K_2|p' - p| + K_3|q' - q|,$$

K_1, K_2, K_3 being positive numbers. Let M be an upper bound of $|F|$ in this domain D, and R the rectangle bounded by the lines $x = 0$, $x = \alpha$, $y = 0$, $y = \beta$. We shall take for the first value of the desired integral $z_0(x, y) = 0$, and then we shall set in a general manner

$$z_n(x, y) = \int_0^x d\xi \int_0^y F\left[\xi, \eta, z_{n-1}(\xi, \eta), \frac{\partial z_{n-1}}{\partial \xi}, \frac{\partial z_{n-1}}{\partial \eta}\right] d\eta.$$

Let ρ and ρ' be two positive numbers at most equal to α and β respectively, and satisfying, in addition, the conditions $M\rho' < H$, $M\rho' < P$, $M\rho < Q$. We see easily, step by step, that all the functions $z_n(x, y)$ are regular in the rectangle R' of dimensions ρ and ρ' analogous to R, and that in this rectangle $|z_n| < H$, $|p_n| < P$, $|q_n| < Q$. To prove that $z(x, y)$ approaches a limit when n increases indefinitely, let us notice that according to condition (58) we have

$$z_n(x, y) - z_{n-1}(x, y)| < \int_0^x d\xi \int_0^y \{K_1|z_{n-1}(\xi, \eta) - z_{n-2}(\xi, \eta)|$$
$$+ K_2|p_{n-1} - p_{n-2}| + K_3|q_{n-1} - q_{n-2}|\} \, d\eta,$$

$$p_n(x, y) - p_{n-1}(x, y)| < \int_0^y \{K_1|z_{n-1}(\xi, \eta) - z_{n-2}(\xi, \eta)| + \ldots\} \, d\eta,$$

. . . .

Let us set, in a general way,

$$u_n(x, y) = \int_0^x d\xi \int_0^y \left[K_1 u_{n-1}(\xi, \eta) + K_2 \frac{du_{n-1}}{\partial \xi} + K_3 \frac{\partial u_{n-1}}{\partial \eta} \right] d\eta,$$

and let us assume that we have taken for $u_1(x, y)$ a function regular in R' and such that we have at any point whatever of this domain $u_1(x, y) > |z_1|$, $\partial u_1/\partial x > |\partial z_1/\partial x|$, $\partial u_1/\partial y > |\partial z_1/\partial y|$; we see, step by step, that we shall have, for every n,

$$|z_n(x, y) - z_{n-1}(x, y)| < u_n(x, y),$$

$$|p_n(x, y) - p_{n-1}(x, y)| < \frac{\partial u_n}{\partial x}, \quad |q_n - q_{n-1}| < \frac{\partial u_n}{\partial y}.$$

Now, we have proven above (III, **38**) that the series Σu_n $\Sigma \partial u_n/\partial x$, $\Sigma \partial u_n/\partial y$ are uniformly convergent; the same is therefore true of the series $z_1(x, y) + [z_2(x, y) - z_1(x, y)] + \ldots + [z_n(x, y) - z_{n-1}(x, y)] + \ldots$ and of those which we derive from it by differentiating term by term with respect to x and to y. The reasoning ends as in section **38**; when n increases indefinitely, z_n approaches a function $Z(x, y)$ which satisfies all the conditions of the problem. Moreover, it is the only integral of equation (57) satisfying these conditions.

The domain in which the existence of the integral is assured is, in general, less extended than for a linear equation. It is an interesting case when this domain is the same; this is the case in which the function $F(x, y, z, p, q)$ remains continuous for every system of real values of z, p, q, when the point (x, y) stays in the domain R, and possesses derivatives $\partial F/\partial z$, $\partial F/\partial p$, $\partial F/\partial q$, remaining less in absolute value than a fixed number, under the same conditions. We do not then have to take account of the conditions which express the fact that z_n, p_n, q_n remain in the domain D and we can take $\rho = \alpha$, $\rho' = \beta$. The series furnished by the successive approximations converges in the rectangle R. Such would be the case of the equation

$$s = ap + bq + c \sin z,$$

where a, b, c are continuous functions of x, y in R; the equation obtained by setting

$$z = \phi(x) + \psi(y) - \phi(0) + u$$

evidently satisfies the desired conditions, provided $\phi'(x)$ and $\psi'(y)$ are continuous in the intervals $(0, \alpha)$ and $(0, \beta)$, respectively.

III. EQUATIONS IN MORE THAN TWO VARIABLES

It was natural to seek to extend Riemann's method, so simple, to equations of hyperbolic type in more than two variables. Kirchhoff, Volterra, Tedone, Coulon, d'Adhémar had treated a certain number of particular examples. Hadamard was the first to obtain a general solution, by proving that it was sufficient to know an integral of the adjoint equation, having at an arbitrary point a singularity of a specified kind, in order to derive from it by quadratures the solution of Cauchy's problem; as in Riemann's method, this particular integral is independent of the surface on which the given values lie. We shall return to the works[12] of the geometrical scholar for the study of this difficult question, and we shall content ourselves with indicating the elegant method of Volterra[13] for the equation of cylindrical waves.

45. Fundamental formula. Let $U(x, y, z)$ be a continuous function possessing continuous partial derivatives. It is often convenient to introduce the derivative of U taken *in a fixed direction.* Let us consider x, y, z as the rectangular coordinates of a point of space, and let L be a direction coming from a point M. On this direction let us take a point M' at a distance h from M; we call the derivative of $U(x, y, z)$ in the direction L the limit of the ratio $[U(M') - U(M)]/MM'$ as the point M' approaches indefinitely the point M, while remaining on the half-line considered. We write for brevity $U(M)$ instead of $U(x, y, z)$, M being the point with coordinates (x, y, z). If α, β, γ are the direction angles of L (made with the positive directions of the axes), we have

$$\frac{U(M') - U(M)}{MM'}$$

$$= \frac{U(x + h \cos \alpha, y + h \cos \beta, z + h \cos \gamma) - U(x, y, z)}{h};$$

the limit of this ratio, that is to say the derivative sought dU/dL, has therefore for its expression, according to the formula which

---

[12] *Annales de l'École Normale supérieure*, 1904 and 1905; *Acta mathematica*, Vol. XXXI, 1908.

[13] *Acta mathematica*, Vol. XVIII, 1894. See also the paper by Kirchhoff, *Sitzungsberichte der Berliner Akademie*, 1882.

gives the derivative of a composite function,

$$(59) \qquad \frac{dU}{dL} = \frac{\partial U}{\partial x} \cos \alpha + \frac{\partial U}{\partial y} \cos \beta + \frac{\partial U}{\partial z} \cos \gamma.$$

Let MV be the vector having its origin at M, and whose components are $\partial U/\partial x$, $\partial U/\partial y$, $\partial U/\partial z$; relation (59) expresses the fact that dU/dL is equal to the algebraic value of the projection of vector MV on the direction L. It follows immediately that derivatives taken in two opposite directions differ only in sign. Let us recall again that the vector MV is directed along the normal to the surface at the level $U(x, y, z) = C$, which passes through the point M and on the side where the function U is increasing, and that the length of this vector is in inverse ratio to the portion of the normal included between two arbitrarily close level surfaces. All these definitions evidently apply to a function of two variables, replacing space by plane.

This being granted, let

$$F(u) = \frac{\partial^2 u}{\partial x^2} + \frac{\partial^2 u}{\partial y^2} - \frac{\partial^2 u}{\partial z^2}.$$

We have the identity (cf. III, **41**, note)

$$vF(u) - uF(v) = \frac{\partial}{\partial x} \left(v \frac{\partial u}{\partial x} - u \frac{\partial v}{\partial x} \right)$$

$$+ \frac{\partial}{\partial y} \left(v \frac{\partial u}{\partial y} - u \frac{\partial v}{\partial y} \right) - \frac{\partial}{\partial z} \left(v \frac{\partial u}{\partial z} - u \frac{\partial v}{\partial z} \right),$$

for any functions u and v. If these functions are continuous, as well as their partial derivatives up to the second order, in a finite domain D, bounded by a surface Σ, we deduce from the preceding identity the relation

$$(60) \qquad \iiint_{(D)} [vF(u) - uF(v)] \, dx \, dy \, dz$$

$$= \iint_{(\Sigma)} \left(v \frac{\partial u}{\partial x} - u \frac{\partial v}{\partial x} \right) dy \, dz + \left(v \frac{\partial u}{\partial y} - u \frac{\partial v}{\partial y} \right) dz \, dx - \ldots,$$

the surface integral being taken on the side exterior to Σ. Let α,

β, γ be the angles which the direction exterior to the normal at Σ makes with the axes; the surface integral is identical with

$$\int\int_{(\Sigma)} v \left(\frac{\partial u}{\partial x} \cos \alpha + \frac{\partial u}{\partial y} \cos \beta - \frac{\partial u}{\partial z} \cos \gamma \right) d\sigma,$$

$$-\int\int_{(\Sigma)} u \left(\frac{\partial v}{\partial x} \cos \alpha + \frac{\partial v}{\partial y} \cos \beta - \frac{\partial v}{\partial z} \cos \gamma \right) d\sigma.$$

Now $\cos \alpha$, $\cos \beta$, $- \cos \gamma$ are the direction cosines of the symmetric direction of the exterior normal with respect to the plane parallel to the plane $z = 0$ drawn through the foot of the normal; following an expression due to d'Adhémar, we shall call this line the *conormal* to the surface Σ at the point under consideration. The positive direction on the conormal corresponds to the exterior direction on the normal. The coefficients of v and of u, in the preceding surface integrals, represent respectively the derivatives of the functions u and v, taken in the positive direction of the conormal. We shall represent these derivatives by du/dN, dv/dN, which permits us to write formula (60) in the abbreviated form

$$(61) \quad \int\int\int_{(D)} [vF(u) - uF(v)] \, dx \, dy \, dz = \int\int_{(\Sigma)} \left(v\frac{du}{dN} - u\frac{dv}{dN} \right) \partial\sigma.$$

46. Volterra's method. Let us consider the equation

$$(62) \quad F(u) = \frac{\partial^2 u}{\partial x^2} + \frac{\partial^2 u}{\partial y^2} - \frac{\partial^2 u}{\partial z^2} = Z,$$

whose second member is a known function of (x, y, z); it would be sufficient to assume $Z = 0$ and to replace z by at in order to regain the equation of cylindrical waves (III, **29**). This equation is of the hyperbolic type, and the characteristic surfaces are the integral surfaces of the partial differential equation

$$(63) \quad \left(\frac{\partial z}{\partial x} \right)^2 + \left(\frac{\partial z}{\partial y} \right)^2 - 1 = 0$$

which expresses the fact that the tangent plane makes an angle of $45°$ with the plane $z = 0$. The conormal at each point therefore lies in the tangent plane, and this property, it is easy to see, belongs only to the characteristic surfaces. The locus of the characteristic curves of equation (63) passing through any point P of space is a cone of revolution with vertex at P, whose axis is parallel to the z-axis, and whose vertex angle is a right angle; this is the *characteristic cone*.

In Volterra's method, Riemann's function is replaced by an integral of the equation $F(u) = 0$, which is zero all along the characteristic cone with vertex (x_1, y_1, z_1). To obtain such an integral, let us first look for an integral depending only upon z/r, where

$$r = \sqrt{x^2 + y^2}.$$

If we make the change of variables $x = r \cos \phi$, $y = r \sin \phi$, the equation $F(u) = 0$ becomes

$$\frac{\partial^2 u}{\partial r^2} + \frac{1}{r^2} \frac{\partial^2 u}{\partial \phi^2} + \frac{1}{r} \frac{\partial u}{\partial r} = \frac{\partial^2 u}{\partial z^2};$$

seeking an integral depending only upon $w = z/r$, we are led to the differential equation

$$(w^2 - 1) \frac{d^2 u}{dw^2} + w \frac{du}{dw} = 0,$$

whose integration is easy. We thus obtain the particular integral

$$\log \frac{\pm z + \sqrt{z^2 - r^2}}{r},$$

which is zero at every point of the characteristic cone having the origin as its vertex, provided that we take a suitable sign before z. Since the equation $F(u) = 0$ is not changed by a translation with arbitrary origin, we see that the function

$$(64) \quad v = \log \left(\frac{z_1 - z + \sqrt{(z_1 - z)^2 - (x_1 - x)^2 - (y_1 - y)^2}}{\sqrt{(x_1 - x)^2 + (y_1 - y)^2}} \right)$$

is a particular integral of the equation $F(u) = 0$, which is zero at every point of the lower nappe of the characteristic cone whose vertex is the point P, with coordinates (x_1, y_1, z_1). This function v presents a discontinuity all along the axis of this characteristic cone.

Let us suppose that we know the value of an integral u of equation (62) and of its first partial derivatives along a surface Σ, and that we would like to calculate the value of this integral at a point $P(x_1, y_1, z_1)$, exterior to Σ. Assuming this point P above Σ, as indicated in Figure 9, let us consider the domain D bounded by the lower nappe of the characteristic cone Λ with vertex at P, and by the portion Σ' of Σ below this cone; assuming that there exists an integral of equation (62) satisfying the Cauchy condition and regular in D, we are going to show how we can calculate the value of this integral at the point P. We cannot immediately apply the general formula (61) to the two functions u and v in the domain

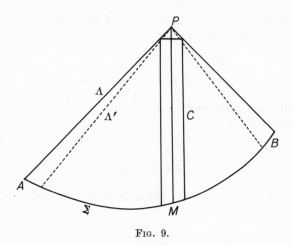

Fig. 9.

D, because the function v is discontinuous along the axis of the cone, and also because the derivatives of v are discontinuous on the cone Λ. To avoid these difficulties, we first of all isolate the singular line by means of a cylinder of revolution C of a very small radius η having the same axis as the cone, and then replace the cone Λ by a cone of revolution Λ' with the same vertex and the same axis whose vertex half-angle ϕ is a little less than $\pi/4$, $\phi = (\pi/4) - \epsilon$, then we consider the domain D' formed by the portion of the domain D which is outside the cylinder C and inside the lower nappe of the cone Λ'. The two functions u and v being regular in this domain D' formula (61) is applicable. The surface which bounds D' is composed of three distinct portions, a portion Σ'' of Σ', a cylindrical surface Σ_1, and a portion of the surface arising from the cone Λ'. Upon replacing $F(u)$ by Z and $F(v)$ by zero, formula (61) becomes

$$\int\int\int_{(D')} vZ\,dx\,dy\,dz = \int\int_{(\Sigma'')} \left(v\frac{du}{dN} - u\frac{dv}{dN} \right) d\sigma$$

$$+ \int\int_{(\Sigma_1)} \left(v\frac{du}{dN} - u\frac{dv}{dN} \right) d\sigma$$

$$+ \int\int_{(\Lambda')} \left(v\frac{du}{dN} - u\frac{dv}{dN} \right) d\sigma.$$

At a point of the surface of the cone Λ', at a distance l from the vertex, we have, as an easy calculation shows,

$$v = \log\left(\cot\phi + \sqrt{\cot^2\phi - 1}\right), \qquad \frac{dv}{dN} = -\frac{1}{l}\frac{\sqrt{\cos 2\phi}}{\sin\phi};$$

when the angle ϕ approaches $\pi/4$, v, dv/dN, and consequently the double integral along Λ', approach zero.[14] The double integral taken over the surface Σ_1 of the cylinder cannot be calculated, since we do not know the values of u and of du/dN on this surface. But we can find the limit of this integral as the radius η of the cylinder approaches zero. In fact, we can take for the element of area on this cylinder $d\sigma = \eta\,d\omega\,dz$, the angle ω varying from 0 to 2π. At a point of the surface, we have the expression

$$v = \log\left(z_1 - z + \sqrt{(z_1 - z)^2 - \eta^2}\right) - \log\eta;$$

the direction of the conormal coincides with the direction of the interior normal to the cylinder, and we have

$$\frac{dv}{dN} = -\frac{dv}{dr} = \frac{1}{\eta} + \frac{\eta}{\sqrt{(z - z_1)^2 - \eta^2}\,[z_1 - z + \sqrt{(z_1 - z)^2 - \eta^2}]}.$$

The product ηv has zero as a limit, while $\eta(dv/dN)$ has $+1$ as its limit. From this we deduce readily that the limit of the double integral taken over the surface of the cylinder is equal to

$$- 2\pi \int_{z_0}^{z_1} u(x_1, y_1, z)\,dz,$$

[14] The function v being zero along Λ, the derivative of v along any direction whatever in the tangent plane must also be zero. Now, the conormal is precisely in the tangent plane.

z_0 being the coordinate of the point where the axis of the cone meets the surface Σ. Moreover, when ϵ and η approach zero, the integrals taken over D' and Σ'' respectively have as limits the integrals taken over D and Σ'. We therefore have in the limit

$$(65) \quad \int \int \int_{(D)} vZ \, dx \, dy \, dz = \int \int_{(\Sigma')} \left(v \frac{du}{dN} - u \frac{dv}{dN} \right) d\sigma$$

$$- 2\pi \int_{z_0}^{z_1} u(x_1, y_1, z) \, dz.$$

Taking the derivatives of the two members of the preceding equality with respect to z_1, we finally find

$$(66) \quad u(x_1, y_1, z_1) = -\frac{1}{2\pi} \frac{\partial}{\partial z_1} \left[\int \int \int_{(D)} vZ \, dx \, dy \, dz \right.$$

$$\left. - \int \int_{(\Sigma')} \left(v \frac{du}{dN} - u \frac{dv}{dN} \right) d\sigma \right].$$

The auxiliary function v is known; u and du/dN are assumed known on Σ and consequently the second member of this formula is a determined function of the coordinates (x_1, y_1, z_1) of the vertex P of the cone Λ. Formula (66) therefore furnishes the solution of Cauchy's problem, by assuming that this solution exists, which is by no means evident *a priori*. It is therefore necessary to prove inversely that the function $u(x_1, y_1, z_1)$ represented by this formula is an integral of equation (62), whose value, as well as those of its first derivatives, approached the given values when the point P approaches a point of Σ. This question, which Volterra had abandoned, has been studied by d'Adhémar, who has established the converse.[15]

When the surface Σ on which the given values lie is a characteristic surface, the direction of the conormal at each point lies in the tangent plane to the surface. If we are given the value of u at each point of Σ, the value of du/dN is likewise known. An integral is therefore determined if we know its value along a characteristic surface (cf. III, **38**).

---

[15] *Journal de Liouville*, 5th series, Vol. X, p. 131–207; *Rendiconti del Circolo matematico di Palermo*, Vol. XX, 1905. — For anything that concerns equations of hyperbolic type, see the work of Hadamard, *Lectures on Cauchy's Problem in Linear Partial Differential Equations* (Yale University Press, 1923).

Example. Let us suppose that the surface Σ is the plane $z = 0$, and that, in addition, we have $Z = 0$. We must find an integral of the equation $F(u) = 0$, knowing that for $z = 0$ it reduces to a function $f(x, y)$, while $\partial u/\partial z$ reduces to $\phi(x, y)$. We shall again content ourselves with calculating the value of this integral at a point $P(x_1, y_1, z_1)$ whose coordinate z_1 is positive. At each point of the plane $z = 0$, the direction of the conormal is parallel to the z-axis, and we therefore have to take

$$u = f(x, y), \qquad \frac{du}{dN} = \phi(x, y)$$

on that portion of the xy-plane which is involved in the calculation of the integral. Besides, we have on the xy-plane

$$v = \log\left(\frac{z_1 + \sqrt{z_1^2 - r^2}}{r}\right), \qquad \frac{dv}{dN} = \frac{dv}{dz} = \frac{-1}{\sqrt{z_1^2 - r^2}}.$$

The domain of integration Σ' is here the circle of radius z_1, having the point with coordinates (x_1, y_1) as center, in the $z = 0$ plane. Suppressing the indices, we can therefore write formula (66) as:

(67) $u(x, y, z)$

$$= \frac{1}{2\pi}\frac{\partial}{\partial z}\left\{ \int \int \left[\log\left(\frac{z + \sqrt{z^2 - r^2}}{r}\right)\phi(\alpha, \beta) + \frac{f(\alpha, \beta)}{\sqrt{z^2 - r^2}}\right] d\alpha\, d\beta\right\},$$

where $r^2 = (\alpha - x)^2 + (\beta - y)^2$, the double integral being taken over the circle Γ with radius z having the point (x, y) as center, in the xy-plane. The first double integral, in polar coordinates, becomes

$$I_1 = \int\int_{(\Gamma)} \log\left(\frac{z + \sqrt{z^2 - r^2}}{r}\right)\phi(\alpha, \beta)\, d\alpha\, d\beta$$

$$= \int_0^{2\pi} d\theta \int_0^z \log\left(\frac{z + \sqrt{z^2 - r^2}}{r}\right)\phi(x + r\cos\theta, y + r\sin\theta)\, r\, dr.$$

The integral of the second member is uniformly convergent if the function ϕ is bounded, and we can apply the usual differentiation formula which gives the expression

$$\frac{\partial I_1}{\partial z} = \int_0^{2\pi} d\theta \int_0^z \frac{\phi(x + r\cos\theta, \, y + r\sin\theta)}{\sqrt{z^2 - r^2}} \, r \, dr$$

$$= \int\int_{(\Gamma)} \frac{\phi(\alpha, \beta) \, d\alpha \, d\beta}{\sqrt{z^2 - r^2}}$$

for $\partial I_1/\partial z$. It is sufficient to replace z by t to come back to formula (20) of III, **29**, where we should have $a = 1$.

Comments and Exercises

1. Study the motion of a vibrating string, given that for $t = 0$ it has the form of a parabolic arc, symmetric with respect to the perpendicular bisector of the segment joining the extremities, and that the initial velocity is zero at each point.

2. Solve Cauchy's problem for the equation $(\partial^2 z/\partial x^2) = (1/a^2) (\partial^2 z/\partial t^2)$ by applying the general method of **33**.

If the initial conditions are $z = f(x)$, $\partial z/\partial t = \phi(x)$, for $t = 0$, then setting $x + at = \xi$, $x - at = \eta$, the equation becomes $\partial^2 z/\partial\xi \, \partial\eta = 0$, and the initial conditions become the following: along the line $\xi = \eta$ we must have

$$z = f(\xi), \qquad \frac{\partial z}{\partial \xi} = \frac{1}{2} f'(\xi) + \frac{1}{2a} \phi(\xi), \qquad \frac{\partial z}{\partial \eta} = \frac{1}{2} f'(\xi) - \frac{1}{2a} \phi(\xi).$$

3. Solve Hugoniot's problem (footnote 3, this chapter) assuming

$$\psi(p) = \frac{1}{k} \log(1 + p), \qquad f(t) = \alpha t^2.$$

What must the function $f(t)$ be for the surface S to be a cone?

4. Establish by the method of successive approximations Cauchy's formula (II, 2, **39**)

$$y = \int_{x_0}^x f(\alpha) \, \phi(x, \alpha) \, d\alpha,$$

for the integral of the linear equation $F(y) = f(x)$, which, along with its first $(n - 1)$ derivatives, is zero for $x = x_0$ (cf. III, **39**).

We write the equation in the form

$$\frac{d^n y}{dx^n} = \lambda \left(a_1 \frac{d^{n-1}y}{dx^{n-1}} + \ldots + a_n y \right) + f(x) = \lambda Fx \, [y(x)] + f(x)$$

and notice that the desired integral satisfies the integro-differential equation

$$y(x) = \lambda \int_{x_0}^x \frac{(x - s)^{n-1}}{(n - 1)!} F_s[y(s)] \, ds + \int_{x_0}^x \frac{(x - s)^{n-1}}{(n - 1)!} f(s) \, ds,$$

which permits us to expand it in powers of λ. We thus find as an expression for this integral

$$y(x) = \int_{x_0}^x f(t) \, dt \, [g_0(x, t) + \lambda g_1(x, t) + \ldots + \lambda^m g_m(x, t) + \ldots],$$

where $g_0(x, t) = (x - t)^{n-1}/(n - 1)!$, and where the succeeding coefficients are obtained by the recurrence formula

$$g_m(x, t) = \int_t^x \frac{(x - s)^{n-1}}{(n - 1)!} F_s[g_{m-1}(s, t)] \, ds.$$

5. *Riemann's equation.* The function $u(x, y, \xi, \eta)$ of Riemann for the equation

$$\frac{\partial^2 z}{\partial x \, \partial y} - \frac{\beta'}{x - y} \frac{\partial z}{\partial x} + \frac{\beta}{x - y} \frac{\partial z}{\partial y} = 0$$

can be expressed as

$$(u, x, y; \xi, \eta)$$
$$= (\eta - x)^{-\beta'} (y - \xi)^{-\beta} F \left(\beta, \beta', 1, \frac{(x - \xi)(y - \eta)}{(x - \eta)(y - \xi)} \right) (\xi - \eta)^{\beta + \beta'},$$

F designating the hypergeometric series (II, 2, **51**) (see Darboux, *Théorie des surfaces*, Vol. II, p. 81 and following). One may also consult an article of M. Jamet (*Bulletin des Sciences mathématiques*, 2nd series, Vol. XIX, 1895, p. 208).

CHAPTER V

LINEAR EQUATIONS OF ELLIPTIC TYPE

I. HARMONIC FUNCTIONS. POISSON'S INTEGRAL

47. General properties.[1] Laplace's equation plays the same role in the study of linear equations of elliptic type as the equation $\partial^2 u/\partial x \partial y = 0$ does in the theory of equations of hyperbolic type. But the problems which arise for the new equation are entirely different from those which we have studied up till now.

We say that a function $u(x, y)$ of the two real variables x, y is *harmonic in a domain* D when it is *regular* in this domain, that is to say, when it and its partial derivatives up to the second order are continuous, and when at every point of this domain it satisfies Laplace's equation, which we shall write (suppressing the index)

$$(1) \qquad \Delta u = \frac{\partial^2 u}{\partial x^2} + \frac{\partial^2 u}{\partial y^2} = 0.$$

The real part of a function $f(z)$ of the variable $z = x + iy$, holomorphic in a domain D, is harmonic in this domain (**II,I,3**). Conversely, with every harmonic function $z(x, y)$ we can associate another function $v(x, y)$, defined within an additive constant, satisfying the two relations[2]

$$(2) \qquad \frac{\partial v}{\partial x} = -\frac{\partial u}{\partial y}, \quad \frac{\partial v}{\partial y} = \frac{\partial u}{\partial x}$$

---

[1] I have made much use in the writing of this Chapter of Picard's *Traité d'Analyse*, in particular of Chapters I, III, X of Volume II.

[2] Let mt and mt' be two rectangular directions such that the angle tmt' has the same orientation as angle xOy; d/dt, d/dt' representing the derivatives

continued on page 171

and such that $u + iv$ is an analytic function of $z = x + iy$. This function $v(x, y)$ is also an integral of equation (1); it is also uniform and regular in the domain D, and therefore harmonic in D, if this domain has a simple contour,[3] and $u + iv$ is holomorphic in this domain. From this connection with the theory of functions of a complex variable, we easily deduce several important properties of harmonic functions. Thus we are going to prove that *every harmonic function is an analytic function of the variables* x *and* y, in the sense which we have attached to this word (I, **191**). Let us assume that $u(x, y)$ is regular in the interior of a circle C of radius R described about the point (x_0, y_0) as center; the same is true of $v(x, y)$ and consequently $f(z) = u + iv$ is holomorphic function of z in this circle. We have, therefore, in the interior of C,

$$(3) \quad f(z) = a_0 + a_1(z - z_0) + \ldots + a_n(z - z_0)^n + \ldots,$$

$$z_0 = x_0 + iy_0$$

the coefficients a_n being, in general, complex numbers. Let us replace $z - z_0$ by $x - x_0 + i(y - y_0)$ and let us separate the real parts and the coefficients of i in the series (3); $u(x, y)$ appears in the form of a double power series

$$(4) \quad u(x, y) = \sum_{p, q} b_{p, q}(x - x_0)^p(y - y_0)^q.$$

---

continued from page 170

taken at the point m in these directions, we can replace relations (2) by the equivalent relations

$$(2a) \quad \frac{du}{dt} = \frac{dv}{dt'}, \quad \frac{du}{dt'} = -\frac{dv}{dt}.$$

The direct proof is easy, but it is sufficient to observe that from their meaning in the theory of functions, relations (2) do not change when we turn the axes through any angle whatever; it is therefore sufficient to rotate them in such a way as to make them parallel to the directions mt, mt'.

Let us suppose that the point m describes a closed curve C in the positive sense; if we take for mt the direction of the tangent in the sense of transversal, mt' will be the direction mn of the interior normal and relations (2a) become

$$(2b) \quad \frac{du}{ds} = \frac{dv}{dn}, \quad \frac{du}{dn} = -\frac{dv}{ds},$$

d/ds and d/dn designating the derivatives taken in these two directions.

[3] If the domain D is bounded by several distinct curves, the function $v(x, y)$ can have multiple determinations. Let us take, for example, the function Log z; the real part is harmonic on the exterior of a circle described about the origin as center, while the coefficient of i has the period 2π.

Equality (3) proves that $u(x, y)$ is equal to the sum of this double series, when we group together all the terms of same degree in $x - x_0$, $y - y_0$, but this is not sufficient to prove the *absolute* convergence of the series. To establish this essential point, we must show that it remains convergent when we replace each term by its absolute value, provided that $|x - x_0|$ and $|y - y_0|$ are sufficiently small. Now, the set of terms of degree n in series (4) is equal, setting $a_n = \alpha_n + i\beta_n$, to

$$\alpha_n \left[(x - x_0)^n - \frac{n(n - 1)}{1.2} (x - x_0)^{n-2}(y - y_0)^2 + \ldots \right]$$

$$+ \beta_n \left[- n(x - x_0)^{n-1}(y - y_0) \right.$$

$$\left. + \frac{n(n - 1) \ (n + 2)}{1.2.3}(x - x_0)^{n-3}(y - y_0)^3 - \ldots \right].$$

It is clear that if we replace each term by its absolute value, the sum obtained is less than

$$|a_n| \left\{ |x - x_0| + |y - y_0| \right\}^n ;$$

R being the radius of convergence of the power series (3), the series

$$\Sigma \ |a_n| \ r^n$$

is convergent provided that we have $r < R$ and, therefore, series (4) is absolutely convergent provided that we have

(5) $$\qquad |x - x_0| + |y - y_0| < R,$$

that is, when the point (x, y) is interior to a square easy to define.

From this important proposition there results a whole set of consequences entirely like those which have been developed for analytic functions of a complex variable. Thus, all the derivatives of a function harmonic in a domain D are themselves analytic functions regular in this domain; they are also harmonic functions, as we see immediately upon differentiating equation (1). If two harmonic functions coincide in a *region*, however small its dimensions, they are identical, for all their partial derivatives are equal at a point of this region, and we could repeat for the analytic continuation of a harmonic function all that has been said concerning functions of a complex variable (Volume II). We shall not begin it again.[4]

The set of terms of degree n in the series (4) is of the form

$$C_1\,\rho^n\,\cos n\phi\,+\,C_2\,\rho^n\,\sin n\phi$$

if we set

$$x\,-\,x_0 = \rho\,\cos\phi, \quad y\,-\,y_0 = \rho\,\sin\phi.$$

We see therefore that the most general harmonic and homogeneous polynomial of degree n in $x - x_0$, $y - y_0$ depends upon only the *two* arbitrary constants C_1 and C_2. From the general form of the terms of series (4), we deduce also that a harmonic function can have *neither a maximum nor a minimum* at the point (x_0, y_0). Indeed, if the development of $u(x, y) - u(x_0, y_0)$ begins with terms of degree n, the set of these terms being of the form

$$\rho^n(C_1\,\cos n\phi\,+\,C_2\,\sin n\phi),$$

it changes sign for n distinct values of ϕ.[5]

---

[4] Every harmonic function, being an analytic function of x, y, is virtually defined for the *complex* values as well as for the *real* values of these variables as soon as we know an element of the function. Here is an interesting consequence. Let $f(z)$ be a holomorphic function of the complex variable $z = x + iy$ in the domain of $z_0 = x_0 + iy_0$

$$f(z) = \alpha_0 + i\beta_0 + \ldots + (\alpha_n + i\beta_n)(z - z_0)^n + \ldots.$$

The real part $u(x, y)$ of $f(z)$ is represented in the same domain by the series

$$u(x, y) = \alpha_0 + \sum_{n=1}^{+\infty} \left\{ \frac{\alpha_n + i\beta_n}{2}[x - x_0 + i(y - y_0)]^n \right.$$
$$\left. + \frac{\alpha_n + i\beta_n}{2}[x - x_0 - i(y - y_0)]^n \right\}.$$

In this formula let us replace $x - x_0$ by $\dfrac{z - z_0}{2}$, $y - y_0$ by $\dfrac{z - z_0}{2i}$; it becomes

$$u\left(x_0 + \frac{z - z_0}{2}, y_0 + \frac{z - z_0}{2i}\right) = \alpha_0 + \frac{1}{2}f(z) - \frac{\alpha_0 + \beta_0 i}{2};$$

this relation, established when we have $|z - z_0| < R$, holds evidently in the entire domain of existence of $f(z)$, since the two members are analytic functions of z. In particular, if $u(x, y)$ is a rational function or an algebraic function of x, y, $f(z)$ is a function of z of the same nature.

[5] The point (x_0, y_0) can only be an ordinary point or a multiple point with distinct tangents on the curve $u(x, y) = u(x_0, y_0)$, but never an isolated point nor a cusp.

From the study which has been made of the isolated singular points of a uniformly analytic function, we can derive the general expression for a harmonic function in the neighborhood of an isolated singular point. Let $u(x, y)$ be a harmonic function regular at every interior point of a circle C with center A (a, b), except perhaps at point A itself. Adjoining to it the harmonic function

$$v(x, y) = \int_{(x_0, y_0)}^{x, y} - \frac{\partial u}{\partial y} dx + \frac{\partial u}{\partial x} dy,$$

taken from a point (x_0, y_0) of the circle, different from the center, we obtain an analytic function $u + iv$ of the complex variable $z = x + iy$ which has no other singular point, in the interior of the circle C, than the point A, but it is not necessarily uniform, for the function $v(x, y)$ may have a period arising from a circuit in the positive sense around the center. Let $2\pi\alpha$ be this period—necessarily real; the difference

$$u + iv - \alpha \operatorname{Log}(z - z_0), \qquad \text{where } z_0 = a + ib,$$

is a uniform function $\alpha f(z)$ in the domain of the point z_0, which can have no singular point in this domain other than the point z_0 itself. We therefore have

$$e^{(u+iv)/\alpha} = (z - z_0)e^{f(z)} = F(z),$$

$F(z)$ also being a uniform function in the neighborhood of the point z_0, incapable of having any singular point other than z_0 in this neighborhood, and different from zero at every other point of the domain. We therefore have

(I) $u(x, y) = \log |F(z)|,$

and conversely from every uniform function $F(z)$ having the stated properties, we could derive by the preceding formula a function harmonic in every neighborhood of the point A, except perhaps at the point A itself. Formula (I) can be extended immediately to the case where the function $v(x, y)$ is itself uniform.

We deduce easily from the preceding several elementary theorems of Picard.[6] Let $u(x, y)$ be a harmonic function regular in a domain D, except possibly at a point A of this domain, in the neighborhood of

---

[6] É. Picard, *Quelques théorèmes élémentaires sur les functions harmoniques* (*Bulletin de la Société mathématique de France*, Vol. LII, 1924, p. 162). See also in Vol. 176 of the *Comptes rendus* (1923) various notes on this subject by Picard, Lebesgue, and Bouligand.

which we know only that its absolute value is less than a fixed number. The function $F(z)$ which occurs in formula (I) cannot have the point A as an essential singular point, nor as a pole, nor as a zero, for, in each of these cases, the absolute value of $\log|F(z)|$ would surpass every given number in the neighborhood of point A. It follows that in the neighborhood of the point A, the function $F(z)$ is represented by a Taylor's series, beginning with a constant term different from zero; the function $\text{Log}\{F(z)\}$ is also holomorphic in the neighborhood of this point, and the real part $u(x, y)$ of $\alpha \,\text{Log}\{F(z)\}$ is regular in the neighborhood of the point A, and, consequently, *in the entire domain* D. This is the first of Picard's theorems.

Let us suppose in the second place that the absolute value of $u(x, y)$ increases indefinitely when the distance r of the point (x, y) from point A approaches zero. This cannot happen if the point A is an essential singular point of $F(z)$ nor when this point is an ordinary point of $F(z)$, without being a zero. It is therefore necessary that z_0 be a pole or a zero of $F(z)$, which is of the form $(z - z_0)^m \phi(z)$, m being a positive or negative integer, and $\phi(z)$ a holomorphic function which is not zero for $z = z_0$. We have then $u(x, y) = \alpha[m \log r + \log|\phi(z)|]$, that is,

$$u(x, y) = K \log r + U,$$

U being a harmonic function regular at A, which is the second theorem of Picard.

In the first case, the function $F(z)$ is regular at point A, without being zero at this point. In the second case, point A is a pole or zero of $F(z)$. When the point A is an essential singular point of $F(z)$, the function $u(x, y)$ is indeterminate at this point. For example, if we take $F(z) = e^{1/z}$, the origin is an indeterminate point for $u(x, y) = x/(x^2 + y^2)$.

The greater part of the other properties of harmonic functions which are going to be proved could be derived similarly from the theory of functions of a complex variable. However, they will be established directly, in such a manner as to permit the extension of the proof to the case of three variables. Let us observe first of all that we can apply to harmonic functions the remarks made above in connection with linear equations (III, **27**). Thus, from every solution of equation (1) depending upon one or several parameters, we can derive by differentiation or integration an infinity of other solutions. Among the known solutions, the function $u = \log r$, where r is the distance between the two points (x, y), (a, b), which depends upon the two parameters a, b, is going to play an important role.

The partial derivatives of u with respect to any one of the variables a, b, x, y are also harmonic functions and the same is true of every linear combination of these derivatives whose coefficients are independent of x and y. For example, let L be any direction whatever, passing through the point (a, b), and making an angle ϕ with the direction from the point (a, b) to the point (x, y). The derivative of log r, taken in this direction, and considered as a function of the parameters a, b, is a new harmonic function of the variables x and y, for it is a linear combination with constant coefficients of the derivatives $\partial \log r/\partial a$, $\partial \log r/\partial b$. This derivative has the expression $1/r \ (dr/dL)$, that is, $-(\cos \phi)/r$; we verify directly that $(\cos \phi)/r$ is a harmonic function by observing that it is the real part of the function $e^{\theta i} \ 1/(z - a - bi)$, θ being the argument of the direction L. We see similarly that $(\cos \psi)/r$, where ψ is the angle which the direction going from (x, y) to (a, b) makes with a *fixed* direction Λ independent of the point (x, y), is a harmonic function, for this expression is equal, except for sign, to the derivative of log r, considered as a function of (x, y), taken in the direction Λ.

Let us observe again that every pointwise transformation which preserves angles changes a harmonic function into a new harmonic function. This property has already been established implicitly.

48. Uniformly convergent integrals. In order to avoid useless repetitions, we are going first of all to prove a property of certain integrals, to which we shall frequently appeal. Let, in a general manner, $u(M, P)$ be a function of the coordinates of the two points M and P, each of which can range over a certain domain, and which is continuous for every system of positions of these two points, except when the two points are coincident; such, for example, is an expression of the form

$$\frac{v(M,P)}{\overline{MP}^\alpha}$$

$v(M, P)$ being continuous and α being positive. Let us suppose first that the point M describes a fixed plane curve C, while P can have any position whatever in the plane. The integral

$$U(P) = \int_{(C)} u(M, P) \, ds,$$

taken by supposing point P fixed and letting M describe arc C, is a continuous function of the coordinates of point P, as long as this point is not on C. When the point P coincides with a point M_0 of C, the integral $U(M_0)$ may have a meaning even though it has an infinite element, but the presence of this infinite element no longer permits us to state without further examination that the integral is continuous at this point, that is, that $U(P) - U(M_0)$ approaches zero with the distance M_0P.

We shall say that the integral $U(P)$ is *uniformly convergent in the neighborhood of a point* M_0 *of* C if the following condition is satisfied: given any positive arbitrary number ϵ, we can find on arc C an arc C' on which M_0 lies, and a positive number ρ, such that for every point P taken in the interior of the circle c_ρ of radius ρ with M_0 for center, the absolute value of the integral

$$\int_{C'} u(M, P)\, ds$$

is less than ϵ. When this condition is fulfilled, it is sufficient to return to the classical reasoning used so often to prove that $U(P) - U(M_0)$ approaches zero with M_0P. Indeed, we can write

$$U(P) - U(M_0) = U'(P) - U'(M_0) + \{U''(P) - U''(M_0)\},$$

representing by U' and U'' the integrals taken along the arc C' and arc $C'' = C - C'$. Arc C' and the number ρ having been chosen as we have just said, the absolute values of $U'(P)$ and of $U'(M_0)$ are less than ϵ when P is in the interior of c_ρ. But the number ρ being replaceable by any smaller positive number, we can assume arc C'' entirely outside c_ρ. The integral $U''(P)$ is then a continuous function in this circle c_ρ. Let us choose a positive number $\rho' \leq \rho$ such that we have

$$|U''(P) - U''(M_0)| < \epsilon,$$

whenever $M_0P < \rho'$. It is clear that we shall also have

$$|U(P) - U(M_0)| < 3\epsilon,$$

when M_0P is less than ρ'.

The definition of uniformly convergent integrals in the neighborhood of a point can be extended to double and to triple integrals. Let us assume that the point P can assume any position in space, while the point M is constrained to remain on a surface Σ. We shall again say that the surface integral

$$U(P) = \int\int_{(\Sigma)} u(M, P)\, d\sigma$$

is uniformly convergent in the neighborhood of a point M_0 of Σ if, given a positive number ϵ, we can find a part Σ' of Σ surrounding the point M_0 and a positive number ρ, such that for every point P taken in the interior of the sphere of radius ρ with center M_0, the absolute value of the integral

$$\int \int_{(\Sigma')} u(M, P)\, d\sigma$$

will be less than ϵ. Finally, if the point M itself describes a three-dimensional domain, D, we shall say that the triple integral

$$U(P) = \int \int \int_{(D)} u(M, P)\, dv$$

is uniformly convergent in the neighborhood of a point M_0 of D if, given a positive number ϵ, we can find a domain D' containing M_0 in its interior and a positive number ρ such that, for every point P taken in the sphere of radius ρ with M_0 as center, the absolute value of the triple integral

$$\int \int \int_{(D')} u(M, P)\, dv$$

is less than ϵ. There is nothing to change in our demonstration to prove that in these two cases $U(P)$ is continuous at the point M_0.

49. Logarithmic potential. From the particular integrals of equation (1) referred to at the end of section **47** we can derive an infinitude of other harmonic functions by quadratures. We shall first study only functions represented by definite integrals, taken along a curve C. Concerning the curves C which will be involved in the sequel, we shall make the following hypotheses: we shall assume that they are composed of a *finite* number of arcs such that the coordinates of a point which describes one of them are continuous functions of a parameter having continuous derivatives. These conditions are evidently fulfilled by a curve which is composed of a finite number of analytic arcs (**I, 192**), but it is of interest for the theory not to limit ourselves to this case.

Let μ be a function which takes on a fixed value at each point M of C, and which varies continuously with the position of this point, for example, a continuous function of the arc s reckoned from a fixed arbitrary initial point. The definite integral

$$(6) \qquad V = \int_C \mu \log r \, ds,$$

where r is the distance between a variable point M of C and a fixed point P of the plane, and where ds is essentially positive, represents a harmonic function of the coordinates (a, b) of the point P, in every neighborhood not containing any point of C. This is a result of the properties of $\log r$, and of the usual formula for differentiation under the integral sign, which is applicable here since the integral (6) and those which we derive from it by differentiation have no infinite element. We call this function V a *logarithmic potential of single layer* (cf. Chap. VI).

The function $V(a, b)$ *is continuous on the curve* C *itself.* It is sufficient to prove that the integral $\int_C \mu \log (r) \, ds$ is uniformly convergent in the neighborhood of a point M_0 of C. Let us take as origin the point M_0, as x and y axes the tangent and the normal at this point, and let C' be a small arc of C, represented by the equation $y = f(x)$, where x varies from $- h$ to $+ h$, h being a positive number small enough that this arc C' is in the interior of the circle of radius $\frac{1}{2}$ having the origin as center. Let c_ρ be a concentric circle with radius $\rho \leq h$, and $P(a, b)$ be a point interior to c_ρ. The distance r of the point P from a point M of C' is less than unity; designating by H the upper limit of

$$|\mu| \cdot \sqrt{1 + f'^2(x)}$$

on a portion of C containing the arc C', the absolute value of

$$\int_{C'} \mu \log r \, ds$$

is less than

$$- H \int_{-h}^{+h} \log \left[\sqrt{(x - a)^2 + (y - b)^2} \right] dx$$

$$< - H \int_{-h}^{+h} \log (|x - a|) \, dx,$$

a being between $-h$ and $+h$; this last integral is itself less than

$$- 2H \int_0^{2h} \log (t) \, dt$$

and approaches zero with h. We could easily extend the demonstration to the case where M_0 is a corner point of C. On the other hand, the partial derivatives of V have discontinuities when the point P crosses the curve C which will be studied later (Chap. VI).

We again obtain harmonic functions when we replace log r by $1/r \cos (r, \lambda)$ in formula (6), where $\cos (r, \lambda)$ represents the cosine of the angle which the direction MP makes with an arbitrary direction through the point M, independent of the position of the point (a, b), for we have observed that this expression is a harmonic function of (a, b) for any position of the point M. If in particular we take a direction on the normal at M to the contour C, we obtain the *logarithmic potential of double layer*

$$(7) \qquad W = \int_C \mu \, \frac{\cos \, \phi}{r} \, ds,$$

ϕ being the angle between the direction MP and a chosen direction along the normal at M; W is again a harmonic function of the coordinates of P, in every domain not containing any point of C, but it is discontinuous when P traverses the contour of integration. In order to study this discontinuity we shall assume that C is a closed curve with no double point, and that we have taken the interior direction along the normal.

If μ reduces to a constant, the integral $\int_{(C)} [(\cos \phi)/r] \, ds$, to which we are led, has a geometrical significance, which makes the discontinuity conspicuous. It is equal, indeed, to the integral

$$\int_C d \, \text{arc tan} \, \frac{y - b}{x - a} = \int_C \frac{(x - a) \, dy - (y - b) \, dx}{(x - a)^2 + (y - b)^2}$$

taken along C in the positive sense. This is verified by means of the formulas $dx = ds \cos \beta'$, $dy = - ds \cos \alpha'$, where α' and β' are the angles (taken from 0 to π) which the direction of the interior normal makes with Ox and Oy (see section 50). It is once more sufficient to consider the infinitesimal triangle PMM', where M and M' are two arbitrarily close points of C, in order to see that $[(\cos \phi)/r] \, ds$ is equal to the signed angle $d\omega$, the sign depending upon the position of the element of arc MM' from the point P. The integral $\int_C [(\cos \phi)/r] \, ds$ is therefore equal to 2π, if point P is interior to the contour C, and equal to 0 if point P is exterior to this contour. If the point P is an ordinary point of the contour, the integral is equal to π; at a corner point of the contour, it is equal to the angle α in which the two tangents intersect, taken from 0 to 2π in the proper direction.

The study of this particular case is sufficient to show that the integral (7) is not uniformly convergent in the neighborhood of a point M_0 of C. Let us suppose for example that M_0 is an ordinary point of C and let C' be a very small arc on which M_0 lies; if we neglect the variation of μ along C', we see that the integral $\int_{C'} \mu \, [(\cos \phi)/r] \, ds$ for a point P interior to C and very close to M_0, is nearly equal to $\pi\mu_0 = \pi\mu(M_0)$, while it is very close to zero for the point M_0 itself. But the integral

$$(8) \qquad I\,(P) = \int_{C'} (\mu - \mu_0) \, \frac{\cos \phi}{r} \, ds$$

is *uniformly convergent in the neighborhood of the point* M_0. Let us assume, indeed, that the arc C' is sufficiently small that we have

$$|\mu(M) - \mu(M_0)| < \epsilon,$$

for every point M of C'. For any point P nearby to M_0 the absolute value of the integral $\int_{C'} (\mu - \mu_0) \, [(\cos \phi)/r] \, ds$ is less than $2\pi\epsilon$, and consequently can be made less than any given number by taking the arc C' small enough. The integral $I(P)$ is therefore continuous at the point M_0.

This being the case, let us designate by W_0 the value of the integral (7) when the point P is at M_0, by W_{i0} and W_{e0} the limiting values of $W(P)$ when the point P approaches point M_0 while remaining in the interior or in the exterior of C. If point M_0 is an ordinary point of the contour, we have $I(M_0) = W_0 - \pi\mu_0$, and besides the limit of $I(P)$ is $W_{i0} - 2\pi\mu_0$ or W_{e0}, according as the point P approaches M_0 from the interior or the exterior of the contour. Considering that $I(P)$ is continuous at the point M_0, we have the two equations

$$W_0 - \pi\mu_0 = W_{i0} - 2\pi\mu_0 = W_{e0},$$

from which we deduce the fundamental relations

$$(9) \qquad W_{i0} = W_0 + \pi\mu_0, \quad W_{e0} = W_0 - \pi\mu_0.$$

At a corner point where the tangents make an angle α, these relations must be replaced by the following:

$$(9) \qquad W_{i0} = W_0 + (2\pi - \alpha)\mu_0, \quad W_{e0} = W_0 - \alpha\mu_0.$$

50. Green's second formula.

In the particular case of Laplace's equation, the general formula (41) of III, **41** takes on the simple form

$$\phi\Delta\psi - \psi\Delta\phi = \frac{\partial}{\partial x}\left(\phi\frac{\partial\psi}{\partial x} - \psi\frac{\partial\phi}{\partial x}\right) + \frac{\partial}{\partial y}\left(\phi\frac{\partial\psi}{\partial y} - \psi\frac{\partial\phi}{\partial y}\right).$$

If the functions ϕ and ψ are regular in a domain D bounded by a closed contour C, we therefore have, from Green's first formula (I, **126**),

$$\int\int_{(D)} (\phi\Delta\psi - \psi\Delta\phi)\, dx\, dy = \int_C \left(\phi\frac{\partial\psi}{\partial x} - \psi\frac{\partial\phi}{\partial d}\right) dy$$

$$- \left(\phi\frac{\partial\psi}{\partial y} - \psi\frac{\partial\phi}{\partial y}\right) dx,$$

the line integral being taken in the positive sense around the contour C. Let α and β be the angles (taken between 0 and π) which the direction MT of the tangent to C makes in the positive sense with the axes, α' and β' the angles of the *interior direction* MN of the normal with the same axes. It is clear that we have $\cos\alpha\cos\alpha' + \cos\beta\cos\beta' = 0$. Moreover, let us suppose that from a point M of C we draw two half-lines Mx', My', respectively parallel to Ox and to Oy; a rotation which brings Mx' on MT will also place My' on MN, and consequently we shall have $\cos\beta' = \cos\alpha$, which implies $\cos\alpha' = -\cos\beta$. We can therefore replace dx by $\cos\beta'\,ds$ and dy by $-\cos\alpha\,ds$ in the line integral, and the preceding formula becomes

$$\int\int_{(D)} (\phi\Delta\psi - \psi\Delta\phi)\, dx\, dy = \int_C \psi\left(\frac{\partial\phi}{\partial x}\cos\alpha' + \frac{\partial\phi}{\partial y}\cos\beta'\right) ds$$

$$- \int_C \phi\left(\frac{\partial\psi}{\partial x}\cos\alpha' + \frac{\partial\psi}{\partial y}\cos\beta'\right) ds.$$

Now

$$\frac{\partial\phi}{\partial x}\cos\alpha' + \frac{\partial\phi}{\partial y}\cos\beta', \quad \frac{\partial\psi}{\partial x}\cos\alpha' + \frac{\partial\psi}{\partial y}\cos\beta'$$

represents precisely (**III**, **45**) the derivatives $d\phi/dn$, $d\psi/dn$, taken along the interior normal, and we thus obtain the new Green's formula

$$(10) \quad \int\int_{(D)} (\phi\Delta\psi - \psi\Delta\phi)\, dx\, dy + \int_C \left(\phi\frac{d\psi}{dn} - \psi\frac{d\phi}{dn}\right) ds = 0.$$

We shall remark once and for all that in this integral and in all similar integrals, ds is essentially positive, and therefore there is no necessity of specifying in which sense the contour is described. This contour can be composed of several distinct closed curves, but the direction of the normal interior to the contour is always that which pierces the domain D; it therefore coincides with the exterior direction of the normal to the geometric curve when the latter bounds the domain interiorly. It is also essential to observe that this formula (10), in which $d\phi/dn$, $d\psi/dn$ occur, presupposes that the partial derivatives $\partial\phi/\partial x$, $\partial\psi/\partial x$, ... have finite values on the contour. When we say, for example, that $\partial\phi/\partial x$ has a finite value at a point M of C, this means that the value of $\partial\phi/\partial x$ at a point m of D, lying on the parallel to Ox drawn through M, approaches a limit when m approaches M, and similarly for the others. These conditions are certainly satisfied if ϕ and ψ are regular in a domain in the interior of which contour C is situated, but this condition is not necessary; we have no need of any hypothesis on the functions ϕ and ψ outside the contour.

From the general formula (10) several particularly important formulas can be deduced. If ϕ and ψ are two harmonic functions in D, upon replacing ϕ and ψ by U and V, the formula becomes

$$(11) \qquad \int_{(C)} \left(U \frac{dV}{dn} - V \frac{dU}{dn} \right) ds = 0.$$

Again, let us take $\psi = 1$, and let us replace ϕ by a harmonic function U or the square, U^2, of a harmonic function; we obtain the two new formulas

$$(12) \qquad \int_{(C)} \frac{dU}{dn} ds = 0,$$

$$(12a) \qquad \int \int_{(D)} \left[\left(\frac{\partial U}{\partial x} \right)^2 + \left(\frac{\partial U}{\partial y} \right)^2 \right] dx\, dy + \int_{(C)} U \frac{dU}{dn} ds = 0.$$

The first of these relations characterizes harmonic functions; for the first member is equal, according to the general formula (10), to $-\int\int_{(D)}\Delta U\, dx\, dy$ and, consequently, integral (12) can be zero, whatever contour C we have, only if we have identically $\Delta U = 0$.

51. Applications to harmonic functions. Let P be a point of the domain D with coordinates (a, b) and $U(x, y)$ a harmonic function in this domain. Let us set $V = \log r$, where r is the distance of the point P from a variable point (x, y), and let us apply the general formula (11) to the domain D' bounded by the contour C and a circle γ described about P as center with radius ρ small enough that it lies entirely within the interior of D. Since the functions U and V are regular in D', we have the relation

$$\int_C \left(U \frac{d \log r}{dn} - \log r \frac{dU}{dn} \right) ds$$

$$= \int_\gamma \left(U \frac{d \log r}{dn} - \log r \frac{dU}{dn} \right) ds,$$

the derivatives d/dn along γ being taken in the direction interior to γ. The line integral around γ is, consequently, independent of the radius ρ. It is sufficient, therefore, in order to obtain its value, to seek its limit for $\rho = 0$. The second part of this integral can be written

$$\int_0^{2\pi} \frac{dU}{dn} \rho \log \rho \, d\phi,$$

and clearly approaches zero with ρ. As to the first part, let us notice that along γ we have

$$\frac{d \log r}{dn} = - \frac{1}{\rho}, \quad ds = \rho \, d\phi,$$

and this integral can be written

$$- \int_0^{2\pi} [U(a, b) + \epsilon] \, d\phi,$$

ϵ being infinitely small with ρ. The limit is therefore equal to

$$- 2\pi U(a, b)$$

and we obtain the fundamental formula

$$(13) \qquad U(a, b) = \frac{1}{2\pi} \int_C \left(\log r \frac{dU}{dn} - U \frac{d \log r}{dn} \right) ds,$$

the derivatives d/dn always being taken along the interior normal. It is hardly necessary to call attention to the analogy of this result with the fundamental formula of the Cauchy integral (II, 1, **33**) from which we could, moreover, derive it (Exercise 1).

If the contour C is a circle of radius R and center P, we have all along C, $\log r = \log R \, [(d \log r)/dn] = -1/R$ and, taking account of relation (12), we obtain the *mean value theorem* of Gauss

$$(14) \qquad U(a, b) = \frac{1}{2\pi R} \int_C U \, ds = \frac{1}{2\pi} \int_0^{2\pi} U(\psi) \, d\psi,$$

$U(\psi)$ being the value of U at the extremity of a radius which makes an angle ψ with an arbitrary fixed direction. It is easy to deduce from this that *a harmonic function can have neither a maximum nor a minimum* (cf. III, **47**). Let us suppose, for example, that $U(x, y)$ had a maximum at the point P. Let us describe with this point as center a circle C of radius sufficiently small that we have at every point of C, $U(\psi) < U(a, b)$. It is clear that equality (14) would be impossible. The proof applies also to the case in which $U(x, y)$ has an *improper* maximum at P. The hypothesis that $U(\psi)$ is constantly equal to the value of U at the point P, however small the radius of C, must evidently be rejected, for the function would then reduce to a constant (III, **47**).

Let A and B be the maximum and minimum values of a harmonic function along the contour C. This function cannot take on any value greater than A nor less than B in the interior of C, *nor these values A and B themselves*, for it would then necessarily have a proper or improper maximum at an interior point of the contour.

Another important consequence is this: we say that a function $u(x, y)$, defined in the interior of C, assumes the value u_M at a point M of C when the difference $u_P - u_M$ approaches zero simultaneously with the distance MP, P being any point whatever interior to C. There can exist no more than one harmonic function in the interior of a closed contour C, and taking on a given value at each point M of C, this value varying continuously with the position of the point M. Indeed, if there were two of them, their difference would be a harmonic function in the interior of C, vanishing all along C; if this difference were not identically zero, it would necessarily have a maximum or a minimum in the interior of C, which is impossible. Formula (13) does not provide the solution of the problem, called *Dirichlet's problem*, which consists of determining U, knowing its values on C, for the second member involves U and dU/dn. It results, on the contrary, from what we have just said, that we cannot choose arbitrarily the values of U and of dU/dn along C; formula (13) therefore involves the given values *superabundantly*. This is not in contradiction to the Cauchy existence theorems, for the problem to be solved is quite different from Cauchy's problem. For one thing, the contour C on which the values are given, and the given values themselves are not necessarily analytic. For another, it is a question of determining a function in the entire *interior* of a closed contour, and not only in the *neighborhood* of an arc of the curve, on both sides of this arc.

52. Poisson's integral. The properties of the potential of second layer lead readily to the solution of Dirichlet's problem when the contour C is a circle. Let $U(M)$ be a function which varies continuously with the position of the point M on C, and let P be an interior point. The potential of second layer

$$(15) \qquad V(a, b) = \int_C U(M) \frac{\cos \phi}{r} ds,$$

where r and ϕ have the usual meaning, is a harmonic function of the coordinates (a, b) of the point P, in the interior of the circle. When point P coincides with any point of C, we have, for every position of the point M on this contour, $r = 2R \cos \phi$, R being the radius of the circle, and, as a result, integral (15) has a constant value

$$\int_C U(M) \frac{ds}{2R},$$

at any point whatever of C. From the general theorem of III, **49**, when the point P in the interior of the circle approaches a point M_0 on the circumference, the function $V(a, b)$ approaches

$$\pi U(M_0) + \int_C \frac{U(M) ds}{2R}.$$

The function represented by the definite integral

$$(16) \qquad U(a, b) = \frac{1}{\pi} \int_C U(M) \left(\frac{\cos \phi}{r} - \frac{1}{2R} \right) ds$$

therefore provides the solution of Dirichlet's problem for the circle. We usually write this integral in the following form, considered by Poisson. Take the center of the circle as the origin and let (ρ, θ) be the polar coordinates of point P, and (R, ψ) those of a point M of C. Considering the relations

$$\rho^2 = R^2 + r^2 - 2Rr \cos \phi, \quad r^2 = R^2 + \rho^2 - 2R\rho \cos (\psi - \theta),$$

formula (16) can be written in the equivalent forms

$$(17) \qquad U(a, b) = \frac{1}{2\pi} \int_0^{2\pi} f(\psi) \, \frac{R^2 - \rho^2}{r^2} \, d\psi$$

$$= \frac{1}{2\pi} \int_0^{2\pi} f(\psi) \, \frac{(R^2 - \rho^2) d\psi}{R^2 + \rho^2 - 2R\rho \cos (\psi - \theta)},$$

where we have used $f(\psi)$ instead of $U(M)$.

Formula (17) can also be derived from the general formula (13) by means of a device based on a geometric property of the circle, which permits the elimination of dU/dn. Let P_1 be the harmonic conjugate of P with respect to the extremities of the diameter passing through P, and r_1 the distance of P_1 from a point (x, y). The function $\log r_1$ being harmonic in the interior of the circle C, we have the relation

$$(13') \qquad \frac{1}{2\pi} \int_C \left(U \, \frac{d \log r_1}{dn} - \log r_1 \, \frac{dU}{dn} \right) ds = 0,$$

U being the harmonic function sought, whose values on C are given. Combining relations (13) and (13') we have

$$(18) \qquad U(a, b) = \frac{1}{2\pi} \int_C U \left(\frac{d \log r_1}{dn} - \frac{d \log r}{dn} \right) ds,$$

for the coefficient of dU/dn under the integral sign is $\log r/r_1$ which remains constant on C, and, consequently, the corresponding integral is zero, from relation (12). Let ρ, ρ_1, be the distances OP and OP_1, and ϕ_1 the angle of the interior normal at a point M of C with MP_1. We have the relations

$$\frac{d \log r}{dn} = - \frac{\cos \phi}{r}, \quad \frac{d \log r_1}{dn} = - \frac{\cos \phi_1}{r_1}, \quad \rho\rho_1 = R^2, \quad \frac{r_1}{r} = \frac{R}{\rho},$$

$$\rho^2 = R^2 + r^2 - 2Rr \cos \phi, \quad \rho_1^2 = R^2 + r_1^2 - 2Rr_1 \cos \phi_1,$$

from which we deduce, upon eliminating ϕ, ϕ_1, r_1, ρ_1,

$$\frac{\cos \phi}{r} - \frac{\cos \phi}{r_1} = \frac{R^2 - \rho^2}{Rr^2},$$

which clearly establishes the identity of formulas (17) and (18). This second proof is less complete than the first, for it assumes that

dU/dn has a finite value along C, and, besides, it only proves that the value of integral (18) indeed approaches the given value of U at a point M of C when the point P approaches the point M.

   Application. Let us suppose that $f(\psi) \geq 0$ along C; then $U(a, b)$ is positive for every interior point. As r varies from the minimum $R - \rho$ to the maximum $R + \rho$, upon replacing successively r by $R - \rho$ and by $R + \rho$ in formula (17), and upon observing that

$$\int_0^{2\pi} f(\psi) \, d\psi = 2\pi \, U_0,$$

we evidently have

(19) $$\frac{R - \rho}{R + \rho} \, U_0 < Up < \frac{R + \rho}{R - \rho} \, U_0,$$

U_0 and U_P being the values of $U(a, b)$ at the center of the circle and at the point P. We deduce from it that the absolute value of $U_P - U_0$ is less than the difference of the two extreme terms of this double inequality $[4R\rho/(R^2 - \rho^2)] \, U_0$. If a harmonic function U is regular and positive in the entire plane, we can assume the number R as large as we wish, and, as a consequence, $[4R\rho/(R^2 - \rho^2)] \, U_0$ smaller than any given number. We therefore have $U_P = U_0$, which proves that *every harmonic function positive in the entire plane reduces to a constant.*

   More generally, *every function harmonic in the entire plane which is bounded in one direction is a constant.* Indeed, if we have, for example, $U(x, y) < C$, the function $C - U(x, y)$ is a harmonic function positive in the entire plane. This proposition corresponds to Liouville's theorem (II, 1, **36**).

   Let us consider again the case where the function $f(\psi)$ has on the circle a finite number of discontinuities of the *first kind.* Poisson's integral again represents a harmonic function in the interior of the circle. When the point P interior to the circle approaches a point M of the circle where $f(\psi)$ is continuous, the limit of the integral is still $f(\psi)$; there is nothing to change in the reasoning. It remains for us to study the behavior of the function $U(a, b)$ in the neighborhood of a point of discontinuity of $f(\psi)$. Let us first take the particular case where $f(\psi) = \psi$, ψ being the central angle taken in the positive sense from $-\pi$ to $+\pi$ from the radius OA' opposite to the radius OA which terminates at a point of discontinuity A. Integral (16) can be written

$$(20) \qquad u(a, b) = \frac{1}{\pi} \int_C \psi \left(\frac{\cos \phi}{r} - \frac{1}{2R} \right) ds = \frac{1}{\pi} \int_C \psi \, d\omega,$$

ω being the angle, taken positively from 0 to 2π, which the direction PM makes with a fixed direction; it is evident, indeed, that the integral $\int_C \psi \, (ds/R)$ is zero, while $(\cos \phi)/r \, ds$ is equal to $d\omega$ (III, **49**). It is clear that if the point P is on the diameter which passes through point A, we have

$$u(a, b) = 0,$$

for the elements symmetrical with respect to the diameter cancel each other two by two. If P is not on this diameter, let A_1 be one of the extremities of the diameter passing through P, and $u_1(a, b)$ the integral $1/\pi \int_C \psi_1 \, d\omega$, ψ_1 being the angle central, taken positively from $-\pi$ to $+\pi$, starting from the radius OA'_1, opposite to OA_1. From what we have just seen, $u_1(a, b) = 0$. We can therefore write

$$u(a, b) = u(a, b) - u_1(a, b)$$

$$= \frac{1}{\pi} \int_{(A_1MA)} (\psi - \psi_1) \, d\omega + \frac{1}{\pi} \int_{(AM'A_1)} (\psi - \psi_1) \, d\omega;$$

along A_1MA we have $\psi - \psi_1 = \alpha$ (Fig. 10), while along $AM'A_1$, $\psi - \psi_1 = \alpha - 2\pi$. Therefore,

$$u(a, b) = \frac{1}{\pi} \alpha (2\pi - \beta) + \frac{1}{\pi} (\alpha - 2\pi) \beta = 2 (\alpha - \beta) = 2\gamma.$$

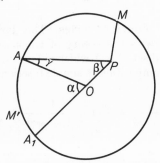

Fig. 10.

Consequently, in the case of the figure, *the integral* u(a, b) *is equal to twice the angle* γ, *taken in the positive sense from* $-\frac{1}{2}\pi$ *to* $+\frac{1}{2}\pi$, *which the direction* AP *makes with the direction* AO. It would be easy to verify that this relation holds in all the cases of the figure, but it is sufficient to observe that if it has been established in one part of the circle, it is valid in the entire circle, for both members are harmonic functions in this circle.

Let us now take the general case, where $f(\psi)$ has a discontinuity of the first kind at *A*. The angle ψ being reckoned, as we have just said, from $-\pi$ to $+\pi$, beginning from the radius OA', let us suppose that we have

$$f(\pi - 0) = l, \quad f(-\pi + 0) = m \ (l \neq m).$$

The difference $f(\psi) - \frac{1}{2}(l - m)/\psi$ is a continuous function $f_1(\psi)$ in the neighborhood of the point *A*, which takes on the value $(l + m)/2$ at this point, and Poisson's integral (17) is the sum of the two integrals

$$\frac{l-m}{2} u\,(a,b), \qquad U_1\,(a,\,b) = \frac{1}{2\pi} \int_{-\pi}^{+\pi} f_1(\psi)\,\frac{R^2 - \rho^2}{r^2}d\psi,$$

which both represent harmonic functions in *C*. When point *P* approaches the point *A*, the limit of $U_1(a, b)$ is equal to $(l + m)/2\pi$, while the limit of $[(l - m)/2\pi]\,u(a, b)$ depends on the manner in which point *P* approaches the point *A*, and varies from $-\,(l - m)/2$ to $(l - m)/2$. In particular, if the point *P* describes the radius *OA*, the limit of $U(a, b)$ is $(l + m)/2$. When point *P* approaches *A* while the direction *AP* has no limit, there is no longer any limit for $U(a, b)$.[7]

53. Relations to Fourier series.
The Poisson integral is intimately connected with the theory of trigonometric series. For simplification, we shall set $R = 1$ which is tantamount to writing ρ in place of ρ/R. A decomposition in simple fractions gives us

$$\frac{1-\rho^2}{1 - 2\,\rho \cos \omega + \rho^2} = -\,1 + \frac{1}{1 - \rho e^{\omega i}} + \frac{1}{1 - \rho e^{-\omega i}};$$

---

[7] Fatou studied the Poisson integral, making much more general hypotheses on $f(\psi)$. (*Acta mathematica*, Vol. XXX, 1907). See also a paper by Lichtenstein in Vol. 141 of the *Journal du Crelle*, p. 12.

moreover, we have, since ρ is less than 1,

$$\frac{1}{1 - \rho \, e^{\omega i}} = 1 + \rho \, e^{\omega i} + \rho^2 \, e^{2\omega i} + \ldots + \rho^n \, e^{n\omega i} + \ldots,$$

and an analogous identity obtained by changing i into $-i$. Combining these results, we shall therefore also have

$$\frac{1 - \rho^2}{1 - 2\rho \cos \omega + \rho^2} = 1 + 2 \sum_1^{+\infty} \rho^n \cos n\omega,$$

the series of the second member being *uniformly convergent* since we are supposing $\rho < 1$. Let us replace ω by $\psi - \theta$, let us multiply by $f(\psi)$ and integrate between 0 and 2π; formula (17) becomes

$$U(a, b) = \frac{1}{2\pi} \int_0^{2\pi} f(\psi) \, d\psi + \frac{1}{\pi} \sum_{n=1}^{+\infty} \rho^n \int_0^{2\pi} f(\psi) \cos n(\psi - \theta) \, d\psi,$$

or again

$$(21) \qquad U(a, b) = \frac{\alpha_0}{2} + \sum_{n=1}^{+\infty} \rho^n (\alpha_n \cos n\,\theta + \beta_n \sin n\,\theta),$$

α_n and β_n being precisely the coefficients of the Fourier series expansion of the continuous function $f(\psi)$ (I, Chap. IX). Let us note that this development of $U(a, b)$ is identical with the real part of the power series in $z = a + ib$

$$F(z) = \frac{\alpha_0}{2} + \sum_{n=1}^{+\infty} (\alpha_n - i\beta_n) \, (a + ib)^n,$$

which is certainly convergent in the circle of unit radius, for the absolute values of the coefficients α_n, and β_n are less than the upper bound of $|f(\psi)|$ (cf. III, **47**).

Formula (21) is established at all interior points of the unit circle; if the Fourier series derived from $f(\psi)$ is convergent for all values of ψ, the equality holds for $\rho = 1$, $\theta = \psi$. Indeed, when the point (a, b) approaches the point $(\cos \psi, \sin \psi)$ of the circle along the radius, the limit of $U(a, b)$ is $f(\psi)$, while, according to Abel's theorem, the limit of the second member is equal to the sum of the series obtained by setting $\rho = 1$, $\theta = \psi$.

But, without making any hypothesis concerning the convergence of the Fourier series, the theory of the Poisson integral shows that, *for any continuous function whatever*, we always have the equality

$$(22) \qquad f(\psi) = \lim_{\rho=1} \left[\frac{\alpha_0}{2} + \sum_{n=1}^{+\infty} \rho^n (\alpha_n \cos n\psi + \beta_n \sin n\psi) \right],$$

α_0, α_n, β_n being the coefficients of the Fourier series derived from $f(\psi)$. Picard has deduced from it an elegant proof of a theorem by Weierstrass (see later, section **75**).

Conversely, one could propose to derive the Poisson integral from Fourier series. Let $f(\psi)$ be a continuous function of period 2π developable in a Fourier series:

$$(23) \qquad f(\psi) = \frac{\alpha_0}{2} + \sum_{n=1} (\alpha_n \cos n\psi + \beta_n \sin n\psi).$$

The series (21) obtained by taking for α_0, α_n, β_n, the same values as in series (23), is uniformly convergent in every circle of radius $\rho < 1$ described about the origin. We can therefore apply to this series the inverse transformations of those which have been made, and go back from this series to the Poisson integral. The function so obtained

$$U(a, b) = \frac{1}{2\pi} \int_0^{2\pi} f(\psi) \, \frac{(1 - \rho^2) \, d\psi}{1 + \rho^2 - 2\rho \cos(\psi - \theta)}$$

indeed represents a harmonic function in the interior of C. But if this integral had not already been directly studied, we would be able to assert only one thing; that the value of $U(a, b)$ approaches $f(\psi)$, when the point (a, b) approaches the point $(\cos \psi, \sin \psi)$ *along the radius which terminates in this point*. The first proof is therefore more complete and, moreover, it only assumes that $f(\psi)$ is developable in a Fourier series.

54. Harnack's theorem.

Harnack's theorem is the analog of Weierstrass's theorem on series of holomorphic functions (II, 1, **39**). Let $u_0(x, y)$, $u_1(x, y)$, ..., $u_n(x, y)$, ... be a sequence of holomorphic functions in a finite domain D, bounded by a contour Γ, which may be composed of one or several closed curves. *If the series $\Sigma u_i(x, y)$ is uniformly convergent along Γ, it is uniformly convergent in the domain* D.

Let U_i be the value of $u_i(x, y)$ at a point of Γ. From the definition of uniform convergence, if ϵ is an arbitrary positive number, we can choose an integer n such that, at any point whatever of Γ, and for any value of p, we have

$$|U_{n+1} + U_{n+2} + \ldots + U_{n+p}| < \epsilon;$$

this inequality will also be satisfied by the maximum value of the first member when we describe Γ. Consequently, if (x, y) are the coordinates of any interior point of D, we then also have

$$|u_{n+1}(x, y) + \ldots + u_{n+p}(x, y)| < \epsilon,$$

which indeed proves the uniform convergence.

The sum of the series

$$F(x, y) = \sum_0^{+\infty} u_i(x, y)$$

is a continuous function in D, *and on the contour itself*; when a point P of D approaches a point M of Γ, the sum of the series at P approaches the sum of the series at M, regardless of the way in which P approaches M. *This function* $F(x, y)$ *is a harmonic function in* D.

It is clearly sufficient to prove that such is the case in the interior of any circle whatever contained in D. Let (x, y) be the coordinates of a point P interior to C; from Poisson's formula we have

$$u_i(x, y) = \frac{1}{2\pi} \int_C U_i \frac{R^2 - \rho^2}{Rr^2} \, ds,$$

R, ρ, r having the same meaning as above (III, **52**), and U_i being the value of u_i at a point of C. From this we deduce

$$F(x, y) = \frac{1}{2\pi} \sum_{i=0}^{+\infty} \int_C U_i \frac{R^2 - \rho^2}{Rr^2} \, ds = \frac{1}{2\pi} \int_C \left(\sum_{i=0}^{+\infty} U_i \right) \frac{R^2 - \rho^2}{Rr^2} \, ds,$$

for since the series ΣU_i is uniformly convergent on C, the same is true of the series $(1/r^2) \Sigma U_i$, and we can interchange the symbols $\int$ and Σ. The last expression for $F(x, y)$ shows clearly that it is a harmonic function in C. We should prove in the same way that the partial derivatives of $F(x, y)$ are the sums of series obtained by differentiating the first expression term by term.

Application. Let C and C_1 be two circles having the origin as center, with radius R and $R_1 (R > R_1)$, and $U(\phi)$, $V(\phi)$ two continuous, periodic functions of period 2π, satisfying the Dirichlet conditions. These functions can be expanded in a *uniformly convergent* Fourier series (III, 37):

$$U(\phi) = \frac{a_0}{2} + \sum_{n=1}^{+\infty} (a_n \cos n\phi + b_n \sin n\phi),$$

$$V(\phi) = \frac{\alpha_0}{2} + \sum_{n=1}^{+\infty} (\alpha_n \cos n\phi + \beta_n \sin n\phi).$$

Harnack's theorem allows us easily to construct a harmonic function in the ring contained between the two circles C and C_1, which reduces to $U(\phi)$ or to $V(\phi)$ respectively on these two circles, ϕ being the angle which corresponds to a point on C or C_1.

Indeed, let us set

$$F(r, \phi) = A_0 + B_0 \log r + \sum_{m=1} [(A_m r^m + B_m r^{-m}) \cos m\phi$$
$$+ (C_m r^m + C_m r^{-m}) \sin m\phi],$$

A_m, B_m, C_m, D_m being constant coefficients. All the terms of this series are harmonic functions in the ring considered, as is evident from the equality $z^{-m} = r^{-m} (\cos m\phi - i \sin m\phi)$. It will be sufficient, therefore, from Harnack's theorem, to choose the coefficients in such a way that the series (r, ϕ) reduces to $U(\phi)$ for $r = R$, and to $V(\phi)$ for $r = R_1$. We thus obtain the relations

$$A_0 + B_0 \operatorname{Log} R = \frac{a_0}{2}, \; A_m R^m + B_m R^{-m} = a_m, \; C_m R^m + D_m R^{-m} = b_m,$$

$$A_0 + B_0 \operatorname{Log} R_1 = \frac{\alpha_0}{2}, \; A_m R_1{}^m + B_m R_1{}^{-m} = \alpha_m, \; C_m R_1{}^m + D_m R_1{}^{-m} = \beta_m,$$

which determine these coefficients.

When all the harmonic functions of a sequence are *positive* in a connected domain D, we have the following theorem:

If the series $\Sigma \, u_i(x, y)$, all of whose terms are positive harmonic functions in the domain D, *converges at one point* O *of the interior of* D, *it converges at all points of* D, *and the sum is a harmonic function.*

With the point O as center, let us describe a circle C of radius R

sufficiently small that the circle lies entirely within D, and let P be any interior point of C at a distance $\rho < R$ from point O. From inequality (19) established above, we have for all values of the index i,

$$(u_i)_P < \frac{R + \rho}{R - \rho}(u_i)_0,$$

which proves that the series $\Sigma\, u_i\,(x, y)$ is convergent at the point P. The same inequality proves that it is uniformly convergent in every circle C' with center O and radius $R' < R$; it therefore represents a harmonic function in this circle C. Let us now start from another point O_1 inside of C and let us describe a new circle C_1 with center O_1 interior to D; reasoning step by step, as in analytic continuation, by means of a chain of circles (II, 1, Chap. IV), we see that the series is convergent at every point of D and represents a harmonic function. It would be easy to establish, in this fashion, that the series converges uniformly in every domain interior to D and not having any point in common with the boundary.

55. Analytic continuation of a harmonic function. Let us recall first the definition of an analytic arc (I, **192**). An arc of the curve AB represented by the equations $x = f(t)$, $y = \phi(t)$, where the parameter t varies from a to b, is *analytic* if the two functions $f(t)$, $\phi(t)$ are developable in ordinary power series in powers of $t - t_0$ in the neighborhood of every value t_0 contained between a and b; it goes without saying that the coefficients of these series must be real numbers. If the two derivatives $f'(t_0)$, $\phi'(t_0)$ are not simultaneously zero, the corresponding point M_0 is an *ordinary* or *regular* point. If these two derivatives are zero for $t = t_0$, M_0 is a singular point, unless to a point M of the arc, close to M_0, there do not correspond several values of t close to t_0, according to the choice of the parameter t. An analytic arc without a singular point is called a *regular* arc.

Let $u(x, y)$ be a function of the two variables x, y defined in a domain D in the interior of which the analytic arc AB is situated. The value of this function at a point of the arc is a function $F(t)$ of the parameter t, which will evidently be analytic if the function $u(x, y)$ is itself analytic in D, and in particular if $u(x, y)$ is harmonic. This being so, let $u(x, y)$ be a harmonic function in a domain D, bounded by a contour Γ, a portion of which is formed by an analytic arc AB. We shall say that this harmonic function $u(x, y)$ can be continued beyond the arc *AB*, if we can find a function $U(x, y)$, harmonic in a domain $\mathcal{D}$, containing *D* and the arc *AB*, which is equal to $u(x, y)$ in *D* (cf. II, 1, Chap. IV). In order that this continuation be possible across *AB*, *it is necessary*, we have just seen, *that the set of values taken by* u(x, y) *along* AB *constitute an analytic function of* t. Schwarz has proven that the condition is sufficient if the arc *AB* is regular: *Every harmonic function in a domain whose boundary contains a regular, analytic arc* AB *can be continued beyond this arc, if the set of values which it assumes on this arc themselves form an analytic function.*

Let us assume first of all that the arc *AB* is a segment of the *x*-axis and that a function $u(x, y)$, harmonic in a domain *D* lying above *Ox* and bounded partly by *AB*, is zero all along this segment. Let *D'* be the domain symmetric to *D* with respect to *Ox* and let $v(x, y)$ be the function which at every point $P'(x, -y)$ of *D'* assumes the value $- u(x, y)$, symmetric to the value which $u(x, y)$ assumes at the point *P* symmetric to *P'*. It is clear that $v(x, y)$ is harmonic in *D'*; the function $F(x, y)$, which is equal to $u(x, y)$ in *D*, and to $v(x, y)$ in *D'*, is continuous in the entire domain $D + D'$. It does not follow from this that it is harmonic in this entire domain, for nothing yet permits us to assert that it has continuous derivatives at every point of *AB*. To prove this essential point, let us take about any point whatever of *AB* a segment $\alpha\beta$ of *Ox*, sufficiently small that the circle *C* described on $\alpha\beta$ as diameter will be entirely in the domain $D + D'$; the theorem will be established if we prove that $F(x, y)$ is harmonic in this circle. Let γ, γ' be the two semicircles lying respectively above and below $\alpha\beta$.

Let us consider the function represented by the Poisson integral, where R, ρ, r have their usual meanings (III, **52**),

$$U(x, y) = \frac{1}{2\pi} \int_C \mu \frac{R^2 - \rho^2}{Rr^2} \, ds,$$

in which we take $\mu = u(x, y)$ along γ and $\mu = v(x, y)$ along γ'. This function $U(x, y)$ is harmonic in *C*; it is zero along $\alpha\beta$, for the symmetrical elements of the integral cancel each other.

This function $U(x, y)$ coincides with $u(x, y)$ in the upper semicircle, and with $v(x, y)$ in the lower semicircle, for it takes on the same values as $u(x, y)$ along $\alpha\beta$ and γ, and the same values as $v(x, y)$ along $\alpha\beta$ and γ'. We therefore have $U(x, y) = F(x, y)$ in the entire circle *C*.

Let us suppose, in the second place, that along the segment *AB* of Ox, a function $u(x, y)$, harmonic in the domain D lying above Ox, takes on a set of values which constitute an analytic function $f(x)$. This function $f(x)$, being developable in a power series in the neighborhood of every point x_0 of AB, is in that way defined in a domain R of the plane of the complex variable $z = x + iy$, containing the segment AB. The real part $u_1(x, y)$ of this function $f(z)$ is harmonic in R and reduces to $f(x)$ along AB. Let us suppose this domain D lies in R; the difference $u(x, y) - u_1(x, y)$ is harmonic in D and zero along AB; we have just proved that it can be continued below AB. Since the function $u_1(x, y)$ can be continued below AB, the same is true of $u(x, y)$.

Finally, let us take the case in which AB is any regular, analytic arc whatever, and let $u(x, y)$ be a harmonic function defined on one side of this arc, and such that the set of values which it assumes on AB forms an analytic function of the parameter t. We are going to prove that given any point M_0 whatever on AB, we can take around M_0 an arc $\alpha\beta$ sufficiently small so that the function $u(x, y)$ can be continued across $\alpha\beta$. Let

$$x = a_0 + a_1(t - t_0) + \ldots + a_n(t - t_0)^n + \ldots$$

$$y = b_0 + b_1(t - t_0) + \ldots + b_n(t - t_0)^n + \ldots$$

be the developments of x, y in the neighborhood of the value t_0 which corresponds to the point M_0. Let us set

$$(24) \qquad z = x + iy = a_0 + ib_0 + (a_1 + ib_1)(Z - t_0) + \ldots$$

$$+ (a_n + ib_n)(Z - t_0)^n + \ldots$$

and let r be a sufficiently small positive number that the series (24) is convergent when $Z - t_0 \leq r$. The preceding relation makes correspond to each point of the circle γ with radius r described about the point $(X = t_0, Y = 0)$ as center, in the plane of the complex variable $Z = X + iY$, a point (x, y) of a domain d around the point M_0 of the xy-plane. Since the two coefficients a_1 and b_1 are not simultaneously zero, dz/dZ is not zero for $Z = t_0$. Equation (24) therefore has conversely one and only one root $Z = \phi(z)$ which approaches t_0 when z approaches $z_0 = a_0 + ib_0$, and this root $\phi(z)$ is holomorphic in the neighborhood of the point z_0. We shall assume that we have taken the radius r of γ sufficiently small so that $\phi(z)$ is holomorphic in the entire corresponding domain d. Relation (24) therefore establishes a one-to-one correspondence between the points of the circle γ of the XY-plane and the domain d of the

xy-plane, with preservation of angles; to the arc $\alpha\beta$ of AB lying in d corresponds a segment $\alpha'\beta'$ of the real axis in the XY-plane. The harmonic function $u(x, y)$ defined on one side of the arc $\alpha\beta$ is transformed into a harmonic function $U(X, Y)$ of the variables X, Y, defined on one side of the segment $\alpha'\beta'$ of the real axis, and it follows from the hypotheses that the set of values which it assumes along $\alpha'\beta'$ is an analytic function. This function $U(X, Y)$ can therefore be extended to the other side of the segment $\alpha'\beta'$, and consequently $u(x\ y)$ can be extended across the arc $\alpha\beta$.

When the arc AB has singular points, it may happen that the analytic extension is not possible completely across the arc. For example, the real part of $\sqrt{x + iy}$, which is positive to the right of the origin on the x-axis, is harmonic to the right of the semi-cubical parabola $y^2 = x^3$. The set of values which it assumes on this curve is analytic, for if we set $x = t^2, y = t^3$, we have $\sqrt{x + iy} = t \sqrt{1 + it}$, and yet the origin is a singular point for this function. This point divides the curve into two regular arcs; the harmonic function can be extended across each of them, but the two extensions do not agree with one another on the left of the parabola.

If a function $u(x, y)$ is harmonic in the interior of a contour C composed of a certain number of regular analytic arcs, and takes on analytic values on the contour, it can be extended beyond each of these arcs, and the only possible singular points are the points of the contour where two regular analytic arcs join one another. In particular, if the contour is composed of a single regular analytic arc, such as a circle or an ellipse, every harmonic function in the interior, which assumes analytic values on C, can be extended in a domain containing this contour.[8]

---

[8] Schwarz's theorem proves that the Cauchy problem appears in an entirely different manner for the Laplace equation than for the hyperbolic equation. Let $u(x, y)$, $v(x, y)$ be two harmonic functions in a domain D, to the right of Oy, bounded partly by a segment AB of Oy. If, along AB, these two functions u and v reduce to *one* single function, $f(y)$, of y, the difference $u - v$ is a harmonic function which can be extended to the left of Oy, and as a consequence $d(u - v)/dx$ is an analytic function of y along the segment AB. It follows that we cannot propose to find a harmonic function $u(x, y)$ in the domain D which reduces for $x = 0$ to a given function $f(y)$ along AB, while $\partial u/\partial x$ is equal to another given function of y, $g(y)$, these two functions $f(y)$ and $g(y)$ being arbitrary.

Indeed, let $v(x, y)$ be a harmonic function satisfying the first condition; the difference $(\partial v/\partial x) - (\partial u/\partial x)$ is an analytic function of y along AB, and hence the function $g(y)$ is defined, within an analytic function, when $f(y)$ is given.

II. DIRICHLET'S PROBLEM. GREEN'S FUNCTION

56. Riemann's proof. We have proven above that Dirichlet's problem can have no more than one solution[9] and have actually found this solution in the case when the contour is a circle. We are now going to concern ourselves with the same problem in the general case, and we shall first reproduce the proof by which Riemann established that this problem, which he called the *Dirichlet principle*, always has a solution. Let D be a finite domain, bounded by a contour Γ composed of one or more distinct closed curves. We shall say for brevity that a function $v(x, y)$, defined in D and on the contour Γ, belongs to class (A) when it satisfies the following conditions: 1. it is continuous in the domain D, including the contour Γ; 2. it assumes on this contour given values, the value at each point of Γ varying continuously with the position of that point; 3. it possesses continuous partial derivatives of the first two orders at every *interior* point of D. We make no hypothesis on these derivatives at a point of the contour.

For all functions of class (A), the double integral

$$(25) \qquad 1 = \int \int_{(D)} \left[\left(\frac{\partial u}{\partial x} \right)^2 + \left(\frac{\partial u}{\partial y} \right)^2 \right] dx \, dy$$

is clearly positive, unless u is not constant in D and hence on Γ. Let us put aside this case where the solution is obvious, and let $v(x, y)$ be a function of class (A) for which the integral I is a *minimum*. It is easy to demonstrate with Riemann that v(x, y) *is a harmonic function*. Indeed, let $\eta(x, y)$ be a function vanishing on Γ and continuous, along with its partial derivatives of the first two orders, in the interior of D and on the contour Γ itself, and let α be an arbitrary parameter. The function

$$u = v(x, y) + \alpha \eta(x, y)$$

is of class (A), for any α, and the difference

$$\int \int_D \left[\left(\frac{\partial u}{\partial x} \right)^2 + \left(\frac{\partial u}{\partial y} \right)^2 \right] dx \, dy - \int \int_D \left[\left(\frac{\partial v}{\partial x} \right)^2 + \left(\frac{\partial v}{\partial y} \right)^2 \right] dx \, dy$$

[9] The impossibility of two solutions for Dirichlet's problem can also be deduced from formula (12a) (III, **50**). This formula proves, in effect, that if a function U is zero at every point of a contour C and harmonic in the domain interior to this contour, then at every point of this domain we have $\partial U/\partial y = \partial U/\partial x = 0$. The function is therefore constant, and hence zero, since it is zero on C. But this proof assumes that U possesses continuous derivatives on C, which the first demonstration does not require.

must be positive. Now this difference is equal to

$$2\alpha \int \int_{(D)} \left(\frac{\partial v}{\partial x} \frac{\partial \eta}{\partial x} + \frac{\partial v}{\partial y} \frac{\partial \eta}{\partial y} \right) dx\, dy + \alpha^2 \int \int_D \left[\left(\frac{\partial \eta}{\partial x} \right)^2 + \left(\frac{\partial \eta}{\partial y} \right)^2 \right] dx\, dy.$$

For this difference to be positive regardless of α, it is clearly necessary that the coefficient of 2α be zero.

Taking account of the identity

$$\frac{\partial v}{\partial x} \frac{\partial \eta}{\partial x} + \frac{\partial v}{\partial y} \frac{\partial \eta}{\partial y} + \eta \Delta v = \frac{\partial}{\partial x}\left(\eta \frac{\partial v}{\partial x} \right) + \frac{\partial}{\partial y}\left(\eta \frac{\partial v}{\partial y} \right)$$

and of the first Green's formula (I, **126**), this coefficient can be written

$$\int_{(\Gamma)} \eta \left(\frac{\partial v}{\partial x} dy - \frac{\partial v}{\partial y} dx \right) - \int \int_D \eta \Delta v\, dx\, dy;$$

since μ is zero all along Γ, we see that the double integral

$$\int \int_D \eta \Delta v\, dx\, dy$$

must be zero for all possible forms of the function $\eta(x, y)$ satisfying the stated conditions. But this cannot be so unless we have $\Delta v = 0$ at every point of D. Let us suppose, indeed, that we have $\Delta v > 0$ for example at a point x_0, y_0 interior to D. With this point as center let us describe a circle C of radius ρ sufficiently small so that it is entirely within D, and so that we have $\Delta v > 0$ at every point of C. If we take $\eta(x, y) = 0$ on the exterior of this circle, and

$$\eta(x, y) = [\rho^2 - (x - x_0)^2 - (y - y_0)^2]^m$$

in the interior of C, this function is continuous, as are its partial derivatives of the first and second order if $m > 2$, and it vanishes on Γ. It is clear that the corresponding double integral $\int \int \eta \Delta v\, dx\, dy$, taken over D, would have a positive value. The function $v(x, y)$ is therefore harmonic in the domain D.

The conclusion of the reasoning is unquestionable, but it relies on two postulates which seemed evident to Riemann but whose invalidity has been shown by a more rigorous critique. On the one hand, we suppose that there exist functions of class (A) for which the double integral I has a finite value; on the other hand, we also suppose that there exists at least one of these functions for which integral I actually attains its lower limit. Weierstrass[10] showed first

[10] Weierstrass, *Mathematische Werke*, Vol. II, p. 49.

that this last point cannot be admitted with proof. More recently Hadamard has made known a simple example in which there does not exist a function of class (A) for which the double integral I has a finite value.[11] Therefore Riemann's method does not furnish a rigorous proof of Dirichlet's principle, but it provides us with an example of a method of proof often employed in mathematical physics, and which at the very least makes plausible the result which we wish to establish.

Remark. We have often explained what is to be understood when we say that a harmonic function in a domain D assumes a given value at a point on the contour. If one does not have regard for the precise meaning of the statement, it may seem that in certain cases Dirichlet's problem has several solutions. For example, the function $u = (x^2 + y^2 - 2x)/(x^2 + y^2)$ vanishes at every point of the circle whose equation is $x^2 + y^2 - 2x = 0$, and it is harmonic in this circle, for it is the real part of $1 - (2/z)$; adding Ku to another harmonic function in C, it appears that we would have an infinity of harmonic functions in C, assuming the same values on the contour. To explain this paradox, it is sufficient to observe that the value of $u(x, y)$ at an interior point P of the circle C and near the origin does not approach any limit when this point P approaches the origin. It is therefore wrong to say that the function $u(x, y)$ is zero at the origin.

57. C. Neumann's method. We owe to C. Neumann[12] a celebrated method for solving Dirichlet's problem in the case of a *convex* contour, having only a finite number of corner points. We are going to expound, with a few modifications in detail, this method which is based on the properties of the potential of second layer. To fix the position of a point M on the closed contour C, we shall take as our parameter the length s of the arc AM taken as beginning from an arbitrary origin A. Every function having a fixed value at each point of the contour is therefore a function $f(s)$ of period l, where l is the length of the closed contour. It is only to

---

[11] *Bulletin de la Société mathématique*, Vol. XXXIV, p. 135. In this example, the contour Γ is a circle, and consequently Dirichlet's problem really has a solution. (See Exercise 5).

[12] *Untersuchungen über das logarithmische und Newtonische Potential* (Leipzig, 1877).

make the notations precise that we adopt this convention; the results themselves are absolutely independent of the choice of parameter. Let $\mu(s)$ be a continuous function on C; we have shown (III, **49**) that the potential of double layer

$$(26) \qquad W = \int_{(C)} \mu \, \frac{\cos \, \phi}{r} \, ds$$

is a harmonic function in C, which at a point of this contour with curvilinear abscissa x takes on the value

$$(27) \qquad w(x) = 2\pi\mu(x) + \int_C [\mu(s) - \mu(x)]\left(\frac{\cos \phi}{r}\right)_x ds$$

where $[(\cos \, \phi)/r]_x$ stands for $(\cos \, \phi_x)/r_x$, r_x being the distance of the point x from the variable point s, and ϕ_x being the angle of the direction sx with the interior normal to the contour at s. This formula (27) is general and is also applicable to corner points of the contour.

This granted, let $f(s)$ be a given continuous function of period l. In order to solve Dirichlet's problem, we shall seek with Neumann for an auxiliary function $\mu(s)$, continuous and of period l, such that the potential of second layer W, represented by formula (26) in the interior of C, takes on precisely the value $f(x)$ at each point of C. It is necessary and sufficient for this that this function $\mu(s)$ satisfy the functional relation

$$(28) \qquad 2\pi\mu(x) + \int_C [\mu(s) - \mu(x)]\left(\frac{\cos \phi}{r}\right)_x ds = f(x);$$

we are going to solve this *integral equation* by a method of successive approximations which will be associated later with a general theory. For this purpose, let us write this equation by introducing a parameter λ, which we shall afterwards set equal to unity (cf. III, **38**),

$$(29) \qquad \mu(x) = \frac{1}{2\pi}f(x) + \frac{\lambda}{2\pi}\int_C [\mu(x) - \mu(s)]\left(\frac{\cos \phi}{r}\right)_x ds,$$

and let us look for an expansion of the form

$$(30) \qquad \mu(x) = \frac{1}{2\pi}[\mu_0(x) + \lambda\mu_1(x) + \ldots + \lambda^n\mu_n(x) + \ldots]$$

which *formally* satisfies equation (29). We thus find successively

$$\mu_0(x) - f(x), \quad \mu_1(x) = \frac{1}{2\pi} \int_C [\mu_0(x) - \mu_0(s)]\left(\frac{\cos\phi}{r}\right)_x ds,$$

and, generally,

$$(31) \qquad \mu_n(x) = \frac{1}{2\pi} \int_C [\mu_{n-1}(x) - \mu_{n-1}(s)]\left(\frac{\cos\phi}{r}\right)_x ds.$$

It is clear that all these functions $\mu_i(x)$ have the period l; if they are *continuous*, and if the series (30), when we set $\lambda = 1$, is *uniformly convergent*, then the sum $\mu(x)$ is a continuous function which really satisfies relation (28). This is immediately verified by integrating term by term the series which gives the expansion of $\mu(s) - \mu(x)$, and by making use of relations (31). It will be sufficient to replace $\mu(s)$ by the function thus determined in formula (26) in order to have the solution of Dirichlet's problem.

We are now going to examine the points which remain to be established in order that the solution be not purely formal. In the first case, *the functions $\mu_i(x)$ are continuous*. Generally, if $f(x)$ is continuous, the same is true of the function

$$f_1(x) = \frac{1}{2\pi} \int_C [f(s) - f(x)]\left(\frac{\cos\phi}{r}\right)_x ds;$$

indeed, if x_0 is any value whatever of x, we can write

$$f_1(x) = \frac{1}{2\pi} \int_C [f(s) - f(x_0)]\left(\frac{\cos\phi}{r}\right)_x ds$$

$$+ \frac{1}{2\pi}[f(x_0) - f(x)] \int_C \left(\frac{\cos\phi}{r}\right)_x ds.$$

The reasoning of (III, **49**) is applicable here without modification and proves that the first integral is a continuous function of x for $x = x_0$, and the same is evidently true for the second part. We thus see, step by step, that all the functions $\mu_1, \mu_2, \ldots$ are continuous.

To prove the uniform convergence, we are first going to establish two lemmas related to convex closed contours.

Lemma I. Let P_1, P_2 be any two points of C, and C' any portion of C, possibly composed of several distinct arcs. It is almost evident, from its geometrical significance, that the definite integral

$$I = \int_{C'} \left[\left(\frac{\cos \phi}{r} \right)_{x_1} - \left(\frac{\cos \phi}{r} \right)_{x_2} \right] ds = \int_{C'} \left(\frac{\cos \phi}{r} \right)_{x_1} ds$$

$$- \int_{C'} \left(\frac{\cos \phi}{r} \right)_{x_2} ds$$

is less than π in absolute value. For it to be equal to π, for example, it would be necessary that the first integral be equal to π, and the second zero. Now the first integral cannot be equal to π unless C' is identical with the contour C, or unless C' is composed of an arc AB joining two points A and B, point P_1 being on the segment of the line AB; in the two cases, the second integral cannot be zero, unless C is the contour of a triangle. The absolute value of I therefore remains less than a maximum $h\pi$, h being a positive number *less than unity*, which depends only upon the contour C,[13] and not on C'.

Lemma II. Let $f(s)$ be a function positive or zero at each point of C and let J be the integral

$$J = \int_C f(s) \left[\left(\frac{\cos \phi}{r} \right)_{x_1} - \left(\frac{\cos \phi}{r} \right)_{x_2} \right] ds.$$

Let us divide C into two parts, C_1 and C_2, such that we have

$$\left(\frac{\cos \phi}{r} \right)_{x_1} \geqq \left(\frac{\cos \phi}{r} \right)_{x_2}$$

on C_1 and

$$\left(\frac{\cos \phi}{r} \right)_{x_1} < \left(\frac{\cos \phi}{r} \right)_{x_2}$$

on C_2, and let J_1 and J_2 be the integrals taken over C_1 and C_2, respectively. We have $J = J_1 + J_2$ and, therefore, $|J|$ is less than the larger of the two numbers J_1 and $|J_2|$. Let L be an upper limit of $f(s)$; from the preceding lemma, each of these two numbers is less than $L \times h\pi$. We therefore also have $|J| < \pi h L$, whatever the points P_1 and P_2.

---

[13] This conclusion cannot pass as absolutely rigorous; but it is clear that it is correct for convex contours such as those which we usually consider.

This being granted, let M and m be the maximum and the minimum of $f(s)$ on C; since P_1 and P_2 are two points of the contour, we can write

$$\mu_1(x_1) - \mu_1(x_2) = \frac{1}{2\pi} \left[\mu_0(x_1) \int_C \left(\frac{\cos\phi}{r}\right)_{x_1} ds - \mu_0(x_2) \int_C \left(\frac{\cos\phi}{r}\right)_{x_2} ds \right]$$

$$+ \frac{1}{2\pi} \int_C [\mu_0(s) - m] \left[\left(\frac{\cos\phi}{r}\right)_{x_2} - \left(\frac{\cos\phi}{r}\right)_{x_1} \right] ds$$

$$+ \frac{m}{2\pi} \int_C \left[\left(\frac{\cos\phi}{r}\right)_{x_2} - \left(\frac{\cos\phi}{r}\right)_{x_1} \right] ds.$$

If the points P_1 and P_2 are not corner points, the last integral is zero, and the absolute value of the first term

$$\frac{1}{2} [\mu_0(x_1) - \mu_0(x_2)]$$

is less than $(M - m)/2$. Moreover, $\mu_0(s) - m$ remains between 0 and $M - m$, and, consequently, from lemma II, the absolute value of the first term of the second line is less than $[(M - m)/2]h$. Therefore, the absolute value of $\mu_1(x_1) - \mu_1(x_2)$ is less than $(M - m)$ $(1 + h)/2 = (M - m)\,\rho$, *where ρ is a positive number less than one.* Since the function $\mu_1(x)$ is continuous, this inequality holds whatever the points P_1 and P_2. Hence, calling M_1 and m_1 the maximum and the minimum of $\mu_1(x)$, we have the fundamental inequality

(32) $$M_1 - m_1 < (M - m)\rho.$$

From this we deduce, step by step, that in general we have

$$M_i - m_i < (M - m)\rho^i,$$

where M_i and m_i are the maximum and the minimum of the function μ_i. The absolute value of $\mu_{i-1}(x) - \mu_{i-1}(s)$ being less than or at most equal to $M_i - m_i$, we therefore have *a fortiori*, from formula (31),

$$|\mu_n(x)| < \tfrac{1}{2}(M - m)\rho^{n-1},$$

and, therefore, series (30) is uniformly convergent for $\lambda = 1$. The sum $\mu(x)$ of this series is a continuous function which satisfies the functional equation (28), and upon replacing μ by this function in formula (26) we have the solution of Dirichlet's problem for the convex contour C.

Example. Let us suppose that C is a circle of radius R; in this case we have $[(\cos \phi)/r]_x = 1/(2R)$, for any point x of the contour. Taking $\mu_0 = f(x)$, we therefore have immediately

$$\mu_1(x) = \tfrac{1}{2}[f(x) - K], \quad \text{where } K = \frac{1}{2\pi R} \int_C f(s)\, ds,$$

and the recurrence relation (31) then gives, for any n,

$$\mu_n(x) = \frac{1}{2^n}[f(x) - K].$$

We therefore have

$$\mu(x) = \frac{1}{\pi} f(x) - \frac{1}{4\pi^2 R} \int_C f(s)\, ds$$

and, upon replacing μ by this expression in formula (26), we have once more Poisson's integral (16), where we have written U_M in place of $f(s)$. Moreover, in this particular case, equation (28) is easy to solve directly. We see, indeed, that $\mu(x)$ is of the form $[f(x) + H]/\pi$, where H is a constant which is determined when we replace $\mu(x)$ by this expression in equation (28).

Neumann's method and the analogous method in space for convex surfaces have been extended to more general cases by different geometers.[14] The most important extension comes from the works of Fredholm and will be treated later.

We owe to Poincaré an absolutely general method, called the *method of "balayage,"*[15] for the solution of Dirichlet's problem in space. Paraf[16] has shown that this method, by means of a few modifications, is also applicable to Dirichlet's problem in the plane. The principle of Schwarz's method will be outlined later.

58. Generalization of the problem. It is of interest, for certain investigations, to study a somewhat more general problem than

---

[14] Poincaré, *La méthode de Neumann et le problème de Dirichlet* (*Acta mathematica*, Vol. XX). This paper is fundamental in this theory. We shall find in a recent article by Bouligand on *Les fonctions harmoniques* (*Mémorial des Sciences mathématiques*, Fascicle XI, 1926) a complete bibliography of the latest works on this problem; the theorem of the mean plays an essential role in some of these papers.

[15] *American Journal of Mathematics*, Vol. XII.

[16] *Annales de la Faculté des Sciences de Toulouse*, Vol. VI, 1892.

Dirichlet's. Let D be a domain bounded by a closed contour C which we shall assume composed of a single curve. To each point M of C let us make correspond a number U_M varying, in general, continuously with the position of the point M, except at a finite number of points of discontinuity of the first kind, and let us try to find a harmonic function $u(x, y)$ in D, assuming the value U_M at each point of the contour C where U is continuous.

We do not make *a priori* any hypothesis on the nature of the desired function $u(x, y)$ in the neighborhood of a point of discontinuity of U on the contour; there is therefore no need to speak of the value of $u(x, y)$ at one of these points. *If we know how to solve Dirichlet's problem for the contour* C, *we can always find* one *solution of the generalized problem.*

Let A_i (α_i, β_i) be a point of discontinuity of U on C; when M approaches this point A_i, U_M approaches two different limits a_i, b_i, according as the point M describes C in the positive sense or in the opposite sense. This being granted, the following function where we have chosen for arc tan any particular determination whatever,

$$W_i(x, y) \ = \ \frac{a_i - b_i}{\pi} \text{ arc tan } \frac{y - \beta_i}{x - \alpha_i},$$

is a function harmonic in D, and the value $(W_i)_M$ which it takes on at a point M of the contour varies continuously with the position of the point M, except at the point A_i, where it presents the same discontinuity as the given function U. This presupposes, however, that this point A_i is not a corner point of the contour; if this point were the point of intersection of two arcs making an angle ω, we would have to replace π by ω in the denominator of the preceding formula. Let us proceed in the same fashion with all the points of discontinuity $A_1, A_2, \ldots, A_n$ of U. The difference

$$W_M = U_M - \sum_{i=1}^{n} (W_i)_M$$

varies continuously with the position of the point M on C, even at points where U is discontinuous. Let $v(x, y)$ be a harmonic function in D which assumes the value W_M at each point M of C; the function

$$(33) \qquad u(x, y) \ = \ v(x, y) + \sum_{i=1}^{n} W_i(x, y)$$

is a harmonic function in D, and, from the manner in which it has been obtained, it certainly takes on the value U_m at every point of the contour C which is not a point of discontinuity for U. It is therefore a solution of the generalized problem, and the investigation of this solution is reduced to the study of $v(x, y)$, that is, to Dirichlet's problem.

Formula (33) makes clear the behavior of $u(x, y)$ in the neighborhood of one of the points of discontinuity of U on the contour; it is the sum of a function which approaches a fixed limit, and of an expression of the form K arc tan $(y - \beta)/(x - \alpha)$, which does not have a fixed value at the point (α, β). Let us only remark that this function is *bounded* in D. We cannot assert that $u(x, y)$ is the only solution of the generalized problem, but it is the only one which remains bounded in the entire domain D. We shall deduce this from an elegant theorem due to Zaremba (*Bulletin de l'Académie des Sciences de Cracovie*, 1909).

Let u(x, y) *be a harmonic function in the interior of a domain* D *bounded by a curve* C, *and assuming the value zero at each point of* C, *except at a finite number of points* A_1, A_2, . . ., A_n, *for which we know only that the ratio* u(x, y)/log r_i *approaches zero simultaneously with the distance* r_i *of the point* A_i *from any point whatever* (x, y) *of* D. *This function* u(x, y) *is zero in the entire domain* D.

Indeed, let ϵ be an arbitrary positive number and H a number greater than the distance between any two points whatever of the domain D. It is clear that the auxiliary function

$$v(x, y) = \epsilon \sum_{i=1}^{n} \log\left(\frac{H}{r_i}\right)$$

is a harmonic function in D, which is positive in this domain and on the contour C, where it is continuous except at the points A_i. With each of these points A_i as center let us draw a circle of very small radius ρ, and let σ_i be the arc of the circle interior to D. If we remove from the domain D the portions contained in these tiny circles, we obtain a domain D_ρ bounded by portions of the original contour and by the arcs σ_i. From the hypothesis on $u(x, y)$, we can choose the number ρ so small that the two expressions

$$v(x, y) + u(x, y), \quad v(x, y) - u(x, y),$$

will be positive on the arcs σ_i. Indeed, each of these expressions is the sum of a regular part in the neighborhood of the point A_i and of a term of the form $(\eta_i - \epsilon) \log r_i$, where η_i is indefinitely small with ρ. The number ρ having been chosen in this manner, the two functions $v(x, y) + u(x, y)$, $v(x, y) - u(x, y)$ are harmonic in D and positive on the contour of this domain. We therefore have, at every point of this domain, $u(x, y) < v(x, y)$. Given any point whatever M in D, we can always choose the radius ρ small enough that this point M will also be in $D\rho$, and therefore the preceding inequality is established for every point of D. We can evidently choose the arbitrary positive number ϵ in such a way that at a fixed point $v(x, y)$ will be less than a preassigned number. The inequality can therefore hold for any ϵ only if we have $u(x, y) = 0$.

It is clear that the conclusion applies in particular if the harmonic function $u(x, y)$, satisfying the other stated conditions, remains bounded in D. This being so, if the generalized Dirichlet problem has two bounded solutions in D, their difference will be a harmonic function bounded in D, and assuming the value zero on the contour, except at a finite number of points; this difference, we are going to see, must be identically zero.

Remark I. If we do not impose on the harmonic function the condition of remaining bounded in the interior of D, the generalized problem can have an infinity of solutions. Let us assume for example that C is the circle $x^2 + y^2 - 2x = 0$, and that the origin is the only point of discontinuity for U on this contour. Adding to the solution $u(x, y)$ of the generalized problem, which remains bounded in the interior of C, the expression $K(x^2 + y^2 - 2x)/(x^2 + y^2)$, where K stands for an arbitrary constant, we obtain an infinity of solutions of the same problem, but these solutions are not bounded in the domain (cf. III, **56**, Remark).

Remark II. Let L and l be the maximum and the minimum of the discontinuous function U on C; the harmonic function $u(x, y)$ represented by formula (33) remains between L and l in the domain D. To prove, for example, that $u(x, y)$ does not assume any value greater than L, it is sufficient to replace $v(x, y)$ by

$$L + \epsilon \sum_{i=1}^{n} \log \left(\frac{H}{r_i}\right)$$

in the reasoning of Zaremba. Since the harmonic function $v(x, y) - u(x, y)$ is positive on the contour of the domain $D\rho$, provided that ρ is sufficiently small, it is positive at every point of the domain D, and, since ϵ is an arbitrary positive number, this could not be so if $u(x, y)$ were greater than L. We see similarly that $u(x, y)$ cannot assume a value less than l at a point of D; $u(x, y)$ cannot take on the values L and l, for this function would then have a maximum or a minimum in D (cf. III, 47).

In the neighborhood of a point of discontinuity A_i of the function U on the contour C, we have already noted that $u(x, y)$ is of the form

$$u(x, y) = V(x, y) + K \arctan \frac{y - \beta}{x - \alpha},$$

where $V(x, y)$ approaches a fixed limit when the point (x, y) approaches A. If the point (x, y) approaches the point A along a curve *whose tangent at* A *is not tangent to the contour* C, the limiting value of arc tan lies between the values of the same arc for the two directions of the tangents to the contour C drawn at A, and consequently the limiting value of $u(x, y)$ lies between the two limiting values a and b of the function U_M when the point M approaches A on the contour C.

59. Schwarz's alternate method.

We owe to Schwarz an alternate procedure, applicable to many other problems, permitting us to pass from a convex contour to other contours much less particular. This procedure is based on a lemma which we are first of all going to establish.

Let C be a convex contour or, more generally, a closed contour for which we know the solution of Dirichlet's problem, and let mn be an arc lying in the domain D bounded by C, and joining two points m and n of this contour without being tangent to the contour at either of these points. Points m and n divide C into two parts C_0 and C_1; let us call $u(x, y)$ the harmonic function bounded in D, considered in the preceding section, which takes on the value *zero* on C_0 and the value *one* on C. This function is positive and less than unity at every point P of the arc mn, and if the point P approaches one of the points m or n, we have pointed out that u_P approaches a limit lying between zero and one. The function $u(x, y)$ therefore remains, all along mn, less than a positive number q *less than one*. Let, moreover, $v(x, y)$ be a harmonic function in D, assuming the value zero on C_0, and whose absolute value remains smaller than a positive number g along C_1; we shall assume, for simplicity, that $v(x, y)$ takes on a fixed value at each point of the contour, and that this value varies continuously. The two functions $gu + v$, $gu - v$ are harmonic and bounded in the domain D, zero on C_0 and positive on C_1; they are therefore positive at every point of D, and the absolute value of $v(x, y)$ is less than gu. In particular, along arc mn, the absolute value of $v(x, y)$ is less than gq; it is hardly necessary to note than the number q, just now defined, depends only upon the contour C and the arc mn, and not on the function $v(x, y)$. It is clear that the property holds good if C_0 and C_1 are composed of several distinct arcs; we can also replace the arc mn by a system of several arcs interior to D and joining points of C_0 or the points of partition of C_0 and C_1. The preceding reasoning applies without modification.

To explain the method of Schwarz, let us now consider the simplest case, that of a domain $\mathscr{D}$ resulting from the superposition of two domains D, D', bounded by two closed contours C, C', which intersect in only two points m and n (Fig. 11) without being tangent. We assume that C and C' are convex contours or, more generally, that we know the solution of Dirichlet's problem for each of the domains D and D'. The two points m and n divide C and C' into two distinct arcs (a, α) and (b, β). To arc α corresponds a positive number less than unity relative to the contour C', and similarly to arc β corresponds a positive number less than unity relative to the contour C; we shall represent by q the larger of these two numbers.

We assume a continuous succession of values on (a, b) given, that is, on the set of the two arcs a and b. Let us construct a function

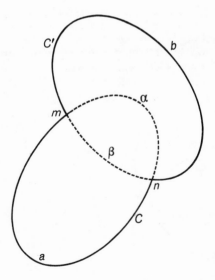

FIG. 11.

u_1, harmonic in D, assuming on a the given values and on α a continuous succession of values uniquely subjected to the condition of assuming on m and n the same values as the first. This function u_1 assumes certain values on arc β. Let us then construct a function v_1, harmonic in D', assuming the same values as u_1 on β and the given values on b; then a function u_2, harmonic in D, assuming the given values on a, and the same values as v_1 on α, and so on alternately. We thus obtain two infinite sequences of functions $(u_1, u_2, \ldots, u_n, \ldots)$ and $(v_1, v_2, \ldots, v_n, \ldots)$. The functions u_i are harmonic in D, and assume the given values on a; the functions v_i assume the given values on b and are harmonic in D'. Moreover u_n and v_n assume the same values on β, while u_n and v_{n-1} assume the same values on α. We shall prove that, *in the domains* D *and* D' *respectively, the functions* u_n *and* v_n *approach a limit when* n *increases indefinitely.*

Let g be an upper limit of $|u_2 - u_1|$ on β; $v_2 - v_1$ is zero on b and equal to $u_2 - u_1$ on β; the absolute value of $v_2 - v_1$ is therefore less than gq on α. The function $u_3 - u_2$ is zero on a and equal to $v_2 - v_1$ on α; we therefore also have $|u_3 - u_2| < q_2 g$ on β. Continuing thus, we see step by step that we have $|u_{n+1} - u_n| < q^{2n-1}g$ on β, and $|v_{n+1} - v_n| < q^{2n-1}g$ on α. The series

$$u_1 + (u_2 - u_1) + \ldots + (u_n - u_{n-1}) + \ldots$$

is therefore uniformly convergent on the contour $(a\alpha)$ and therefore uniformly convergent in the domain D, from Harnack's theorem. The sum of this series $U(x, y) = \lim u_n(x, y)$ is a harmonic function in D, which takes on the given values on a. We see in the same way that v_n has for its limit a function $V(x, y)$ harmonic in D', which

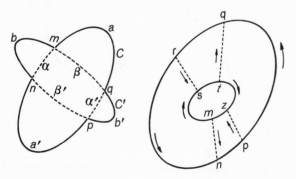

Fig. 12.   Fig. 13.

assumes the given values on b. These two functions U and V assume
the same values on α and on β, since we have $u_n = v_n$ on β, and
$u_n = v_{n-1}$ on α; they therefore coincide in the domain bounded by
the arcs α and β. Consequently, the function $F(x, y)$, which is equal
to U in D and to V in D' is harmonic in the entire domain $\mathscr{D}$ and
gives the solution of Dirichlet's problem for this domain.

The method can be extended of itself to much less simple cases,
where the contours C, C' intersect in more than two points, or even
have certain parts in common. In the case of Figure 12, the contours
C, C' have four common points m, n, p, q; we have marked on the
figure the arcs which must replace the arcs a, b, α, β, in the reasoning. In the case of Figure 13, the contours C and C' are the contours
$mnpqrstzm$ and $mstqrnpzm$ which have certain parts in common.
Replacing in the reasoning a by arcs $npqr$ and $mzts$, α by mn and
rs, b by $qrnp$ and $tsmz$, β by tq and zp, we see that if we can solve
Dirichlet's problem for the domains bounded by C and C', we shall
be able to solve it for the domain bounded by the two contours
$mztsm$ and $mpqrn$.

The latter example shows how we can pass from a domain bounded by a single contour to a domain bounded by several contours.

Application. From the solution of Dirichlet's problem, Lebesgue[17]
has deduced a very simple proof of the first Picard theorem, established above (III, **47**). Let $u(x, y)$ be a harmonic function *bounded*
and regular at every point of a domain D, except perhaps at a point
A of this domain. With the point A as center, let us draw two circles
C and c of radius R and ρ respectively ($\rho < R$), lying in the domain
D. Let $v(x, y)$ be the regular harmonic function in the interior of C
which is equal to $u(x, y)$ along C; Lebesgue's method consists of
showing that at every point (x, y) interior to C, distinct from the
point A, we have $u = v$.

If M is an upper limit of the absolute value of $u(x, y)$ in the
domain D, the absolute value of $u(x, y)$ along C, and therefore in the
interior of C, is also less than M. Let $u_1(x, y)$, $u_2(x, y)$ be two harmonic functions regular in the ring contained between C and c,
equal to $u(x, y)$ along C, and equal to $+ M$ and to $- M$, respectively,
along c. The difference $u_i - u$ is positive on c, zero on C, and, since
it cannot have a minimum between C and c, in this domain we have
$u_1 - u > 0$. We should require in the same way the inequalities

$$u - u_2 > 0, \quad u_1 - v > 0, \quad v - u_2 > 0.$$

[17] *Comptes rendus*, Vol. 176, 1923, p. 1097.

We therefore have in the circular ring considered

$$|u - v| < u_1 - u_2.$$

The harmonic function $u_1 - u_2$, which is equal to $2M$ on c and zero on C, is therefore identical with

$$2M \frac{\log R - \log r}{\log R - \log \rho},$$

r being the distance of the point (x, y) from the point A. Given any interior point (x, y) of C, different from the center, we can choose the number $\rho < r$ so small that the preceding expression will be less than an arbitrarily chosen positive number ϵ. We therefore indeed have at every point of this domain that $u(x, y) = v(x, y)$.

The proof can be extended to harmonic functions in space by replacing $\log r$ by $1/r$.

60. Exterior problem. Up to now we have studied harmonic functions only in a bounded domain. Let us now consider a domain $\mathscr{D}$ formed by the portion of the plane exterior to a closed contour Γ, and let $u(x, y)$ be an integral of the equation $\Delta u = 0$, regular at every point (a, b) of $\mathscr{D}$. In order to study this function when x and y increase indefinitely, it is sufficient to make a transformation by reciprocal radii, for example to set $x = [x'/(x'^2 + y'^2)], y = [y'/(x'^2 + y'^2)]$. To the portion of the xy-plane, exterior to a circle C of radius R, lying in $\mathscr{D}$, and having the origin as center, corresponds in the $x'y'$-plane a circle c of radius $1/R$. The function $u(x, y)$ is changed into a function

$$u'(x', y') = u\left(\frac{x'}{x'^2 + y'^2}, \; \frac{y'}{x'^2 + y'^2} \right)$$

which is also an integral of Laplace's equation (III, **47**), and which is regular at each point of c, except perhaps at the origin. If this function $u'(x', y')$ is also regular at the origin, it is harmonic in c, and we shall say that the function $u(x, y)$ is *regular at infinity*. In the interior of c the function $u'(x', y')$ can be expanded in a series of the form

$$(34) \qquad\qquad u' = \sum_{m=0}^{+\infty} v_m(x', y'),$$

where $v_m(x', y')$ is a homogeneous harmonic polynomial of degree m (III, **47**). Carrying out the inverse transformation, we deduce from it that in the exterior of C, the function $u(x, y)$ is developable in a series of the form

(35)
$$u(x, y) = \sum_{m=0}^{+\infty} \frac{v_m(x, y)}{(x^2 + y^2)^m};$$

inversely, this form of development characterizes a harmonic function regular at infinity, for we return immediately from series (35) to series (34).

We have before us, for the domain $\mathscr{D}$ composed of that portion of the plane exterior to a closed contour Γ, a problem analogous to Dirichlet's:

To find a harmonic function in the domain $\mathscr{D}$ exterior to a contour Γ, regular at infinity, and assuming on Γ a continuous set of given values.

This is what is known as the *exterior problem* relative to the contour Γ; in contradistinction, the problem with which we have been concerned up to now is called the *interior problem*. The exterior problem relative to a closed contour Γ reduces to the interior problem for *another* contour Γ'. Indeed, let O be an interior point of the contour Γ; a transformation by reciprocal radii with the point O as pole replaces Γ by the contour Γ', and the domain $\mathscr{D}$ exterior to Γ by a domain $\mathscr{D}'$ interior to Γ'. Moreover, every harmonic function $u(x, y)$ in $\mathscr{D}$, regular at infinity, is transformed into a function $u(x', y')$ harmonic in $\mathscr{D}'$. If the set of values of $u(x, y)$ along Γ is given, we know from this the set of values of u' along Γ'. If the solution of the interior problem for the contour Γ' is known, we can then derive from it the solution of the exterior problem for the contour Γ.

Remark. Given two functions U and V, harmonic on the exterior of a contour Γ and regular at infinity, we can extend the general formula (11) to cover them. Indeed, let us consider an auxiliary circle C, having a fixed point O for center, and entirely enclosing the contour Γ. Since the two functions U and V are harmonic in the domain bounded by the curves C and Γ, we can apply formula (11) to the set of these two curves. When the radius R and C increase indefinitely, the integral arising from C approaches zero; indeed, $\partial U/\partial x$, $\partial U/\partial y$, ..., and therefore dU/dn, dV/dn are infinitely small quantities of the order of $1/R^2$, and the integral along C is of the form

$$\frac{1}{R} \int_0^{2\pi} F \, d\phi,$$

the function F remaining finite. We are therefore left with the relation

(11′) $$\int_{(\Gamma)} \left(U \frac{dV}{dn} - V \frac{dU}{dn} \right) ds = 0,$$

where the derivatives are taken along the direction of the *exterior* normal to Γ. It is to be noted that formula (13) cannot be extended in the same way to a function harmonic on the exterior of Γ (cf. Exercise 6).

61. Conformal representation. The problem of conformal representation is closely allied with the Dirichlet problem. Let D, D' be two finite domains, bounded by two contours C, C', and such that there is a conformal transformation which establishes a one-to-one correspondence between the points of D and of D', of C and of C'. Every function u harmonic in the domain D is changed, by this transformation, into a function u' harmonic in D', and it is clear that if the values of u along C are known, then the values of u' along C' are also known. We shall therefore be able to solve Dirichlet's problem for the domain D' if we can solve it for the domain D. In particular, if we are given a domain D bounded by a single closed curve C, we shall be able to solve the Dirichlet problem for this domain if we know how to carry out the conformal representation of D on the surface of a circle. Conversely, Riemann has shown the possibility of this application by making use of the Dirichlet principle.

Let $Z = f(z)$ be the analytic function which effects the conformal representation of a domain D on a circle of unit radius; the function $f(z)$ must be holomorphic in D, and for each point of this domain we must have $|f(z)| < 1$. Moreover, to each value of Z with modulus less than one, there must correspond one and only one point z in D. Let $z_0 = a + bi$ be the point in D which corresponds to $Z = 0$; the equation $f(z) = 0$ must have the single root $z = z_0$ in the interior of this domain, and consequently $f(z)$ must be of the form $(z - z_0)e^{\pi(z)}$, $\pi(z)$ being a holomorphic function in D, which can be written, replacing $\pi(z)$ by $P + Qi$, as

$$Z = e^{\log r + P + i(\phi + Q)},$$

where r and ϕ are the modulus and argument of $z - z_0$. For every point of the contour C we must have $|Z| = 1$, and therefore $P + \log r = 0$. The function $P(x, y)$ must therefore be harmonic in D and assume the same values as $-\log r$ on the contour C. We are brought back to a particular case of the Dirichlet problem. Let us suppose that we could solve this problem for the domain under consideration; to the function $P(x, y)$ harmonic in D, we can then adjoin another harmonic function in D, defined within an additive constant, in such a way that $P + Qi$ will be a holomorphic function of z in D. It remains for us to examine whether the function so determined

$$Z = (z - z_0)e^{P+iQ} = e^{u+iv}$$

really satisfies all the required conditions. We can immediately remark that the constant on which Q depends has no importance in the matter, for a change in the value of this constant amounts to increasing the argument of Z by a constant angle without changing its modulus.

1. To every interior point z of the contour C corresponds an interior point Z of the circle Γ with radius 1 described about the origin as center in the Z-plane. Indeed, the function $u = P + \log r$ approaches $-\infty$ when z approaches z_0; we can, therefore, with point z_0 as center, describe a circle c of sufficiently small radius ρ that u will be negative in this circle. Since the function u is harmonic in the domain contained between C and c, and is zero on C, it is negative at every point contained between C and c. Since the radius ρ can be taken as small as we wish, the function u is negative at every point z interior to the domain D, and consequently we do indeed have $|Z| < 1$.

2. Conversely, let Z be any point whatever in the interior of Γ; the equation $f(z) = Z$ has one and only one root in the domain D. This is evident for $Z = 0$. Let us now consider any negative number m whatever. On every arc of the curve joining the point z_0 to a point of C, there is at least one point for which $u(x, y)$ assumes the value m when u varies on this arc from $-\infty$ to 0. The locus of these points forms one or several closed curves, for the analytic curve $u(x, y) = m$ encloses only ordinary points or multiple points with distinct tangents (III, **47**); moreover, an analytic arc can intersect this curve in only a *finite* number of points, since along an arc of this kind $u(x, y)$ is an analytic function of a parameter. I say that this curve is composed of a single closed curve C_m *surrounding the point* z_0. Indeed, in any other case, it would determine a domain S, in the interior of which $u(x, y)$ would be harmonic, while it would have a constant value on the contour; it would consequently reduce

to a constant. The curve C_m thus decomposes the domain D into two regions, an interior region containing the point z_0 for which we have $u < m$, and an annular region contained between C_m and C for which we have $u > m$. As m varies from $-\infty$ to 0 we have a family of curves C_m, each surrounding its predecessor, beginning with an infinitely small closed curve about z_0, and approaching more and more the contour C as m approaches zero. Let us suppose that the point z describes the curve C_m in the positive sense; the corresponding point Z describes a circle of radius e^m always proceeding in the same direction. Indeed, let s be the arc of C_m, taken as positive in the positive description of the contour; the argument of Z is equal to $v = \phi + Q$. The relation $dv/ds = -\,du/dn$ (III, **47**) shows that dv/ds is positive since the derivative du/dn taken along the interior normal is evidently negative; the argument v is therefore constantly increasing and, since this argument is increased by 2π when z describes the curve C_m, it follows that to each point of C_m corresponds one and only one point of the circle $|Z| = e^m$ and conversely. This granted, given any point whatever $Z = e^{m+ni}$ in the interior of Γ $(m < 0)$, every point which is a root of $f(z) = e^{m+ni}$ must be on the curve C_m, and it is clear that there is one and only one point of this curve for which $v = n + 2K\pi$.

3. It remains only to prove that the contours C and Γ also correspond point by point in a one-to-one manner. Riemann does not seem to have been concerned with this point, which is not evident. When the point z approaches a point M of C, $P + \log r$ indeed approaches zero, and the modulus of Z approaches unity, but we can say nothing up to this point about the behavior of the function $Q(x, y)$ in the neighborhood of the point M. Indeed, this function Q is derived by quadratures from the derivatives $\partial P/\partial x$, $\partial P/\partial y$; it is not at all certain *a priori* that these derivatives maintain finite values on C, and it could happen that Q did not approach any limit, or that its modulus increased indefinitely; the argument of Z itself would not approach any limit as z approached the point M.

We remove the difficulty at once when the contour C is composed of a single regular analytic arc. The function $P(x, y)$, which assumes analytic values on this arc, is therefore harmonic in a domain $\mathscr{D}$, enclosing the domain D in its interior (III, **55**). The same is true of the conjugate function $Q(x, y)$, and therefore to each point of C corresponds a fixed point of Γ. The reasoning just now given for the curves C_m proves that conversely to each point of Γ corresponds only one point of C. Let us again take the more general case where

the contour C is composed of a finite number of regular analytic
arcs joined together at the vertices of the contour, a singular point
on an analytic arc being considered as a vertex. Let ab be one of
these arcs; the function $P(x, y)$ can again be extended beyond the
arc ab, and the same reasoning proves that to a point m of ab corresponds a point μ of Γ, the two points m and μ changing their
position at the same time in the positive sense. When m describes
the arc ab, μ can describe only a part of Γ; indeed, if to two points
m and m' of ab corresponded the same point μ of Γ, to an interior
point of Γ, infinitely close to μ, would have to correspond a point of
D infinitely close at one and the same time to m and to m'. To the
arc ab of C therefore corresponds a fixed arc $\alpha\beta$ of Γ, these two arcs
being described at the same time in the positive sense. The entire
difficulty consists in proving *that arcs such as* $\alpha\beta$ *cover the circle* Γ
once and only once.[18]

Remark. All conformal transformations which make self-corres-
ponding the circle of radius *one* having the center as origin are
given by the linear transformation $Z = e^{i\alpha} (z - z_0)/[d (z - z'_0)]$,
z_0 being the coordinate of a point interior to this circle, at a distance
d from the center, z'_0 being the coordinate of the conjugate point,
and α being a real constant. These transformations certainly depend
upon three real constants. If one conformal representation of a
domain with a simple contour D on this circle is known, we have all
the others by combining it with the preceding transformations.

62. Green's function. Let D be a domain with simple contour
C, which satisfies the conditions of the preceding section, and
which we can map conformally on a circle of radius *one*. If we
know how to effect this representation, the Dirichlet problem relative to the domain D is reduced to the Dirichlet problem relative
to the circle, whose solution is known.

Let $U(s)$ be a given continuous function on the contour C, which
we assume expressed in terms of the arc s, oriented in the positive
sense beginning from an arbitrary origin. In order to find the value
of the harmonic function in D, equal to $U(s)$ on C, at a point (a, b)
of the domain D, we return to the function

$$Z = (z - a - bi)e^{P+iQ},$$

[18] The proof has been given by É. Picard (*Traité d'Analyse*, Vol. II, p. 301
and following, 2nd edition). We shall find in Montel's note at the end of
Volume III, Part 2 [of Goursat] a method which is applicable to much more
general cases.

which makes the domain D and the circle of *unit* radius correspond point by point, in such a manner that the center of the circle corresponds to the point (a, b). To a point s of C there corresponds a point with argument

$$\theta = Q + \phi \quad \text{or} \quad z - a - bi = re^{i\phi},$$

on the circle Γ. The function $U(s)$ is transformed into a continuous function $U_1(\theta)$, of period 2π, and the desired harmonic function is changed into a function harmonic in the circle, assuming the value $U_1(\theta)$ on the circumference. The value at the center of the circle, that is, the value $U(a, b)$ at the point (a, b), is given by formula (17) (III, 52)

$$U(a, b) = \frac{1}{2\pi} \int_0^{2\pi} U_1(\theta) \, d\theta,$$

which, upon taking the arc s of C as independent variable, becomes

$$U(a, b) = \frac{1}{2\pi} \int_{(C)} U(s) \left(\frac{dQ}{ds} + \frac{d\phi}{ds} \right) ds,$$

dQ/ds, $d\phi/ds$ representing the derivatives taken along the tangent at C in the positive sense. But these derivatives are equal, respectively, to $- dP/dn$, $- (d \log r)/dn$ (III, 47), where these derivatives are taken along the interior normal to C. The value of $U(a, b)$ may therefore be written as

$$U(a, b) = - \frac{1}{2\pi} \int_{(C)} U \left(\frac{dP}{dn} + \frac{d \log r}{dn} \right) ds,$$

or again

(37) $$U(a, b) = \frac{1}{2\pi} \int_{(C)} U \frac{dG}{dn} \, ds,$$

where we are designating the function $P(x, y) - \log r$ by $G(x, y; a, b)$. This function $G(x, y; a, b)$ is *Green's function*, relative to the contour C and to the interior point (a, b). From the very definition of the harmonic function $P(x, y)$, Green's function is defined by the following properties: 1. it is zero at every point of the contour C; 2. in the interior of C it is equal to the sum of a harmonic function and of $- \log r$. It follows that it is harmonic in the domain of all interior points of C, except in the neighborhood of the point (a, b) where it is infinite in the same manner as

$$- \tfrac{1}{2} \log [(x - a)^2 + (y - b)^2].$$

Knowing this Green's function for the contour C permits us, we see, to solve the interior Dirichlet's problem for this contour, whatever the given function $U(s)$ on C. From this point of view, Green's function resembles the Riemann function $u(x, y; \xi, \eta)$ (III, **42**). But, while Riemann's function is independent of the contour for which we wish to solve Cauchy's problem and depends only upon the coefficients of the equation, Green's function depends upon the contour C itself; moreover, it has a logarithmic infinity, while Riemann's function is continuous. To each closed contour of the type considered there corresponds a Green's function; the investigation of this function is tantamount to finding a conformal representation of the interior domain D on a circle, that is, to solving a particular case of the same Dirichlet problem.

In several simple cases, Green's function is easy to obtain. Let us take first of all a circle of radius R; let P be an interior point at a distance ρ from the center, P_1 the harmonic conjugate point of P with respect to the extremities of the diameter passing through P, and r and r_1 the distances of a point M from the points P and P_1. The ratio r_1/r is equal to R/ρ at every point of the circumference; the function $\log(\rho\, r_1/R\, r) = \log (\rho\, r_1/R) - \log r$ is Green's function relative to the circle, for it is zero on the circumference, and $\log (\rho\, r_1/R)$ is harmonic in the interior. Replacing G by this expression in the general formula (37), we have again precisely formula (16) (III, **52**). Let us take again the contour composed of a semicircle AMB and the diameter AB. Let P be an interior point, P_1 the harmonic conjugate of P with respect to the extremities of the diameter passing through P, P' and P'_1 the points symmetric to P and P_1 relative to the diameter AB; and r, r_1, r', r'_1 the distances of a point M from the points P, P_1, P', P'_1. We easily verify that the expression $\log (r_1 r')/(r r'_1)$ is the Green's function relative to this contour.

The technique in (III, **52**), by which we were able to get rid of the term in dU/dn in the general formula (13), when the contour C is a circle, succeeded precisely because the Green's function for this contour was known *a priori*. The same technique succeeds for any contour whatever, if the corresponding Green's function $G (x, y; a, b)$ is known. Indeed, the function

$$G(x, y; a, b) + \log r$$

being harmonic in the interior of the contour C, we have the relation

$$(38) \quad 0 = \frac{1}{2\pi} \int_{(C)} \left[U\left(\frac{dG}{dn} + \frac{d \log r}{dn}\right) - (G + \log r)\frac{dU}{dn} \right] ds.$$

Adding formulas (13) and (38) member by member, and noting that G is zero on C, we once again have formula (37).

This proof has the advantage of being applicable to a domain of multiple connectivity, or bounded by several distinct closed curves. For such a contour, Green's function is defined by the same conditions as above; it must vanish on the contour, and be equal in the interior to the sum of a harmonic function and of $-\log r$, r always representing the distance of the point (x, y) from an interior point (a, b). But the proof does assume that dU/dn exists on the contour for the desired harmonic function.[19] For the case of a circular ring, we shall find the calculation later on (Exercise 14).

We can also define Green's function for the exterior problem relative to a domain $\mathscr{D}$ extending to infinity and bounded by one or several closed curves which form the contour C of this domain. Let P be any point whatever of $\mathscr{D}$ with coordinates (a, b).

Green's function $G(x, y; a, b)$ relative to the contour C for the *exterior* problem is defined by the following properties: it is zero at

---

[19] When the various parts of the contour C are composed of a finite number of regular analytic arcs, we can easily complete the proof. On the one hand, Schwarz's methods permit us to prove that Dirichlet's problem has a solution for this domain. The Green's function therefore exists, since we can obtain it by adding to $-\log r$ a harmonic function $P(x, y; a, b)$ which assumes the same values as $\log r$ on the contour. This function P, assuming analytic values along the analytic arcs of the contour, can be extended outside the domain, and consequently dG/dn exists on the contour. We cannot assert that dU/dn exists also on the contour for the harmonic function U which takes on a set of given values $U(s)$ on C. To circumvent the difficulty, let us take on each arc of C an analytic function $V(s)$ such that $U(s) - V(s)$ will be $< \epsilon$ at each point of C. The harmonic function V which is equal to $V(s)$ on the contour can be extended outside, and therefore, dV/dn exists on C. We can accordingly apply to this harmonic function V the general formula (37). Besides, the difference $U - V$ is less than ϵ at every interior point. In the identity

$$U - \frac{1}{2\pi} \int_{(C)} U(s)\frac{dG}{dn} ds = (U - V) + \frac{1}{2\pi} \int_{(C)} (V - U)\frac{dG}{dn} ds,$$

the two parts of the second member are less than ϵ (see section **63**), and consequently the absolute value of the first member is less than 2ϵ; but since ϵ is arbitrary, this first member is therefore zero.

every point of C, regular at infinity and harmonic in the neighborhood of every point of $\mathscr{D}$, except in the neighborhood of the point (a, b), where it is infinite in the same way as

$$- \tfrac{1}{2} \log \left[(x - a)^2 + (y - b)^2\right].$$

In order to find the value $U(a, b)$ at the point P of a harmonic function in $\mathscr{D}$, regular at infinity, and assuming the given values on the contour C, it is sufficient to apply formula (11') to the two functions U and $G(x, y; a, b)$, which are harmonic in the domain $\mathscr{D}'$ obtained by removing from $\mathscr{D}$ the portion interior to a circle γ of very small radius, having the point P as center. Making the radius of γ approach zero, and returning to the calculation in III, **51**, we readily obtain the formula

$$(39) \qquad\qquad U(a, b) = \frac{1}{2\pi} \int_{(C)} U \frac{dG}{dn} ds,$$

where the derivative is taken in the direction which penetrates the domain $\mathscr{D}$.[20]

In the case of a circle, Green's function for the exterior problem is $\log \left[(MP_1/MP)(d/R)\right]$, P_1 being the harmonic conjugate point of P with respect to the extremities of the diameter passing through P, M being any point whatever, R the radius, and d the distance of the point P from the center. Upon calculation, we find a formula just like that of Poisson,

$$U(a, b) = \frac{1}{\pi} \int_{(C)} U \frac{d^2 - R^2}{2Rr^2} ds,$$

which is verified in the same way by using a potential of double layer

$$U(a, b) = \frac{1}{\pi} \int_{(C)} U \frac{ds}{2R} - \frac{1}{\pi} \int_{(C)} U \frac{\cos \phi}{r} ds,$$

and applying the known properties of this potential (III, **49**).

63. Properties of Green's function.   Green's function $G(x, y; \xi, \eta)$ depends upon two pairs of variables (x, y) and (ξ, η).

---

[20] It is essential to remark that the function $G + \log r$ is not regular at infinity, so that we cannot apply formula (11) to the two functions U and $G + \log r$ along C. On the contrary, the method followed to establish formula (39) in the case of the exterior problem is applicable without modification to the interior problem.

Up to now it has not been defined (in restricting ourselves to the interior problem) when the point (ξ, η) is *interior* to the contour C, the point (x, y) itself being in the interior of or on the contour C, but *different* from the point (ξ, η). Let (a, b), (a', b') be any two points whatever interior to C, γ and γ' two circles of very small radii, ρ, ρ', described about these points as centers and lying entirely within the domain D. The two functions

$$G(x, y; a, b) \text{ and } G' = G(x, y; a', b')$$

are harmonic in the domain D' bounded by C and the two circles γ, γ'. Observing that $G = G' = 0$ along C, the general formula (11) leads to the relation

$$\int_{(\gamma)} \left(G\frac{dG'}{dn} - G'\frac{dG}{dn} \right) ds + \int_{(\gamma')} \left(G\frac{dG'}{dn} - G'\frac{dG}{dn} \right) ds = 0;$$

the derivative being taken along the direction of the exterior normal to the circle. In the neighborhood of the point (a, b) the function

$$G\,(x, y; a, b)$$

is of the form $- \log r + g(x, y)$, $g(x, y)$ being harmonic and r being the distance from the point (x, y) to the point (a, b). The integral along γ therefore reduces to

$$\int_{(\gamma)} \left(g\frac{dG'}{dn} - G'\frac{dg}{dn} \right) ds - \int_{(\gamma)} \left(\log r\frac{dG'}{dn} - G'\frac{d \log r}{dn} \right) ds$$
$$= 2\pi\,G'(a, b; a', b').$$

The integral along γ' is similarly equal to

$$- 2\pi G(a', b'; a, b).$$

Replacing (a, b) by (x, y) and (a', b') by (ξ, η), we obtain the fundamental relation

$$(40) \qquad\qquad G(x, y; \xi, \eta) = G(\xi, \eta; x, y).$$

The function $G(x, y; \xi, \eta)$ is therefore *symmetric* with respect to the two pairs of variables (x, y), (ξ, η) and, as a result, is a harmonic function of (ξ, η) at every point of the domain D, except at the point $\xi = x$, $\eta = y$. To sum up, let us consider in a space of four dimensions $(x, y; \xi, \eta)$ the domain R_1 defined by describing about each of the points (x, y), (ξ, η) the domain D and the contour C; the function $G(x, y; \xi, \eta)$ has a fixed value at each point of R_1 except on the two-dimensional variety $\xi = x$, $\eta = y$. It is zero when one of the points (x, y), (ξ, η) falls on the contour C. It is harmonic with respect to each of the two pairs of variables (x, y), (ξ, η) in the neighborhood of every interior point of the domain R_1 not lying on the singular variety; it does not change when we permute the two pairs of variables (x, y), (ξ, η).

This function is continually positive, if the two points (x, y), (ξ, η) are in the interior of C. Indeed, considered as a function of (x, y), it is zero on C and equal to $+ \infty$ at the point (ξ, η). It follows that the derivative dG/dn is positive at every point of C, since G can only increase as we move toward the interior. The integral $\int_{(C)} (dG/dn)\, ds$, all of whose elements are positive, is equal to 2π; for if the function U is equal to *one* on C, we also have at every interior point, $U(a, b) = 1$.

Let $x = \phi(x', y')$, $y = \psi(x', y')$ be formulas defining a conformal transformation, permitting us to map the domain D, bounded by the contour C, onto another domain D', bounded by the contour C', in such a way that there is a one-to-one correspondence between the points of the two domains and of the two contours. Green's function $G(x, y; \xi, \eta)$, relative to the contour C, is transformed into a function $G(\phi, \psi; \xi, \eta)$ of the variables x', y' which is zero on C' and harmonic in the domain D', except in the neighborhood of the point (ξ', η') which corresponds to the point (ξ, η). Indeed, $G(x, y; \xi, \eta)$ is the real part of an analytic function $F(z)$ of the form

$$g(z) - \log (z - \xi - \eta i),$$

where $g(z)$ is a holomorphic function in the domain D. After the transformation $x + iy = \phi + i\psi$, F is changed into an analytic function

$$F_1(z') = F_1(x' + iy'),$$

which is of the form

$$g_1(z') - \log (z' - \xi' - \eta' i),$$

where $g_1(z')$ is holomorphic in D'. It follows from this that in the domain of the point (ξ', η') the function $G(\phi, \psi; \xi, \eta)$ is equal to

$$- \tfrac{1}{2} \log [(x' - \xi')^2 + (y' - \eta')^2],$$

augmented by a regular part. We therefore have

$$g[\phi(x', y'), \psi(x', y'); \xi, \eta] = G'(x', y'; \xi', \eta'),$$

where G' is Green's function for the contour C', in which the singular point (ξ', η') corresponds to the point (ξ, η) by the transformation being considered.

In particular, if the domain D is bounded by a single closed curve C, we can map this domain on a circle; certain properties of the Green's function make this intuitive.[21] If, by an inversion, we replace the circle by a half-plane, for example by the upper half-plane of the xy-plane, Green's function is replaced by a function $g(x, y; \xi, \eta)$ which must be zero along the x-axis, harmonic at every point of this half-plane, except at a point (ξ, η) which it has as a logarithmic infinity, and approach zero when $(x^2 + y^2)$ increases indefinitely. This function is clearly

$$\frac{1}{2} \log \left[\frac{(x - \xi)^2 + (y + \eta)^2}{(x - \xi)^2 + (y - \eta)^2} \right].$$

III. GENERAL EQUATION OF THE ELLIPTIC TYPE

64. Extension of Dirichlet's problem. The reasoning by which we have established that Dirichlet's problem, for the Laplace equation, cannot have several solutions, is easily extended, in certain cases, to the general equation of the elliptic type, reduced to canonical form (III, 23)

$$(41) \qquad F(u) = \frac{\partial^2 u}{\partial x^2} + \frac{\partial^2 u}{\partial y^2} + a\frac{du}{\partial x} + b\frac{\partial u}{\partial y} + cu = f(x, y),$$

where a, b, c, f are continuous functions of the variables x, y in the domains involved. The generalized Dirichlet problem still consists of determining an integral of equation (41), regular in a finite domain D, bounded by the contour, C, and assuming on this contour a continuous set of given values. This problem cannot have more than one solution *if the coefficient c is negative or zero* at every point of D. The following elementary method is due to Paraf.

Let us suppose first of all that the coefficient c has a negative value at every point of D. If the proposed problem had two solutions their difference v would be an integral of the homogeneous equation $F(v) = 0$, regular in the domain D, and zero on the contour. If this difference is not identically zero, it assumes positive or negative values in the interior of D, and consequently passes through a positive maximum or a negative minimum at a point (x_0, y_0) of this domain. The second case reducing to the first by the change of v

[21] J. Hadamard, *Bulletin de la Société mathématique* (session of June 28th, 1911).

into $- v$, we can assume that at the point (x_0, y_0) the function $v(x, y)$ has a *positive* maximum v_0. From the general theory we must have at this point

$$\left(\frac{\partial v}{\partial x}\right)_0 = \left(\frac{\partial v}{\partial y}\right)_0 = 0, \quad \left(\frac{\partial^2 v}{\partial x^2}\right)_0 \leqq 0, \quad \left(\frac{\partial^2 v}{\partial y^2}\right)_0 \leqq 0,$$

conditions which are incompatible with the equations $F(v) = 0$, $v_0 > 0$, for the point (x_0, y_0). Therefore there cannot exist an integral of $F(v) = 0$ satisfying the desired conditions.

The case where the coefficient c is not positive at any point of the domain D reduces to the preceding case by setting $v = zw$, z being a function of x and of y, regular in D and not vanishing at any point of this domain nor its contour. The equation $F(v) = 0$ is replaced by an equation of the same form in which the coefficient of w is $F(z)/z$. In order for the preceding conclusion to hold, it is sufficient to be able to choose the function z in such a way that we have in the entire domain D, $z > 0$, $F(z) < 0$, the equality being excluded. Now, if we take for z a function of the form $A - e^{\alpha x}$, where A and α are two positive constants, we have $F(z) = cA - (\alpha^2 + \alpha x + c)e^{\alpha x}$, and this result is negative, whatever the value of A, in the domain considered, provided that $\alpha^2 + a\alpha + c$ is positive at every point of D, a condition which can always be satisfied by taking the number positive α large enough. This number α once thus determined, it is sufficient to take for A a positive number greater than the maximum of $e^{\alpha x}$ in D. We see in particular that when c is zero, equation (41) cannot have more than one regular integral in the domain D, assuming the given values on the contour.

The conclusion cannot be extended to the case where the coefficient c takes on positive values in D. For example, the equation $\Delta u + 2u = 0$ has the integral $u = \sin x \cdot \sin y$, which is regular in the interior of a square bounded by the lines $x = 0$, $x = \pi$, $y = 0$, $y = \pi$, and which is zero on the contour.

We also deduce from the preceding the following conclusion: the problem proposed for equation (41) cannot have several solutions when the equation $F(u) = 0$ possesses a particular integral u_1, regular in this domain and not vanishing in D nor on the contour. The transformation $u = u_1 v$ will, indeed, lead to an equation of the same form in v, whose coefficients will be continuous functions and where the coefficient of v will be zero. We have just seen that the new equation cannot have several regular integrals assuming the same values on C.

Let (x_0, y_0) be any point of the plane; every integral u_1 of the equation $F(u) = 0$, regular in the neighborhood of this point and assuming a positive value for $x = x_0$, $y = y_0$ is certainly positive in the neighborhood. If we take a closed curve γ surrounding the point (x_0, y_0) and sufficiently close to this point for the integral u_1 to be positive in the interior, we can apply the preceding to the domain bounded by the curve γ. Consequently, equation (41) cannot have more than one integral assuming a set of given values on a closed curve c surrounding any point whatever (x_0, y_0), and regular in the interior of γ, provided that this curve is *sufficiently small*. The preceding explains the meaning which must be attached to these words.

65. Study of the equation $\Delta u = f(x, y)$. Following the same order as for equations of hyperbolic type (Chap. IV), we shall begin by studying the simple equation

$$(42) \qquad \frac{\partial^2 u}{\partial x^2} + \frac{\partial^2 u}{\partial y^2} = f(x, y).$$

We propose to find an integral of this equation which is regular in the interior of a domain D, bounded by a contour C, and zero on this contour; we shall further make the hypothesis that the function $f(x, y)$ possesses continuous partial derivatives of the first order in this domain and on the contour C. From the preceding section, this problem cannot have several solutions; this can also be seen directly by observing that if there were two, their difference would be a harmonic function in D, and zero on C. If any regular integral $u_1 (x, y)$ of equation (42) is known, the problem reduces immediately to the Dirichlet problem; to obtain the desired function it is sufficient to adjoin to $u_1 (x, y)$ the harmonic function in D which takes on the same value as $- u_1$ at each point of the contour. For example, when $f(x, y)$ reduces to unity, we obtain the integral of the equation $\Delta u = 1$, which is zero on C, by adding to $(x^2 + y^2)/4$ the harmonic function which is equal to $- (x^2 + y^2)/4$ at each point of C.

Let us assume the existence of an integral $U(x, y)$ of equation (42) satisfying the desired condition, and let us apply the general Green's formula to the two functions $U(\xi, \eta)$ and $G(x, y; \xi, \eta)$ of the variables ξ, η, where G is the Green's function relative to the contour C for the interior problem. These two functions are regular in the domain D' bounded by C and by a circle γ of very small radius ϵ

having as center the point (x, y) in D. Taking account of equation (42) itself and of the fact that the two functions U and G are zero on C, we obtain the relation

$$\int \int_{(D)} f(\xi, \eta) G(x, y; \xi, \eta) \, d\xi \, d\eta = \int_{(\gamma)} \left[U(\xi, \eta) \frac{dG}{dn} - G \frac{dU}{dn} \right] ds,$$

where the derivatives are taken in the direction of the exterior normal to the circle γ. In the neighborhood of the point (x, y), we can replace G by $g(x, y; \xi, \eta) - \log r$, where g is a harmonic function and r designates the distance between the two points (x, y), (ξ, η). When the radius ϵ approaches zero, the only term of the line integral which does not approach zero is

$$- \int_{(\gamma)} U \frac{d \log r}{dn} \, ds,$$

which has $- 2\pi U(x, y)$ as its limit. The desired function, if it exists, therefore has for its expression,

$$(43) \qquad U(x, y) = - \frac{1}{2\pi} \int \int_{(D)} f(\xi, \eta) G(x, y; \xi, \eta) \, d\xi \, d\eta.$$

Conversely, the function $U(x, y)$, represented by this formula, satisfies all the conditions desired. Let us consider first a domain Δ, entirely interior to D; when the point (x, y) remains in the domain Δ, we can write

$$U(x, y) = \frac{1}{2\pi} \int \int_{(D)} f(\xi, \eta) \log \left[\sqrt{(x - \xi)^2 + (y - \eta)^2} \right] d\xi \, d\eta$$

$$- \frac{1}{2\pi} \int \int_{(D)} f(\xi, \eta) g(x, y; \xi, \eta) \, d\xi \, d\eta,$$

where g is a harmonic function of (x, y). Consequently $U(x, y)$ is the sum of a harmonic function and of a logarithmic potential (see below, section **81**). Since the function $f(x, y)$ has continuous derivatives, we can apply Poisson's formula (III, **81**), and the function $U(x, y)$ indeed satisfies relation (42) at every interior point of the domain D. It remains to prove that this function $U(x, y)$ approaches zero when the point (x, y) approaches any point whatever of the contour C. Now it is clear that the absolute value of U is less than

$$\frac{M}{2\pi} \int \int_{(D)} G(x, y; \xi, \eta) \, d\xi \, d\eta,$$

where M is an upper bound of $|f(x, y)|$. Moreover, the double integral

$$-\frac{1}{2\pi} \int \int_{(D)} G(x, y; \xi, \eta) \, d\xi \, d\eta$$

represents precisely the integral of the equation $\Delta u = 1$ which is zero on the contour C, a function whose existence has just now been established. This expression therefore approaches zero when the point (x, y) approaches a point of the contour C, and therefore the same is true of the function $U(x, y)$, represented by formula (43).

Remark. When the function $f(x, y)$ is analytic, every integral of equation (42) is itself analytic. Indeed, let (x_0, y_0) be any point whatever; equation (42) clearly has an infinity of regular analytic integrals in the domain of this point. Let $u_1(x, y)$ be one of them; every other regular integral in this domain is the sum of $u_1(x, y)$ and of a harmonic function, that is, an analytic function.

66. Picard's method. The first method used by É. Picard to solve the Dirichlet problem related to equation (41) is once more a method of successive approximations, very analogous, at least in the general procedure of the calculations, to that of III, **38, 39, 44.** Let us write equation (1) in the following form:

$$(44) \qquad \Delta u = \lambda \left(a \frac{\partial u}{\partial x} + b \frac{\partial u}{\partial y} + cu \right) + f(x, y),$$

where λ is an auxiliary parameter which we shall then replace by -1 in the result. We propose to determine an integral of this equation, regular in the interior of a closed contour C, and assuming on this contour a continuous set of given values. For this purpose, we shall first of all seek a formal solution

$$(45) \qquad u(x, y) = u_0(x, y) + \lambda u_1(x, y) + \ldots + \lambda^n u_n(x, y) + \ldots,$$

where all the functions $u_0, u_1, \ldots, u_n, \ldots$ are regular in the interior of the contour C, $u_0(x, y)$ assuming the given values on C, and all the other functions $u_1, u_2, \ldots$ being zero on this contour. These functions are determined by the equations

$$
(46)
\begin{cases}
\Delta u_0 = f(x, y), \\[2mm]
\Delta u_1 = a\dfrac{\partial u_0}{\partial x} + b\dfrac{\partial u_0}{\partial y} + cu_0, \\[2mm]
\Delta u_2 = a\dfrac{\partial u_1}{\partial x} + b\dfrac{\partial u_1}{\partial y} + cu_1, \\[2mm]
\cdots\cdots\cdots\cdots\cdots\cdots\cdots\cdots,
\end{cases}
$$

in conjunction with the boundary conditions. The first function $u_0(x, y)$ is obtained by adding to the function $U(x, y)$ given by formula (43) the harmonic function which assumes the given values on C. Once this function $u_0(x, y)$ is known, the following functions $u_1(x, y)$, $u_2(x, y)$, ... are calculated step by step by the repeated application of formula (43). By means of certain hypotheses on the contour C, the given values of the unknown function on this contour, and the coefficients, a, b, c, f, Picard succeeded in proving that series (45) and those derived from it by taking partial derivatives up to the second order are uniformly convergent for $\lambda = -1$, so that the function $u(x, y)$ indeed gives the solution of the problem. His method is also applicable, in certain cases, to the equations

$$
\Delta u = f\left(x, y, u, \frac{\partial u}{\partial x}, \frac{\partial u}{\partial y}\right),
$$

but, generally, the conclusions are less precise than for equations of hyperbolic type. We shall see the reason for this later on. We shall return to the works cited above for the proofs.

This method of calculation puts us on the track of an important theorem. When the coefficients a, b, c, f are analytic functions, all the terms of the series (45) are themselves analytic functions (III, **65**). A deeper study of this series shows that the same is true for the sum of the series, which led Picard to an important theorem: *When the coefficients of equation (41) are analytic, all the integrals are themselves analytic functions.* This proposition has since been generalized by Serge Bernstein.[22]

[22] Doctoral thesis (1904). We can also extend Harnack's theorem (III, **54**) on series with positive, harmonic terms to series with positive terms, these terms being integrals of equation (41), where we have set $f = 0$. (Lichtenstein, *Rendiconti del Circolo matematico di Palermo*, Vol. XXXIII, 1912, p. 201).

67. Green's function for the general equation of elliptic type.

We have seen above that knowledge of Green's function for a contour C permits us to solve the Dirichlet problem for this contour, whatever the given values on C. We shall similarly be able to solve the Dirichlet problem relative to a contour C, for any equation of elliptic type, if we can determine a unique function satisfying certain conditions which are going to be explained.

Let us return first of all to the general formula (41) of III, **41**, which plays a fundamental role in Riemann's method. In the case of the elliptic equation

$$(47) \qquad \mathscr{F}(u) = \frac{\partial^2 u}{\partial x^2} + \frac{\partial^2 u}{\partial y^2} + a\frac{\partial u}{\partial x} + b\frac{\partial u}{\partial y} + cu = 0,$$

the adjoint equation is

$$(48) \qquad \mathscr{G}(v) = \frac{\partial^2 v}{\partial x^2} + \frac{\partial^2 v}{\partial y^2} - \frac{\partial(av)}{\partial x} - \frac{\partial(bv)}{\partial y} + cv = 0,$$

and we have, for any functions u and v, the identity

$$(49) \qquad v\mathscr{F}(u) - u\mathscr{G}(v) = \frac{\partial}{\partial x}\left[v\frac{\partial u}{\partial x} - u\frac{\partial v}{\partial x} + auv\right]$$

$$+ \frac{\partial}{\partial y}\left[v\frac{\partial u}{\partial y} - u\frac{\partial v}{\partial y} + buv\right].$$

Let us suppose that the functions u and v are regular in a domain D bounded by a contour C, on which the functions a, b, c, $\partial a/\partial x$, $\partial b/\partial y$ are continuous. Then we also have, from the preceding identity,

$$\int\int_{(D)} [v\mathscr{F}(u) - u\mathscr{G}(v)]\,dx\,dy = \int_{(C)} \left[v\frac{\partial u}{\partial x} - u\frac{\partial v}{\partial x} + auv\right]dy$$

$$- \left[v\frac{\partial u}{\partial y} - u\frac{\partial v}{\partial y} + buv\right]dx,$$

where the line integral is taken in the positive sense. Replacing dx and dy by $\cos \beta' ds$ and $\cos \alpha' ds$, where α' and β' are the angles made by the interior normal with the axes (III, **50**), the preceding formula becomes

(50) $\displaystyle\int\int_{(D)} [v\mathscr{F}(u) - u\mathscr{G}(v)]\,dx\,dy = \int_{(C)} \left(u\frac{dv}{dn} - v\frac{du}{dn}\right) ds$

$$- \int_{(C)} (a\cos\alpha' + b\cos\beta')\,uv\,ds,$$

where du/dn, dv/dn represent the derivatives taken along the interior normal.

This formula assumes, of course, that the derivatives $\partial u/\partial x$, $\partial v/\partial x$, $\partial u/\partial y$, $\partial v/\partial y$ remain finite on the contour.

That being granted, let $u(x, y)$ be any integral of the equation $\mathscr{F}(u) = f(x, y)$, regular in the domain D, and remaining finite, along with its partial derivatives $\partial u/\partial x$, $\partial u/\partial y$, on the contour. Moreover, let $v(x, y; \xi, \eta)$ be a *particular* integral of the adjoint equation $\mathscr{G}(v) = 0$, satisfying the following condition:

A. *In the domain* D *it is of the form* U log r $+$ V, *where* U *and* V *are regular in this domain, and* r *is equal to*

$$\sqrt{(x - \xi)^2 + (y - \eta)^2};$$

the point (ξ, η) *is a point of the domain* D *and we further suppose that* $U(\xi, \eta) = -1$.

On the contour C, we are only assuming that v, $\partial v/\partial x$, $\partial v/\partial y$, remain finite. Let us apply the general formula (50) to the domain D' bounded by C and by a circle γ of very small radius ρ having the point (ξ, η) as center. Since we have $\mathscr{F}(u) = f(x, y)$ and $\mathscr{G}(v) = 0$ in this domain, the formula becomes

$$\int\int_{(D')} vf(x, y)\,dx\,dy = \int_{(C)} \left(u\frac{dv}{dn} - v\frac{du}{dn}\right) ds$$

$$- \int_C (a\cos\alpha' + b\cos\beta')\,uv\,ds$$

$$+ \int_{(\gamma)} \left(u\frac{dv}{dn} - v\frac{du}{dn}\right) ds$$

$$- \int_{(\gamma)} (a\cos\alpha' + b\cos\beta')\,uv\,ds,$$

where the interior normal at a point of γ is the exterior normal to the geometric curve. When the radius ρ approaches zero, the integral $\int_\gamma (a, \cos\alpha' + b\cos\beta')uv\,ds$ approaches zero, for an element of this integral is of the form $\rho d\theta(A + B \log \rho)$, where A and B remain finite.

For the same reason, the integral $\int_\gamma v(du/dn)\ ds$ also approaches zero. As for the integral $\int_\gamma u\ ds$, it can be written as

$$\int_0^{2\pi} \left[(-1 + \epsilon)\frac{1}{\rho} + \log \rho \frac{dU}{dn} + \frac{dV}{dn} \right] u\rho\ d\theta$$

and its limit is clearly $- 2\pi u(\xi, \eta)$. Passing to the limit, we therefore have

$$(51) \quad u(\xi, \eta) = \frac{1}{2\pi} \int_{(C)} \left[u\frac{dv}{dn} - v\frac{du}{dn} \right] ds$$

$$-\frac{1}{2\pi} \int_{(C)} (a \cos \alpha' + b \cos \beta')\ uv\ ds - \frac{1}{2\pi} \int \int_{(D)} vf\ dx\ dy.$$

If the value of $u(x, y)$ is given at all points of the contour, we shall be able to calculate all the terms which occur in the second member, with the exception of $\int_C v(du/dn)\ ds$, which contains du/dn. In order for this term to disappear, it will be sufficient to take for v an integral of the adjoint equation satisfying condition A and which is zero at all points of C. Knowledge of an integral $v(x, y; \xi, \eta)$ of the adjoint equation satisfying these various conditions will allow us to solve the Dirichlet problem for the contour C, whatever values are given on the contour, for formula (51) then becomes

$$(52) \quad u(\xi, \eta) = \frac{1}{2\pi} \int_C u\frac{dv}{dn}\ ds - \frac{1}{2\pi} \int \int_{(D)} vf(x, y)\ dx\ dy$$

and reduces to formula (37) itself when $f(x, y) = 0$.

The function $v(x, y; \xi, \eta)$, if it exists, therefore plays exactly the same role as Green's function for the Laplace equation. The determination of this function is composed of two distinct problems. We must first of all look for a *fundamental* solution of the adjoint equation $\mathscr{G}(v) = 0$, that is, for an integral having at an arbitrary point (ξ, η) a logarithmic discontinuity of the type specified above.[23]

This first problem is independent of the contour C.

In the particular case of the equation $\Delta u = 0$, a fundamental solution is $\log (1/r)$. In the general case, once having obtained a

---

[23] The existence of this solution when the coefficients a, b, c are analytic, was first of all established in a particular case by Picard, then in the general case by Hilbert, Hedrick and Hadamard (see Hadamard's paper, already cited, *Annales de l'École Normale*, 1903, p. 535 and following).

fundamental solution $V(x, y; \xi, \eta)$, in order to have the solution $v(x, y; \xi, \eta)$ relative to the contour C, it will be sufficient to add to this fundamental solution an integral of the adjoint equation, regular in the interior of the contour, and assuming the same value as $- V$ at each point of this contour. Thus we have a reduction to a particular case of the same Dirichlet problem. We shall return later to this second part of the problem.

We can also extend to the function $v(x, y; \xi, \eta)$ the property established above for the Green's function concerning the interchange of the two pairs of variables (x, y), (ξ, η). Let $u(x, y; \xi, \eta)$ be an integral of the equation $\mathscr{F}(u) = 0$, defined in the same way as v, that is, zero at all points of C, and having the form $U_1 \log r + V_1$, U_1 and V_1 being regular functions in the domain D, and $U_1 (\xi, \eta)$ being equal to $- 1$. Let us take any two points whatever (a, b), (a', b') of the domain D, and let us apply the general formula (50) to the two functions $u(x, y; a', b')$, $v(x, y; a, b)$ in the domain D' formed by the portion of D which is exterior to the two circles γ, γ' of very small radii ρ, ρ', having for centers, respectively, the two points (a, b), (a', b'). The line integral along C is zero, and we can prove as just above that the integrals along γ and γ' have for limits respectively, $- 2\pi u(a, b; a', b')$ and $2\pi v(a', b'; a, b)$, when ρ, ρ' approach zero. Replacing (a, b) by (x, y), and (a', b') by (ξ, η) we therefore have the interchange relation

$$(53) \qquad u(x, y; \xi, \eta) = v(\xi, \eta; x, y),$$

entirely similar to those which have been established for Riemann's function (III, **42**) and for Green's function, and from which we can draw the same conclusions. But it is essential to notice that the function $u(x, y; \xi, \eta)$ does not depend only upon the equation itself, as does Riemann's function, but also on the contour C.

68. Positive mixed problems. Formula (51) allows us to attack more general problems than the Dirichlet problem. In this formula we have under the integral sign a bilinear expression with respect to the two pairs of variables $[u, (du/dn)]$, $[v, (dv/dn)]$. Let us suppose that instead of being given the value of u on the contour C, we are given a linear relation between u and du/dn which must be satisfied at every point of C,

$$(54) \qquad Hu + K\frac{du}{dn} = L,$$

where H, K are constants, or else known functions at each point of the contour, which may, besides, have any number of points of discontinuity on this contour, and where L is a function given on C. For example, we may be given the value of du/dn at each point of C, or the value of u on certain parts of C and the value of du/dn on the remainder of the contour. The function under the integral sign in formula (51) will itself be known if the coefficients of u and of du/dn are proportional to the coefficients H and K, which requires that the integral v of the adjoint equation itself satisfies along the contour C the relation

$$(55) \qquad K\frac{dv}{dn} + v(H - aK\cos\alpha' - bK\cos\beta') = 0.$$

We would again obtain this function v by adding to a fundamental solution $V(x, y; \xi, \eta)$ an integral v_1 of the adjoint equation, regular in the interior of the contour C, and satisfying on this contour the relation

$$\left(\frac{dv_1}{dn} + \frac{dV}{dn}\right) + (v_1 + V)(l - a\cos\alpha' - b\cos\beta') = 0, \quad l = \frac{H}{K};$$

this is a particular case of the general problem with whose solution we are concerned. Knowledge of this function $v(x, y; \xi, \eta)$ again allows us to solve the proposed mixed problem, whatever the values of L in formula (54) which express the boundary conditions.

We thus understand the existence of an infinity of functions depending upon two pairs of variables (x, y), (ξ, η) each of which plays the role of Green's function for a problem with boundary conditions of the elliptic type. These functions depend simultaneously upon the equation, the contour C, and also upon the very nature of the problem, that is, upon the coefficients H and K. It is clear that these are only general remarks, which must necessarily be made precise in each particular case, and it may happen that the conditions which the function v is to satisfy are incompatible.

A simple example of this case is furnished by *Neumann's problem* which consists of *determining a function* u(x, y), *harmonic in the interior of a contour, when the value of* du/dn *on the contour is known*. Let $U'(M)$ be the given value of du/dn at each point M of the contour C; from the general property expressed by relation (12) (III, **50**), this function $u(x, y)$ can exist only if the given function $U'(M)$ satisfies the condition

$$(56) \qquad \int_C U'(M)\, ds = 0.$$

This is sufficient to prove that there does not exist a solution of the equation $\Delta v = 0$, whose normal derivative dv/dn is zero on C, and which is regular in the interior, except in the neighborhood of a point (ξ, η) which is a logarithmic infinity. Indeed, this function v would be harmonic in the domain bounded by C and a circle γ of very small radius ρ described about the point (ξ, η) as center, and we would have to have $\int_\gamma (dv/dn)\,ds = 0$, since dv/dn is zero on C. But the calculation just now made proves that this integral would approach 2π when ρ approaches zero.

When condition (56) is satisfied, Neumann's problem reduces to Dirichlet's problem; we shall restrict ourselves to the case of an area with a simple contour. Indeed, let us consider on the contour C the function

$$V(s) = \int_0^s U'(M)\,ds,$$

where the measurement of the arc begins at an arbitrary origin; this function $V(s)$ is continuous and has a unique value at each point, according to relation (56). Let $V(x, y)$ be the harmonic function in the domain D which assumes the value $V(s)$ on C; with this function $V(x, y)$ we can associate another harmonic function $U(x, y)$ such that $V + iU$ is a holomorphic function of $x + iy$ in the interior of C. By virtue of the general relations of III, **47**, on this contour we have $dU/dn = dV/ds = U'(M)$, and therefore the function $U(x, y)$ provides the solution of Neumann's problem. This function is only determined within an additive constant, as was evident *a priori* (see Exercise 12).

Comments and Exercises

1. Derive the general formula (13) (III, **51**) from Cauchy's integral (II, 1, **33**).

Let $U(x, y) + iV(x, y)$ be a holomorphic function in the interior of a contour C. Replacing in Cauchy's formula x by $a + bi$, where a and b are the coordinates of an interior point P, and equating the real parts, we obtain the relation

$$U(a, b) = \frac{1}{2\pi} \int_{(C)} \left(V \frac{d \log r}{ds} - U \frac{d \log r}{dn} \right) ds,$$

observing that $[dz/(z - a - bi)] = [(d \log r)/ds] - i\,[(d \log r)/dn]\,ds$

along C. An integration by parts applied to the first integral is sufficient to get formula (13), after having replaced dV/ds by $-dU/dn$.

2. Prove that the function $U(a, b)$, given by formula (18), solves Dirichlet's problem for the circle by using the fact that the second member is the difference of two potentials of double layer.

3. Prove, by means of Cauchy's theorems, that the integral

$$- \frac{1}{2\pi} \int_{-\pi}^{+\pi} \psi \, \frac{d \log r}{dn} \, d\psi$$

is equal to the argument of $(1 + a + bi)$, taken between $- \pi/2$ and $+ \pi/2$; r is the distance of a point of the unit circle about the origin from a point (a, b) interior to this circle (cf. **III, 52**).

We begin by establishing the relation

$$\int_C \text{Log } z \, \frac{dz}{z - x} = 2\pi i \text{ Log } (1 + x),$$

where $x = a + bi$, the argument of z being taken between $- \pi$ and $+ \pi$, and the argument of $1 + x$ between $- \pi/2$ and $+ \pi/2$. To do this we apply the theorem of residues to the contour formed by C and the two edges of the cut joining the origin to the point $(- 1)$.

4. Show by an inversion that Poisson's formula (17) can be written as

$$U(a, b) = \frac{1}{2\pi} \int_0^{2\pi} f(\psi) \, d\psi',$$

where ψ' is the polar angle of the second point of intersection of the line PM with the circle C. Let P and Q be any two points interior to the circle, ρ and ρ' their distances from the center, d their distance, D the oscillation of the given function $f(\psi)$ on the circle; we have the inequality

$$|V_Q - V_P| < \frac{2D}{\pi} \text{ Arc tan } \frac{Rd}{\sqrt{R^2 - \rho^2} \, \sqrt{R^2 - \rho'^2}}.$$

[Darboux, *Bull. des Sc. math.*, 2nd series, Vol. **XXXIV**, 1910, p. 287.]

5. *Hadamard's example* (note 11, this chapter). The function

$$U = \sum_{n=1}^{+\infty} \frac{\rho^{2^n}}{2n} \cos (2^{2n}\theta)$$

is harmonic in the interior of the circle C of *unit* radius and reduces on this circle to a continuous function of θ, $\Sigma\, 1/2^n \cos{(2^{2n}\theta)}$. The double integral

$$\int \int \left[\left(\frac{\partial U}{\partial x} \right)^2 + \left(\frac{\partial U}{\partial y} \right)^2 \right] dx\, dy,$$

taken over the area of a concentric circle of radius $\rho < 1$, has the value

$$\pi \sum_{n=1}^{+\infty} \rho^{2^{2n+1}}$$

and increases indefinitely when ρ approaches unity.

6. Let $U(x, y)$ be a harmonic function in the part of the plane exterior to a contour C and regular at infinity. Show that for this part of the plane the general formula (13) should be replaced by the following

$$U(a, b) - U_\infty = \frac{1}{2\pi} \int_C \left(\log r \frac{dU}{dn} - U \frac{d \log r}{dn} \right) ds,$$

where the derivatives are taken in the exterior direction of the normal.

We first apply formula (13) to the contour formed by C and circle Γ with center at (a, b), whose radius we then make increase indefinitely.

7. Calculate the potentials of single layer

$$I_1 = \int_0^{2\pi} \cos n\psi \log r\, d\psi, \quad I_2 = \int_0^{2\pi} \sin n\psi \log r\, d\psi,$$

where r is the distance between the two points with polar coordinates (ρ, ω) and $(1, \psi)$, and n is a positive integer.

From the classic formula which gives the expansion of $\text{Log}\,(1 - z)$, we have, setting $z = \rho e^{i\theta}$, where $\theta = \psi - \omega$, and assuming $\rho < 1$,

$$\log{(1 + \rho^2 - 2\rho \cos \theta)^{1/2}} = -\rho \cos \theta - \rho^2 \frac{\cos 2\theta}{2} - \cdots$$

$$- \rho^n \frac{\cos n\theta}{n} - \cdots,$$

replacing log r by its expansion and integrating term by term we obtain $I_1 = - (\pi/n)\rho^n \cos n\omega$, $I_2 = - (\pi/n)\rho^n \sin n\omega$, if $\rho < 1$. We shall have the values of I_1, and of I_2, when ρ is greater than 1 by replacing ρ by $1/\rho$. Since the potential is continuous, the formulas hold for $\rho = 1$, and this gives the relations

$$\int_0^{2\pi} \cos n\psi \, \log\left\{2\left|\sin\frac{\psi - \omega}{2}\right|\right\} d\psi = -\frac{\pi}{n} \cos n\omega,$$

$$\int_0^{2\pi} \sin n\psi \, \log\left\{2\left|\sin\frac{\psi - \omega}{2}\right|\right\} d\psi = -\frac{\pi}{n} \sin n\omega.$$

8. Verify that the only functions $F(\psi)$ satisfying a relation of the form

$$\int_0^{2\pi} F(\psi) \log\left\{2\left|\sin\frac{\psi - \omega}{2}\right|\right\} d\psi = KF(\omega),$$

where K is constant, are of the form $A \cos n\psi + B \sin n\psi$.

We consider the potential

$$V(\rho, \omega) = \int_0^{2\pi} F(\psi) \log r \, d\psi,$$

and, calculating $\partial V/\partial \rho$, we prove after several easy transformations, that this potential satisfies a relation $\rho(\partial V/\partial \rho) + (\pi/K)V = C$, where C is a constant. This coefficient must be zero since V is zero at the center of the circle, and consequently V is a homogeneous harmonic function.

9. Calculate the potentials of double layer

$$\int_0^{2\pi} \cos n\psi \, \frac{\cos \phi}{r} d\psi, \qquad \int_0^{2\pi} \sin n\psi \, \frac{\cos \phi}{r} d\psi,$$

where r and ϕ have the usual meanings.

10. Let U be a continuous function along the circle C of radius R; if x is the affix of an interior point, the integral

$$F(x) = \frac{1}{\pi i} \int_C \frac{U \, dz}{z - x} - \frac{1}{\pi} \int_C U \frac{ds}{2R}$$

represents a holomorphic function of x in the interior of circle C, whose real part approaches U when the point x approaches a point on the circle C.

We observe that this real part is a potential of double layer. We derive from this the relation

$$F(x) - F(0) = \frac{x}{\pi i} \int_C U \frac{dz}{z(z - x)} = -\frac{x}{\pi R} \int_C U \frac{d \operatorname{Log}(z - x)}{dx} ds.$$

11. Let u and v be two conjugate harmonic functions in a circle C with origin as center, such that $u + iv = F(z)$. Show that $\rho(\partial u/\partial \rho)$ and $\rho(\partial v/\partial \rho)$ are also harmonic functions, are conjugates, and that we have

$$\rho \frac{\partial u}{\partial \rho} + i\rho \frac{\partial v}{\partial \rho} = zF'(z).$$

12. *Neumann's problem for the circle.* Let $u(a, b)$ be a harmonic function in the circle C of radius R with origin as center, whose derivative du/dn assumes a given value at each point of C, such that $\int_C (du/dn) \, ds = 0$; if $v(a, b)$ is the conjugate function, set

$$f(x) = u + iv, \quad x = a + ib.$$

From Exercise 11 we have

$$\rho \frac{\partial u}{\partial \rho} + i\rho \frac{\partial v}{\partial \rho} = xf'(x).$$

The real part of the holomorphic function $xf'(x)$ is equal to $-R(du/dn)$ on C; we therefore have (Ex. 10)

$$xf'(x) = \frac{x}{\pi} \int_C \frac{du}{dn} \frac{d \operatorname{Log}(z - x)}{dx} ds,$$

$$f'(x) = \frac{1}{\pi} \int_C \frac{du}{dn} \frac{d \operatorname{Log}(z - x)}{dx} ds$$

and, therefore,

$$f(x) = \frac{1}{\pi} \int_C \frac{du}{dn} \operatorname{Log}(z - x) \, ds.$$

Taking the real part, we obtain Dini's formula which represents in the circle the desired harmonic function

$$u = \frac{1}{\pi} \int_C \frac{du}{dn} \log r \, ds.$$

This result is easily verified by appealing to the properties of normal derivatives of the potential of single layer [III, **82**, formulas (54)], or to the formulas of Exercise 7. (See an article by Tommaso Boggio, *Reale Accademia delle Scienze di Torino* 1911–1912).

13. *Generalization.* Determine a harmonic function u' in a circle C of radius R, such that on this circle we have

$(a/R)\,u' - du'/dn = U$ (given function on C).

[Tommaso Boggio, Ibid.]

Let u be the harmonic function equal to U on C; we must have

$$au' + \rho\frac{\partial u'}{\partial \rho} = Ru,$$

for the two members are harmonic functions equal on C. Let v and v' be the conjugate harmonic functions of u and u', respectively; we may also assume that we have

$$av' + \rho\frac{\partial v'}{\partial \rho} = Rv.$$

Let $u' + iv' = f(z)$, $u + iv = F(z)$. We derive from these equations that the function $f(z)$ satisfies the differential equation

$$af(z) + zf'(z) = RF(z),$$

which has a holomorphic solution in C, provided that a is not a negative integer.

14. *Dirichlet's problem for an annular area.* This problem, a solution to which we have already indicated (III, **54**), has been made the object of an extended investigation by Villat (*Rendiconti del Circolo matematico di Palermo*, Vol. XXXIII, 1912, p. 134). The corresponding Green's function can be expressed simply enough in terms of elliptic functions.

Let D be the domain between the two circles C, C' of radius 1 and $R > 1$, having the origin as center in the plane of the variable z. Setting $u = i \log z$, we set up a correspondence between the circle C and the real axis in the u-plane, and the circle C' and a parallel to the real axis with ordinate $\log R$, while to the circular ring corresponds an infinite band D', of width $\log R$, contained between these two lines. To a point of D corresponds an infinity of points of the band D' which have the same ordinate and whose abscissas form an arithmetic progression of common difference 2π. Let us consider the system of periods $2\omega = 2\pi$, $2\omega' = 2i \log R$; e_1, e_2, e_3, g_2, g_3 are real and the functions σ, σ_1, σ_2, σ_3, formed with these periods, are represented by developments in power series with real coefficients; η is real, as is η'/i (see, for example, Tannery and Molk, *Fonctions elliptiques*, Vol. I, p. 188 and following).

Let $\alpha + \beta i$ be a point taken in the band D'. The quotient

$$\frac{\sigma(u - \alpha - \beta i)}{\sigma(u - \alpha + \beta i)}$$

has a modulus equal to unity when u describes the real axis; it is holomorphic in D' and has no other zeros there than the points $\alpha + \beta i + 2k\pi$. The product

$$\phi(u) = e^{\frac{2\beta\eta i u}{\pi}} \left\{ \frac{\sigma(u - \alpha - \beta i)}{\sigma(u - \alpha + \beta i)} \right\}$$

also possesses these properties, but we easily see besides that this function has the period $2\omega = 2\pi$ by considering the relation between $\sigma(u)$ and $\sigma(u + 2\omega)$. The modulus of $\phi(u)$ remains constant when u describes the upper boundary of the strip D'. From the general relations

$$\sigma(u + \omega') = e^{\eta' u}\sigma\omega'\sigma_3 u, \quad \eta\omega' - \eta'\omega = \frac{\pi}{2}i,$$

we have, indeed,

$$\phi(u + \omega') = e^{-\beta} e^{\frac{2\beta\eta i u}{\pi}} \left\{ \frac{\sigma_3(u - \alpha - \beta i)}{\sigma_3(u - \alpha + \beta i)} \right\},$$

and as the coefficients of σ_3 are real, the modulus of $\phi(u + \omega')$ is equal to $e^{-\beta}$ when u is real. This being the case, let us set $v = \text{Log}\,[\phi(u)]$; when z describes a closed contour in the ring D, u increases by $2k\pi$, $\phi(u)$ returns to its initial value, and the real part of v is a uniform function of the variables x, y in this domain, which is zero on C and equal to $-\beta$ on C'. Moreover, the function v has only one logarithmic singular point in D, the point $e^{-i(\alpha+\beta i)} = e^{\beta-\alpha i}$. Adding on to the real part of v the real part of $(\beta/\text{Log}\,R)\,\text{Log}\,z$, we have the required Green's function.

CHAPTER VI

HARMONIC FUNCTIONS IN THREE VARIABLES

I. DIRICHLET'S PROBLEM IN SPACE

69. General properties. The definition of harmonic functions can be extended immediately to functions of three variables. We shall say that a function $u(x, y, z)$ of the three variables x, y, z is *harmonic* in a domain D of space if it is regular, that is, continuous with continuous partial derivatives up to the second order, and if the partial derivatives of the second order satisfy Laplace's equation

$$(1) \qquad \Delta u = \frac{\partial^2 u}{\partial x^2} + \frac{\partial^2 u}{\partial y^2} + \frac{\partial^2 u}{\partial z^2} = 0$$

at every point of this domain. The function $1/r$, where r is the distance of the variable point $M(x, y, z)$ from the fixed point $P(a, b, c)$, is harmonic in every domain not containing the point P, and this function plays the same role as $\log 1/r$ in the theory of the equation in two variables. The partial derivatives of this function, whether with respect to the variables x, y, z, or with respect to the parameters a, b, c, are harmonic in the same domain, and the same is true of every linear combination of these derivatives whose coefficients are independent of x, y, z. For example, the expression $(\cos \phi)/r^2$, where ϕ designates the angle made by the direction PM with any line whatever starting from P, is a harmonic function, for it is equal to the derivative of $1/r$ taken in the direction mentioned when we regard $1/r$ as a function of the coordinates (a, b, c) of the point P.

Similarly $(\cos \psi)/r^2$, where ψ is the angle made by the direction MP with a *fixed* direction, independent of M, is also harmonic, for it is the derivative of $1/r$, considered as a function of x, y, z, taken along this direction. The properties of harmonic functions derived from potential theory or from Green's formula, can be extended with few easily discoverable changes to harmonic functions of three variables; we shall often restrict ourselves to some indications, leaving to the reader the details of developing the proofs, entirely similar to those of III, **49–51**.

To the contrary, the theory of analytic functions of a complex variable and the theory of conformal transformations do not have analogs when we pass from two to three variables. Every harmonic function is changed into a harmonic function when we replace x, y, z by kx, ky, kz, or when we carry out on these variables any orthogonal substitution, or when we change x, y, z into $x + a$, $y + b$, $z + c$, respectively; the verification is immediate. Similarly, if $U(x, y, z)$ is harmonic, the function

$$\frac{1}{\sqrt{x^2 + y^2 + z^2}} \, U \left(\frac{x}{x^2 + y^2 + z^2}, \frac{y}{x^2 + y^2 + z^2}, \frac{z}{x^2 + y^2 + z^2} \right)$$

is also harmonic.[1] Combining the preceding transformations, we obtain all the transformations

$$X = f_1(x, y, z), \qquad Y = f_2(x, y, z), \qquad Z = f_3(x, y, z),$$

$$U = \phi(u, x, y, z)$$

by which the equation $\Delta U = 0$ is changed into an equation of the same form[2] $\Delta u = 0$.

We have seen (III, **47**) that the most general harmonic and homogeneous polynomial of the nth degree in two variables depends upon *two* arbitrary constants. A homogeneous polynomial of the nth degree in three variables contains $[(n + 1)\,(n + 2)]/2$ coefficients; requiring it to satisfy Laplace's equation establishes $[n(n - 1)]/2$ relations among these coefficients; therefore there remain $[(n + 1)\,(n + 2) - n(n - 1)]/2 = 2n + 1$ arbitrary coefficients. We can also see this by observing that Laplace's equation and those derived from it by differentiation permit us to express all the derivatives of nth order in terms of derivatives of this order in which either x does not occur at all or else occurs only once.

In a homogeneous harmonic polynomial of the nth degree we can therefore choose arbitrarily only the coefficients of the terms

---

[1] This property is due to Lord Kelvin [*Journal de Liouville*, Vol. X (1st series), 1845, p. 364]. It is easily proven by using Laplace's equation in polar coordinates.

[2] Painlevé, *Mémoires des Facultés de Lille*, Vol. I, 1889.

not containing x or containing x in the first degree; the number of these terms is definitely equal to $2n + 1$. These harmonic polynomials $V_n(x, y, z)$ can be derived from the partial derivatives of the harmonic function

$$\frac{1}{\sqrt{x^2 + y^2 + z^2}}.$$

Indeed, all these derivatives also satisfy Laplace's equation, and a derivative of order n is of the form $V_n(x, y, z) (x^2 + y^2 + z^2)^{-n-\frac{1}{2}}$, where $V_n(x, y, z)$ is a homogeneous polynomial of degree n; the harmonic function derived by Lord Kelvin's transformation is precisely the polynomial $V_n(x, y, z)$. All these polynomials reduce to $2n + 1$ linearly independent polynomials, since the number of linearly independent partial derivatives of nth order of a harmonic function is equal to $2n + 1$. For $n = 1, 2, 3$, respectively, we have

$$V_1(x, y, z) = \lambda_1 x + \lambda_2 y + \lambda_3 z,$$

$$V_2(x, y, z) = \lambda_1(x^2 - z^2) + \lambda_2(y^2 - z^2) + \lambda_3 xy + \lambda_4 xz + \lambda_5 yz,$$

$$V_3(x, y, z) = \lambda_1(x^3 - 3xy^2) + \lambda_2(x^3 - 3xz^2) + \ldots + \lambda_7 xyz,$$

where the coefficients λ_i are arbitrary, and the terms not written in V_3 are derived from the first two by circular permutation.

70. Newtonian potential of single layer.

Let us first recall some definitions concerning surfaces. We say that a point $M_0(x_0, y_0, z_0)$ of a surface S is an ordinary point if the coordinates (x, y, z) of a nearby point M of S are functions $x = f(u, v)$, $y = \phi(u, v)$, $z = \psi(u, v)$ of the two parameters u, v, which are continuous and have continuous partial derivatives of the first order in the neighborhood of the system of values (u_0, v_0) which correspond to the point M_0, and if moreover the three Jacobians

$$\frac{D(y, z)}{D(u, v)}, \frac{D(z, x)}{D(u, v)}, \frac{D(x, y)}{D(u, v)}$$

are not all simultaneously zero for this system of values. A portion of the surface is called *regular* if it contains only regular points. The surfaces in the discussion to follow are not necessarily analytic, but we shall always assume that they are composed of a finite number of portions of regular surfaces. They can have a finite number of edges along which intersect two nappes of regular surfaces with

two distinct tangent points, and a finite number of isolated singular
points, as conical points, or as vertices where several edges come
together. It is clear that a surface integral taken over a surface of
this character always has a meaning if the function under the
integral sign is continuous, or if it is discontinuous yet bounded at
certain points or along certain lines, finite in number. For example,
if the function under the integral sign depends upon the direction
of the normal, it is discontinuous along edges, but if we have chosen
a fixed direction for the normal on each portion of the surface, the
double integral has a finite value.

Let Σ be a surface of the kind considered, closed or not, but
lying entirely at a finite distance, and μ a continuous function
on Σ. The integral taken over this surface

$$(2) \qquad V(a, b, c) = \int\int_{(\Sigma)} \frac{\mu}{r}\, d\sigma,$$

where r represents the distance of a point M of Σ from a fixed
point with coordinates (a, b, c), is a *Newtonian potential of single
layer*. We prove as in III, **49** that $V(a, b, c)$ is a harmonic function
of the coordinates (a, b, c) in every domain D having no point in
common with Σ, and *that it is continuous in the entire space*. To
prove this last point it is sufficient to prove that the integral (2)
is uniformly convergent in the neighborhood of every point M_0
of Σ (III, **48**). Let us assume that the point M_0 is an ordinary point
of Σ; let us take this point as the origin and the normal as the z-
axis. Let Σ' be a portion of Σ surrounding M_0 which is intersected
in only one point by a parallel to the z-axis, and which projects
onto the xy-plane into the interior of a closed curve enclosing the
origin. The integral

$$V'(a, b, c) = \int\int_{(\Sigma)} \frac{\mu\, d\sigma}{r} = \int\int \frac{\mu\sqrt{1 + p^2 + q^2}\, dx\, dy}{\sqrt{(x - a)^2 + (y - b)^2 + (z - c)^2}},$$

taken over the portion of the xy-plane interior to the curve γ, is
less in absolute value than

$$M \int\int \frac{dx\, dy}{\sqrt{(x - a)^2 + (y - b)^2}},$$

where M stands for an upper limit of

$$|\, \mu\,\sqrt{1 + p^2 + q^2}\,|$$

on a portion of Σ containing Σ'. If we change to polar coordinates by setting $x = a + \rho \cos \phi$, $y = b + \rho \sin \phi$, we see that the absolute value of $V'(a, b, c)$ is smaller than the integral

$$M \int \int d\rho \, d\phi,$$

and consequently less than $2\pi M l$, if the curve γ lies entirely inside a circle of diameter l. Since this number l can be taken as small as we wish, the same is therefore true of $|V'|$. The proof is easily extended to the case where the point M_0 lies on a double curve of Σ.

Outside of Σ, $V(a, b, c)$ *is an analytic function of* a, b, c. Since we can take for the origin any point whatever outside of Σ, it is sufficient for us to prove that U can be expanded in a power series of powers of a, b, c, when the origin is outside of Σ. The function $1/r$, where x, y, z are the coordinates of a point of Σ, is a holomorphic function of a, b, c in the neighbourhood of the values $a = b = c = 0$. Let us consider these variables as complex variables; if the modulus of each of them is less than ρ, the modulus of r^2 is greater than

$$x^2 + y^2 + z^2 - 2\rho \left[|x| + |y| + |z| \right] - 3\rho^2.$$

Since the number ρ has been chosen small enough so that the preceding expression does not vanish when the point (x, y, z) describes Σ, the function $1/r$ of the complex variables a, b, c, is holomorphic in the preceding domain, and its modulus remains less than a positive number M whatever the position of the point (x, y, z) on Σ. Therefore, if we expand this function in a power series of powers of a, b, c, the moduli of the coefficients will be less than the corresponding coefficients of the development of

$$\frac{M}{\left(1 - \dfrac{a}{\rho} \right) \left(1 - \dfrac{b}{\rho} \right) \left(1 - \dfrac{c}{\rho} \right)}.$$

This series is therefore uniformly convergent when the point (x, y, z) describes Σ, provided that the absolute values of a, b, c are less than ρ. Multiplying each of these terms by $\mu(x, y, z)$ and integrating term by term along Σ, we obtain for $V(a, b, c)$ a power series arranged in powers of a, b, c; this proves the theorem.

It is essential to remark that this property is no longer true for a point of Σ; on both sides of a portion of this surface, $V(a, b, c)$ represents two distinct analytic functions, which are not analytic extensions of one another when we cross this surface. For example, in the case where Σ is a sphere of radius R, if we have $\mu = 1$, in the interior of the sphere $V = 4\pi R$, and on the exterior $V = 4\pi(R^2/d)$, where d is the distance of the point P from the center. The discontinuity of the partial derivatives $\partial V/\partial a, \ldots$, when we cross Σ, really explains this result (see III, 82).

To study the potential $V(a, b, c)$ when the point P recedes indefinitely, it is sufficient to interchange the role of the two systems of variables (x, y, z) and (a, b, c) in the preceding reasoning. Let S be a sphere of radius ρ with the origin as center which contains the surface Σ in its interior; since the point P is exterior to S, let us consider $1/r$ as a function of the complex variables x, y, z, where the moduli of these variables remain less than ρ. In this domain, the modulus of r^2 remains greater than

$$a^2 + b^2 + c^2 - 2\rho\{|a| + |b| + |c|\} - 3\rho^2$$

$$= \{|a| - \rho\}^2 + \{|b| - \rho\}^2 + \{|c| - \rho\}^2 - 6\rho^2;$$

if we assume the point $P(a, b, c)$ to be on the exterior of a sphere S', concentric with S and of radius $R = 5\rho$, we easily see that this modulus is greater than $3\rho^2$. Consequently, the function $1/r$ of the complex variables x, y, z is holomorphic, and its modulus remains less than a fixed positive number, whatever the position of P outside of S', when the moduli of x, y, z are less than ρ. From this we conclude that $1/r$ can be expanded in a power series in powers of x, y, z, and *uniformly convergent* when the point (x, y, z) describes the surface Σ,

$$(3) \qquad \frac{1}{r} = \frac{1}{\sqrt{a^2 + b^2 + c^2}} + \Sigma A_{mnp} x^m y^n z^p,$$

where for the coefficient A_{mnp} we have the expression

$$A_{mnp} = (-1)^{m+n+p} \frac{\partial^{m+n+p}}{\partial a^m \, \partial b^n \, \partial c^p} \left(\frac{1}{\sqrt{a^2 + b^2 + c^2}}\right) \frac{1}{m! \, n! \, p!}.$$

Multiplying both members of formula (3) by $\mu(x, y, z)$ and integrating term by term, we obtain a development of $V(a, b, c)$ which is valid for every position of the point P on the exterior of S':

(4) $V(a, b, c) = \dfrac{Q}{\sqrt{a^2 + b^2 + c^2}}$

$\qquad + \Sigma B_{mnp} \dfrac{\partial^{m+n+p}}{\partial a^m \, \partial b^n \, \partial c^p} \left(\dfrac{1}{\sqrt{a^2 + b^2 + c^2}} \right),$

where P and B_{mnp} are constant coefficients. We shall remark that all the terms of this development are harmonic functions of a, b, c, and that the coefficient Q is equal to the integral $\iint \mu \, d\sigma$, taken over Σ.

The same calculations applied to the logarithmic potential of single layer prove that it is an analytic function, but for values greater than a, b, the expansion begins with a term in

$$Q \log (\sqrt{a^2 + b^2}).$$

71. Potential of double layer. Let MN be a fixed direction on the normal at each point M of a surface Σ, varying continuously with the position of the point M on the entire surface or on each portion of the surface; let us call ϕ the angle of the direction MN with the direction MP joining the point M to the point P with coordinates (a, b, c). We prove as in III, **49** that the double integral

(5) $W(a, b, c) = \displaystyle\int\int_{(\Sigma)} \mu \, \frac{\cos \phi}{r^2} \, d\sigma = \int\int \mu \, \frac{d\left(\frac{1}{r}\right)}{dn} \, d\sigma,$

where μ is a function which varies continuously with the position of the point M on Σ, is a harmonic function of the coordinates of the point P, in every domain having no point in common with Σ. We have given to this function the name of *potential of double layer*, borrowed from the theory of magnetism. It is also an *analytic function*. To prove this, let us make the same hypotheses as in the preceding paragraph; we can write

$$-\frac{\cos \phi}{r^2} = \frac{\partial\left(\frac{1}{r}\right)}{\partial a} \cos \alpha + \frac{\partial\left(\frac{1}{r}\right)}{\partial b} \cos \beta + \frac{\partial\left(\frac{1}{r}\right)}{\partial c} \cos \gamma,$$

where α, β, γ are the angles of the direction MN with the axes.

When the moduli of the complex variables a, b, c are smaller than a suitable positive number ρ, we have seen that the function $1/r$ can be expanded in a power series which remains uniformly convergent when the point (x, y, z) describes Σ. The same is evidently true of the partial derivatives of $1/r$ with respect to the variables a, b, c, and consequently of $(\cos \phi)/r^2$. The reasoning is concluded as in the case for the potential of single layer.[3]

From the relation

$$\frac{\cos \phi}{r^2} = \frac{\partial\left(\frac{1}{r}\right)}{\partial x} \cos \alpha + \frac{\partial\left(\frac{1}{r}\right)}{\partial y} \cos \beta + \frac{\partial\left(\frac{1}{r}\right)}{\partial z} \cos \gamma$$

we should similarly deduce that the function $W(a, b, c)$ can be expanded in a series of the form (4), when $\sqrt{a^2 + b^2 + c^2}$ is greater than a suitably chosen positive number, but it must be noted that there will be no term in $(a^2 + b^2 + c^2)^{-\frac{1}{2}}$, so that at infinity W is of the order of $(a^2 + b^2 + c^2)^{-1}$.

The function $W(a, b, c)$ is discontinuous at a point of Σ. Let us take first of all the simple case when we have $\mu = 1$; the integral thus obtained,

$$(6) \qquad W_1(a, b, c) = \int \int_{(\Sigma)} \mu \, \frac{\cos \phi}{r^2} \, d\sigma = \int \int_{(\Sigma)} \frac{d\left(\frac{1}{r}\right)}{dn} \, d\sigma,$$

called *Gauss's integral*, has a geometrical significance which makes the discontinuity obvious. Given a point O and a portion of the surface σ, such that a half ray coming from O cannot intersect it in more than one point, the locus of the half rays coming from O and passing through a point of σ is a solid cone; the area cut out by this cone on a sphere of *unit* radius with center at O is the measure of the *solid angle* under which we see the surface σ from point O. This granted, the expression $[(\cos \phi)/r^2] \, d\sigma$ is equal to $\pm$ the solid angle under which we see the element of the surface $d\sigma$, from the point P, for $\cos \phi \, d\sigma$ is, apart from sign, the element of area cut out on the sphere of radius r and center P by the elementary cone with vertex

[3] When the surface Σ is analytic, if μ is also an analytic function on Σ, the two potentials $V(a, b, c)$, $W(a, b, c)$ can be extended analytically across the surface Σ. (Bruns, *Journal de Crelle*, Vol. 81; Erhard Schmidt, *Mathematische Annalen*, Vol. LXVIII).

P and the element $d\sigma$ for base. As to the sign, it is determined by the following convention: Let us call the positive side of Σ the side which corresponds to the direction chosen on the normal, and the negative side the opposite one; it is clear that $\cos \phi \, (d\sigma/r^2)$ is positive if a half ray coming from P and crossing the element of surface passes from the positive side to the negative side, and is negative in the contrary case. We immediately see from this the value of the integral (6): it is the sum of the elementary solid angles, with the appropriate signs, under which the various elements of Σ are seen from the point P. Let us suppose in particular that Σ is a closed surface and that we have chosen for the direction of MN the interior normal; $W_1(a, b, c)$ is equal to 4π if the point P is in the interior of the domain D bounded by Σ, and is equal to zero if the point P is on the exterior. At a non-singular point P taken on Σ, the integral is equal to 2π; at a point where the surface does not have a unique tangent plane, the integral is equal to the measure of the solid angle α formed by the tangents to the surface coming from this point.[4]

Let us now return to the general case, always assuming that the surface Σ is closed and that we have chosen the direction of the interior normal. We prove as above (III, **49**) that the integral

$$I(P) = \int \int_{(\Sigma)} [\mu - \mu_0] \frac{\cos \phi}{r^2} \, d\sigma,$$

where μ_0 is the value of μ at a point M_0 of Σ, is a continuous function of the coordinates of the point P at this point M_0, such that the difference $I(P) - I(M_0)$ approaches zero with the distance M_0P. That being the case, let us call by W_0 the value of integral (5) itself when the point P coincides with the point M_0, and by W_{0i}, W_{0e} the limits which $W(a, b, c)$ approaches when the point P approaches the point M_0, either from the interior or the exterior of Σ.

When P is at M_0, I is equal to $W_0 - 2\pi\mu_0$; when P approaches M_0 from the interior of Σ, the first term of I has W_{0i} as its limit, while the coefficient of μ_0 is constantly equal to -4π. On the other

---

[4] These results are also very easily derived from the formulas of III, **72**. If the point P is exterior to the domain D, $U = r/1$ is harmonic in this domain, and formula (12) gives $W_1 = 0$. If the point P is interior to D, formula (14) applied to the harmonic function $U = 1$ gives $W_1 = 4\pi$. If the point P is on Σ, we shall apply formula (12) to the function $U = r/1$ which is harmonic in the portion of the domain D exterior to a sphere of radius ρ having the point P as center, and we shall make the radius ρ of this sphere decrease indefinitely.

hand, when P approaches M_0 from the exterior of Σ, the first term of I has W_{0e} as a limit, and the coefficient of μ_0 is zero. Since the function I is continuous at the point M_0, we therefore have $W_0 - 2\pi\mu_0 = W_{0i} - 4\pi\mu_0 = W_{0e}$, from which we derive the two relations exactly like those of III, **49**:

(7) $$W_{0i} = W_0 + 2\pi\mu_0, \qquad W_{0e} = W_0 - 2\pi\mu_0.$$

At a singular point, these relations must be replaced by the following:

(8) $$W_{0i} = W_0 + (4\pi - \alpha)\mu_0, \qquad W_{0e} = W_0 - \alpha\mu_0,$$

where α has the meaning given above.

72. Green's second formula. If we are given any two functions whatever, $\phi(x, y, z)$, $\psi(x, y, z)$, we have identically

$$\phi\Delta\psi - \psi\Delta\phi = \frac{\partial}{\partial x}\left(\phi\frac{\partial\psi}{\partial x} - \psi\frac{\partial\phi}{\partial x}\right)$$
$$+ \frac{\partial}{\partial y}\left(\phi\frac{\partial\psi}{\partial y} - \psi\frac{\partial\phi}{\partial y}\right) + \frac{\partial}{\partial z}\left(\phi\frac{\partial\psi}{\partial z} - \psi\frac{\partial\phi}{\partial z}\right).$$

If the functions ϕ and ψ are regular in a finite domain D, bounded by one or several closed surfaces, and continuous with continuous partial derivatives of the first order on the surfaces which bound this domain, we have, according to Green's first formula (**I, 149**),

(9) $$\begin{cases} \displaystyle\int\!\!\int\!\!\int_{(D)} (\phi\Delta\psi - \psi\Delta\phi)\, dx\, dy\, dz \\[2ex] \displaystyle= \int\!\!\int_{(\Sigma)} \phi\left(\frac{\partial\psi}{\partial x}\, dy\, dz + \frac{\partial\psi}{\partial y}\, dz\, dx + \frac{\partial\psi}{\partial z}\, dx\, dy\right), \\[2ex] \displaystyle- \int\!\!\int_{(\Sigma)} \psi\left(\frac{\partial\phi}{\partial x}\, dy\, dz + \frac{\partial\phi}{dy}\, dz\, dx + \frac{\partial\phi}{dz}\, dx\, dy\right), \end{cases}$$

where the double integrals are taken over the *exterior* side of the surface Σ which bounds D. Let α, β, γ be the angles which the direction of the *interior* normal at a point of Σ makes with the axes; the first double integral can be written

$$-\int\int_{(\Sigma)} \phi \left(\frac{\partial \psi}{\partial x} \cos \alpha + \frac{\partial \psi}{\partial y} \cos \beta + \frac{\partial \psi}{\partial z} \cos \gamma \right) d\sigma$$

$$= -\int\int_{(\Sigma)} \phi \frac{d\psi}{dn} d\sigma.$$

We can similarly transform the second double integral, and formula (9) becomes

(10) $$\int\int\int_{(D)} (\phi \Delta \psi - \psi \Delta \phi) \, dx \, dy \, dz$$

$$+ \int\int_{(\Sigma)} \left(\phi \frac{d\psi}{dn} - \psi \frac{d\phi}{dn} \right) d\sigma = 0,$$

where the derivatives $d\phi/dn$, $d\psi/dn$ are taken in the direction of the interior normal, that is, the one which penetrates the domain D.

When the functions ϕ and ψ are two harmonic functions U and V in D, the triple integral disappears and there remains the relation

(11) $$\int\int_{(\Sigma)} \left(U \frac{dV}{dn} - V \frac{dU}{dn} \right) d\sigma = 0.$$

We once more obtain two important formulas by assuming $\psi = 1$, $\phi = U$, or $\phi = U^2$, where U is a harmonic function,

(12) $$\int\int_{(\Sigma)} \frac{dU}{dn} d\sigma = 0,$$

(13) $$\int\int\int_{(D)} \left[\left(\frac{\partial U}{\partial x} \right)^2 + \left(\frac{\partial U}{\partial y} \right)^2 + \left(\frac{\partial U}{\partial z} \right)^2 \right] dx \, dy \, dz$$

$$+ \int\int_{(\Sigma)} U \frac{dU}{dn} d\sigma = 0;$$

the first characterizes harmonic functions (III, **50**).

Let $P(a, b, c)$ be a point of the domain D and $U(x, y, z)$ be a harmonic function in this domain. The two functions U and $V = 1/r$, where r is the distance of the point P from a variable point (x, y, z), are harmonic in the portion of D exterior to a sphere S with center P and radius ρ small enough that S is entirely interior to D. Let us apply formula (11) to this domain bounded by Σ and S; letting ρ approach zero and reasoning as in III, **51**, we obtain the formula

$$(14) \qquad U(a, b, c) = \frac{1}{4\pi} \int \int_{(\Sigma)} \left[U \frac{d\left(\frac{1}{r}\right)}{dn} - \frac{1}{r} \frac{dU}{dn} \right] d\sigma,$$

exactly like formula (13) of III, **51**. The factor 2π has been replaced by 4π, which is the area of a unit sphere, and log $1/r$ by $1/r$. In particular, if the surface Σ is the surface of a sphere of radius R having P as center, all along this sphere we have

$$r = R, \quad \frac{d(1/r)}{dn} = \frac{1}{R^2},$$

and we have the *mean value formula* for harmonic functions in three variables

$$(15) \qquad U(a, b, c) = \frac{1}{4\pi R^2} \int \int_{(S)} U \, d\sigma.$$

From it we could deduce, as above (III, **51**), that a harmonic function of three variables can have neither a maximum nor a minimum.

The second member of formula (14) is the sum of a potential of single layer and a potential of double layer, that is, of two analytic functions (III, **70–71**). We conclude from this *that every harmonic function is an analytic function.* Indeed, if we are given a point P, lying in the domain D where the function U is harmonic, we can always apply formula (14) by taking for Σ a closed surface surrounding the point P and lying entirely within this domain D. Let x_0, y_0, z_0 be the coordinates of any point of D; in the neighborhood of this point, the harmonic function $U(x, y, z)$ can be expanded in power series arranged according to powers of $x - x_0$, $y - y_0$, $z - z_0$. The set of terms of nth degree is a polynomial

$$V_n(x - x_0, y - y_0, z - z_0)$$

where $V_n(x, y, z)$ represents a homogeneous harmonic polynomial of degree n (III, **69**).[5]

---

[5] Known theorems concerning power series of a complex variable have been extended to series of this nature (see Appell, *Acta mathematica*, Vol. IV, 1884, pp. 313–374).

Formula (14) permits the extension of the second Picard theorem to harmonic functions in three dimensions (III, 47). Let $V(x, y, z)$ be a harmonic function in a domain D, with the exception of a point O of that domain, where it becomes equal to $+ \infty$. The family of surfaces $V(x, y, z) = K$ is therefore composed, for very large values of K, of closed surfaces surrounding point O and approaching this point when K increases indefinitely. The derivative dV/dn taken over the exterior side of one of these surfaces is negative and the integral $\iint (dV/dn) \, d\sigma$, taken over the exterior side, has a negative value $- 4\pi H$, independent of K, since the function V is harmonic in the region contained between any two of these surfaces. This being the case, let S be a sphere with center O lying in the domain D, let $M(a, b, c)$ be any interior point of S other than O, and let Σ be one of the surfaces $V = K$, interior to S but having point M on its exterior. Formula (14) gives for $V(a, b, c)$ the sum of two integrals, one taken over the interior side of S, the other over the exterior side of Σ. The integral taken over the interior side of S represents a harmonic function $U(a, b, c)$ in S. The integral taken over the exterior side of Σ reduces to

$$- \frac{1}{4\pi} \int \int_{(\Sigma)} \frac{1}{r} \frac{dV}{dn} \, d\sigma.$$

Since the derivative dV/dn has a constant sign on Σ, we can apply to this integral the theorem of the mean; when the surface Σ reduces to the point O, this integral reduces to H/ρ, ρ designating the distance OM. The function $V(a, b, c)$ is therefore of the form $(H/\rho) + U(a, b, c)$, where $U(a, b, c)$ is harmonic in the domain D.

Formula (14) also permits an affirmative response to the following question: *Let* U *be a continuous function with continuous first partial derivatives in the domain* D; *we further know that the second order partial derivatives are continuous and satisfy Laplace's equation at all points of the domain* D, *except perhaps along a finite number of certain surfaces lying in this domain. Can we conclude from this that* U *is harmonic in the entire domain?*

Let S be one of the surfaces of the domain D along which the second derivatives of U may be assumed discontinuous. With a point A of this surface as center let us draw a sphere Σ of sufficiently small radius that it lies entirely within D, and does not contain any other surface analogous to S. The portion S' of S interior to Σ decomposes the interior of the sphere into two domains D' and D'', bounded respectively by S' and by two portions Σ' and Σ'' of Σ.

In each of these two domains the function U is harmonic; let us designate by U' and U'' the two harmonic functions with which they coincide in the two domains D' and D'', respectively. We wish to show that these two functions U' and U'' are the analytic extensions each of the other when we cross S' or, what amounts to the same thing, that there exists a harmonic function in the domain $D' + D''$ which coincides with U' in D' and with U'' in D''.

Let P be any point of the domain D'; since U' is harmonic in D', we have according to formula (14)

$$U'_p = -\frac{1}{4\pi} \int \int_{(\Sigma)} \left[\frac{1}{r} \frac{dU'}{dn} - U' \frac{d(1/r)}{dn} \right] d\sigma$$

$$-\frac{1}{4\pi} \int \int_{S'} \left[\frac{1}{r} \frac{dU'}{dn'} - U'' \frac{d(1/r)}{dn'} \right] d\sigma$$

where d/dn' designates the derivative at a point of S' along the interior normal to D'. Since the two functions U'' and $1/r$ are harmonic in the domain D'', the second member of the preceding formula is zero when we replace U' in it by U'', Σ' by Σ'', and d/dn', by the derivative d/dn'' taken along the interior normal to D'' at a point of S'. Now, since the given function U is continuous with continuous first partial derivatives along S', we have $(dU'/dn') + (dU''/dn'') = 0$; adding the two supposedly written equations, we therefore have

$$U'_p = -\frac{1}{4\pi} \int \int_{(\Sigma')} \left[\frac{1}{r} \frac{dU'}{dn} - U' \frac{d(1/r)}{dn} \right] d\sigma$$

$$-\frac{1}{4\pi} \int \int_{(\Sigma'')} \left[\frac{1}{r} \frac{dU''}{dn} - U'' \frac{d(1/r)}{dn} \right] d\sigma.$$

It is clear that we should have the same expression for U''_P, where P is an interior point of D''. Now the second member of this formula, considered as a function of the coordinates of the point P, is harmonic in the interior of Σ; this proves the result stated above.

73. The interior problem and the exterior problem. The interior Dirichlet problem for three dimensions is stated like the analogous problem in the plane. Given a finite domain D bounded by one or several closed surfaces, we wish to find a harmonic function in D, assuming given values on the bounding surfaces, where these values form a continuous set on each of these surfaces. The absence of a maximum or minimum for a harmonic function again proves that this problem has at most one solution, and Riemann's demonstration to prove the existence of a solution is subject to the same objections as in the two-dimensional case. The reader can easily reestablish this demonstration for himself.

Before taking up the *exterior problem*, we must first give a few definitions. Let $U(x, y, z)$ be a harmonic function in the neighborhood of every point P lying outside a sphere of radius R with the origin as center. The function obtained by Lord Kelvin's transformation

$$V(x, y, z)$$

$$= \frac{1}{\sqrt{x^2 + y^2 + z^2}} U\left(\frac{x}{x^2 + y^2 + z^2}, \frac{y}{x^2 + y^2 + z^2}, \frac{z}{x^2 + y^2 + z^2}\right)$$

is a solution of the equation $\Delta V = 0$, regular at every interior point of the sphere with radius $1/R$ and origin as center, except perhaps for the origin.

If this function $V(x, y, z)$ is also regular at the origin, it can be expanded in a power series of the form

$$A_0 + \sum_{n=1}^{\infty} A_n V_n(x, y, z),$$

and consequently, the function $U(x, y, z)$, derived from $V(x, y, z)$ in the same way as V is derived from U, can be expanded in a series of the form

$$U(x, y, z) = \frac{A_0}{\sqrt{x^2 + y^2 + z^2}}$$

$$+ \sum_{n=1}^{+\infty} \frac{A_n}{\sqrt{x^2 + y^2 + z^2}} V_n\left(\frac{x}{x^2 + y^2 + z^2}, \dots\right),$$

provided that $\sqrt{x^2 + y^2 + z^2}$ is greater than a suitable positive number. We then say that *the harmonic function* U *is regular and zero at infinity*. The same is true for a potential of single layer or of double layer (III, **70–71**). Formulas (4) and (16) differ in fact only in notation, for we have noticed (III, **69**) that the nth derivatives of $1/r$ are of the form

$$V_n(x, y, z) (x^2 + y^2 + z^2)^{-n-\frac{1}{2}},$$

where $V_n(x, y, z)$ is a harmonic polynomial and homogeneous of the nth degree.

In a general way, we shall say that a harmonic function $U(x, y, z)$ is *regular at infinity* if there exists a constant C such that the difference $U(x, y, z) - C$ is regular and zero at infinity. This function approaches the value C when the distance of the point (x, y, z) from the origin increases indefinitely.

This being granted, let us consider, for the sake of definiteness, a single closed surface Σ, and let $\mathcal{D}$ be the unbounded domain exterior to Σ. The exterior problem, relative to the surface Σ, is stated thus: *Find a harmonic function in $\mathcal{D}$, regular and* zero *at infinity, assuming on Σ a continuous set of given values.*

Thus stated the problem reduces immediately to the interior problem. Let us suppose, indeed, that the origin is in the interior of the surface Σ, and let us carry out an inversion with the point O as pole and with unity as modulus. The surface Σ is replaced by a closed surface Σ', and the domain $\mathcal{D}$ by the domain $\mathcal{D}'$ interior to Σ'. Moreover, Lord Kelvin's transformation makes correspond to the desired harmonic function $U(x, y, z)$ a function $V(x, y, z)$, harmonic in $\mathcal{D}'$, and assuming on Σ' the known values which are derived from the given values of U on Σ. We shall therefore obtain this function $V(x, y, z)$, and consequently the function $U(x, y, z)$ itself, by solving the interior problem.

We see from this that there is an essential difference between the exterior problem in the case of the plane and in the case of three dimensions. If, in this latter case, we did not impose on the harmonic function $U(x, y, z)$ the condition of being zero at infinity, the problem would be indeterminate.

Indeed, let $U(x, y, z)$ be the harmonic function which gives the solution of the exterior problem, properly so called, for the surface Σ; moreover, let $U_1(x, y, z)$ be the harmonic function in $\mathcal{D}$, regular and zero at infinity, assuming the value *one* on Σ. The function $U(x, y, z) + C[1 - U_1(x, y, z)]$ is harmonic in $\mathcal{D}$, regular at infinity, and assumes the same values as $U(x, y, z)$ on Σ, whatever the constant C; it takes on the value C at infinity. In order for the problem to be completely determined, it is necessary that the value of the desired harmonic function at infinity be given; we obtain the ordinary exterior problem if we choose *zero* for the value of U at infinity. For example, when Σ is a sphere of radius R, all functions

$1 + C[(R/r) - 1]$, where r represents the distance from the center, are harmonic on the exterior, regular at infinity, and assume the value *one* on the sphere; we must take $C = 1$ to have the one which is zero at infinity.

Remark. Let U and V be two functions harmonic on the exterior of Σ, regular and *zero* at infinity. We can again apply formula (11) to these two functions, provided that we represent by d/dn the derivative taken along the *exterior* normal to Σ. Indeed, let S be a sphere having a fixed point O as center and of radius R sufficiently large that the surface Σ is in the interior of this sphere. Since the two functions U and V are harmonic in the domain bounded by S and Σ, we can apply formula (11) to the set of the two surfaces S and Σ. If we now let R increase indefinitely, the double integral taken over S is infinitely small, since U and V are zero at infinity, and since dU/dn and dV/dn are of the order of $1/R^2$.

Let us consider in particular a function $U(x, y, z)$, harmonic on the exterior of Σ, zero at infinity, and the function $1/r$, where r is the distance of the point (x, y, z) from a fixed point $P(a, b, c)$ exterior to Σ. These two functions are regular on the exterior of Σ and of a sphere σ with center P and radius ρ. Let us apply formula (11) to the set of the two surfaces Σ and σ, then let us make the radius ρ of σ approach zero; we shall again verify that $U(a, b, c)$ is given by formula (14), the derivatives being taken along the exterior normal to Σ (cf. Exercise 6, Chap. V).

74. Solution of the problem for the sphere.

The solution of the interior problem for the sphere is given by a formula analogous to Poisson's integral. Let $U(x, y, z)$ be a harmonic function in the interior of a sphere S of radius R, assuming given values on the surface. If the value of dU/dn at each point of the surface is also known, the value of this function at an interior point with coordinates (a, b, c) will be given by formula (14). dU/dn is eliminated by a device exactly like the one in III, **52**.

Let P_1 be the harmonic conjugate point to P with respect to the extremities of the diameter passing through P, and let r_1 be the distance of P_1 from the point (x, y, z). Since the function $1/r_1$ is harmonic in the interior of S, we have the relation

$$(17) \qquad \frac{1}{4\pi} \int \int_{(S)} \left[U \frac{d(1/r_1)}{dn} - \frac{1}{r_1} \frac{dU}{dn} \right] d\sigma = 0.$$

But at each point of the sphere S, we have $r_1/r = R/\rho$, where ρ is the distance of the point P from the center of the sphere.

Adding formulas (14) and (17), after having multiplied the second by $-(R/\rho)$, we obtain the relation

$$(18) \qquad U(a, b, c) = \frac{1}{4\pi} \int \int_{(S)} U \left[\frac{d(1/r)}{dn} - \frac{R}{\rho} \frac{d(1/r_1)}{dn} \right] d\sigma,$$

where the integral no longer depends only upon the value of U on the surface of the sphere. Let ρ_1 be the distance of P_1 from the center of S, and ϕ and ϕ_1 the angles of the interior normal at a point M of the surface S with MP and MP_1. We have the relations

$$\frac{d(1/r)}{dn} = \frac{\cos\phi}{r^2}, \qquad \frac{d(1/r_1)}{dn} = \frac{\cos\phi_1}{r_1^2}, \qquad \rho\rho_1 = R^2, \qquad \frac{r_1}{r} = \frac{R}{\rho},$$

$$\rho^2 = R^2 + r^2 - 2Rr\cos\phi, \qquad \rho_1^2 = R^2 + r_1^2 - 2Rr_1\cos\phi_1,$$

from which we further derive, upon eliminating ϕ, ϕ_1, r_1, ρ_1,

$$\frac{\cos\phi}{r^2} - \frac{R}{\rho}\frac{\cos\phi}{r_1^2} = \frac{R^2 - \rho^2}{Rr^3}$$

and formula (18) becomes

$$(19) \qquad U(a, b, c) = \frac{1}{4\pi} \int \int_{(S)} U \frac{R^2 - \rho^2}{Rr^3} d\sigma.$$

The preceding proof assumes that the interior problem has a solution, and moreover that dU/dn exists on the surface, which is not always the case. We are going to verify directly that *the function* U(a, b, c) *represented by formula* (19) *furnishes the solution of the Dirichlet problem for the sphere*, regardless of what the given continuous function, U, on the sphere is. This formula can, indeed, be written as

$$(20) \quad U(a, b, c) = \frac{1}{2\pi} \int \int_{(S)} U \frac{\cos\phi}{r^2} d\sigma - \frac{1}{4\pi R} \int \int_{(S)} \frac{U}{r} d\sigma,$$

using the relation $R^2 - \rho^2 = 2Rr\cos\phi - r^2$. The second member is the difference between a potential of double layer and a potential of single layer, and hence is a harmonic function. Let K' be the value of the potential of single layer $(1/4\pi R)\int\int(U/r)\,d\sigma$ when the point P coincides with a point M' of the surface of the sphere, and let U' be the given value of U at this point. When point P, interior to the sphere, approaches the point M', the potential of double layer approaches the limit $U' + K'$ (III, **71**), for we have $2R \cos \phi = r$ for any point whatever of the sphere when P coincides with the point M'. Besides, the limit of the second integral is $- K'$, since the potential of single layer is continuous on the surface (III, **70**). The limit of $U(a, b, c)$ is therefore equal to U' when the point P approaches the point M' and formula (20) indeed gives the solution of the *interior* problem. We shall see in the same way that the formula

$$(21) \qquad U(a, b, c) = \frac{1}{4\pi R} \int \int_{(S)} U \frac{\rho^2 - R^2}{r^3} \, d\sigma$$

gives the solution of the *exterior* problem for the sphere.

We deduce from formula (19) the same consequences as from Poisson's integral (III, **52**). If the given function U is positive at every point of the surface of the sphere, $U(a, b, c)$ is also positive for every interior point, and as r varies between $R - \rho$ and $R + \rho$, we shall have two limits for $U(a, b, c)$ upon replacing r by $R - \rho$, and then by $R + \rho$, in the formula; moreover, the integral $\iint_{(S)} U \, d\sigma$ is equal, from the theorem of the mean value, to $4\pi R^2 U_0$, where U_0 is the value of U at the center of the sphere. We therefore have the two inequalities

$$\frac{R(R - \rho)}{(R + \rho)^2} U_0 < U_P < \frac{R(R + \rho)}{(R - \rho)^2} U_0$$

and since U_0 also lies between the two extreme terms, the absolute value of $U_P - U_0$ is less than the difference of these two terms, that is, less than $U_0 \, [R(6R^2\rho + 2\rho^3)/(R^2 - \rho^2)^2]$. The two terms of this fraction are of the third and fourth degree in R, respectively; it therefore approaches zero if, keeping ρ fixed, we let R increase indefinitely. We conclude from this *that a harmonic function in three dimensions which is always positive, is a constant*, and, consequently, that a harmonic function in three dimensions whose absolute value is bounded reduces to a constant (III, **52**). This extension of Liouville's theorem is due to Picard. Harnack's theorem, the proof of which is based upon Poisson's integral, is similarly extended without difficulty to harmonic functions of three variables.

75. Laplace functions. Let us suppose that the sphere S has the origin for its center and is of unit radius. Modifying the notation a little, let us designate by x, y, z the rectangular coordinates of a point P in the interior of the sphere, and by ρ, θ, ψ its spherical coordinates, related to the first set by the relations

$$x = \rho \sin \theta \cos \psi, \qquad y = \rho \sin \theta \sin \psi, \qquad z = \rho \cos \theta.$$

Formula (19) takes the equivalent form

$$(22) \quad U(x, y, z)$$

$$= \frac{1}{4\pi} \int_0^\pi d\theta' \int_0^{2\pi} \frac{1 - \rho^2}{(1 - 2\rho \cos \gamma + \rho^2)^{3/2}} f(\theta', \psi') \sin \theta' \, d\psi';$$

the coordinates of a variable point M of the sphere are $(1, \theta', \psi')$, and $f(\theta', \psi')$ represents the given function U on the surface of the sphere, expressed in terms of the variables θ', ψ'; γ is the angle made by the radius OM with the direction OP, and from the fundamental relation of spherical trigonometry, we have the expression

$$(23) \quad \cos \gamma = \cos \theta \cos \theta' + \sin \theta \sin \theta' \cos (\psi' - \psi)$$

for $\cos \gamma$. Using a formula already proven (I, **184**, formula (31)), we have

$$(24) \quad \frac{1}{\sqrt{1 - 2\rho \cos \gamma + \rho^2}}$$

$$= P_0 + P_1(\cos \gamma)\rho + \ldots + P_n(\cos \gamma)\rho^n + \ldots,$$

P_n being the nth Legendre polynomial. Adding this formula to the one obtained by differentiating with respect to ρ, and multiplying the two members by 2ρ, we get

$$(24') \quad \frac{1 - \rho^2}{(1 - 2\rho \cos \gamma + \rho^2)^{3/2}} = P_0 + 3P_1(\cos \gamma)\rho + \ldots$$

$$+ (2n + 1) P_n(\cos \gamma)\rho^n + \ldots.$$

This series is *uniformly convergent* when the point M describes the sphere S. Indeed, from the formula recalled just now, $P_n(\cos \gamma)$ is equal to the coefficient of ρ^n in the development of the product $(1 - \rho e^{\gamma i})^{-1/2} (1 - \rho e^{-\gamma i})^{-1/2}$. If each of the factors is developed separately, the coefficients of $\rho^p e^{p\gamma i}$ and of $\rho^p e^{-p\gamma i}$ are *positive* numbers, and, consequently, we can only increase the modulus of the coefficient of any power of ρ if we replace $e^{\gamma i}$ and $e^{-\gamma i}$ by unity. The absolute value of the coefficient of ρ^n in the product is therefore less than the coefficient of ρ^n in the development of $(1 - \rho)^{-1}$, that is to say, less than unity. It follows that the terms of series (24') are less in absolute value than the terms of the series $\Sigma (2n + 1) \rho^n$, which is convergent, since we are assuming $\rho < 1$. Multiplying the two members of formula (24)' by $f(\theta', \psi') \sin \theta'$, and integrating term by term, we have

(25) $U(x, y, z)$

$$= \sum_{n=0}^{+\infty} \frac{2n + 1}{4\pi} \rho^n \int_0^\pi d\theta' \int_0^{2\pi} P_n(\cos \gamma) f(\theta', \psi') \sin \theta' \, d\psi'.$$

The polynomial $P_n(\cos \gamma)$ contains only terms in $\cos \gamma$ whose exponents are the same as n; we can therefore transform it into a homogeneous polynomial in $\sin \gamma$, $\cos \gamma$, containing only even powers of $\sin \gamma$. Replacing $\sin^2 \gamma$ by

$$\sin^2 \theta (\cos^2 \psi + \sin^2 \psi) + \cos^2 \theta - \cos^2 \gamma,$$

and $\cos \gamma$ by its expression (23) we see definitely that $P_n(\cos \gamma)$ is an integral and homogeneous function of degree n in $\cos \theta$, $\sin \theta \cos \psi$, $\sin \theta \sin \psi$, whose coefficients are functions of θ' and of ψ'. The coefficient of ρ^n in series (25) is an expression of the same nature, and we thus obtain an expansion of the desired function $U(x, y, z)$, each term of which is a homogeneous polynomial in x, y, z of degree indicated by its subscript. Since the function $U(x, y, z)$ is harmonic, it is clear that all these polynomials are also harmonic. We shall write this development as

(26) $$U(x, y, z) = \sum_{n=0}^{+\infty} (2n + 1) Y_n \rho^n,$$

where Y_n is a homogeneous polynomial of degree n in $\cos \theta$, $\sin \theta \cos \psi$, $\sin \theta \sin \psi$, which is derived from a harmonic and homogeneous polynomial V_n of degree n by replacing in it x, y, z by $\sin \theta \cos \psi$, $\sin \theta \sin \psi$, $\cos \theta$, respectively. These polynomials Y_n are the Laplace functions; from their very definition, there are $2n + 1$ linearly independent functions Y_n of order n.

Formula (26) has been proven only for interior points of the sphere. If the series of the second member is convergent at a point M of the surface, with coordinates $(1, \theta, \psi)$, the function $U(x, y, z)$ has $f(\theta, \psi)$ as a limit when the point P approaches the point M; assuming that point P remains on the radius OM, we therefore have, from Abel's theorem (I, **177**),

$$(27) \qquad f(\theta, \psi) = \sum_{n=0}^{+\infty} (2n + 1) \, Y_n(\theta, \psi),$$

where $Y_n(\theta, \psi)$ is equal to the double integral

$$(28) \qquad Y_n(\theta, \psi) = \frac{1}{4\pi} \int_0^{\pi} d\theta' \int_0^{2\pi} P_n(\cos \gamma) f(\theta', \psi') \sin \theta' \, d\theta'.$$

This formula gives us a development of a continuous function on the surface of a sphere, entirely analogous to the Fourier series for a function of one variable. Leaving aside for the moment the question of convergence, we shall only remark that from what precedes, no matter what the given continuous function on the surface of the sphere may be, we have

$$(29) \qquad f(\theta, \psi) = \lim_{\rho = 1} \left[\sum_{n=0}^{+\infty} (2n + 1) \, Y_n(\theta, \psi) \rho^n \right].$$

Application. Picard has derived from this formula (29) an elegant extension of Weierstrass's theorem (I, **199**) to continuous functions in two variables. Let U be any continuous function on the surface of the sphere S, and $f(\theta, \psi)$ the function obtained by expressing it in terms of the variables θ and ψ. The function represented by series (26) in the interior of the sphere and which is equal to $f(\theta, \psi)$ on its surface, is continuous in this entire closed domain, and consequently, uniformly continuous. Given a positive number ϵ, we can find a number $\rho_1 < 1$ such that the difference

$$f(\theta, \psi) - \sum_{n=0}^{+\infty} (2n + 1) \, Y_n(\theta, \psi) \rho_1^n$$

will be less in absolute value than $\epsilon/3$ for all points of the sphere. Moreover, the series whose general term is $(2n + 1) \, Y_n \rho_1^n$ is itself uniformly convergent, for, from the expression (28) for Y_n, we have

$$|Y_n| < H,$$

where H is the maximum of $|f(\theta, \psi)|$. We can therefore take in this series the sum of a finite number of terms

$$\Phi = Y_0 + 3Y_1 + \ldots + (2n + 1) \, Y_n,$$

which differs from the sum of the series by less than $\epsilon/3$, for any θ and ψ.

Finally, this sum Φ can itself be developed in a power series in θ and ψ, and we can take a finite number of terms in this series, that is, a polynomial $Q(\theta, \psi)$ in θ and ψ such that we have

$$|\Phi - Q(\theta, \psi)| < \epsilon/3$$

for every system of values of θ and ψ taken between 0 and 2π. It is clear that the difference $f(\theta, \psi) - Q(\theta, \psi)$ will be less in absolute value than ϵ for all these sets of values.

If instead of being determined on the entire sphere, the function $f(\theta, \psi)$ is determined on only a part of it, we can always complete this determination on the remainder of the sphere by considering continuity, and this in an infinite number of ways. The preceding conclusion still applies, and we could derive from it, as in I, **199**, that *every continuous function of two variables in the domain A can be represented in this domain by a uniformly convergent series of polynomials.*

76. Properties of the functions Y_n. The polynomials $V_m(x, y, z)$ are the only homogeneous functions which are harmonic in the interior of a sphere with the origin as center. Indeed, every harmonic function in this sphere is developable in a series of polynomials V_m, and it is clear that the sum of this series can be homogeneous only if it reduces to a single term. Over a sphere of center O and radius R, the derivative dV_m/dn taken along the interior normal is equal because of the homogeneity to $-(m/R) V_m$. If we apply formula (11) to two polynomials V_p, V_q ($p \lessgtr q$), in the interior of a sphere with center O, we see that the double integral

$$\int \int V_p V_q \, d\sigma,$$

taken over the surface of the sphere, is zero; this can be written again as

$$(30) \qquad \int_0^\pi \int_0^{2\pi} Y_p(\theta, \psi) \, Y_q(\theta, \psi) \sin \theta \, d\theta \, d\psi = 0. \qquad (p \neq q)$$

Since the harmonic function $V_m(x, y, z) = \rho^m Y_m(\theta, \psi)$ reduces to $Y_m(\theta, \psi)$ on the sphere S of unit radius, we have, according to the general formula (25), if ρ is less than one,

$$\rho^m \, Y_m(\theta, \psi)$$

$$= \sum_{n=0}^{+\infty} \frac{2n + 1}{4\pi} \rho^n \int_0^\pi \int_0^{2\pi} P_n(\cos \gamma) \, Y_m(\theta', \psi') \sin \theta' \, d\theta' \, d\psi',$$

which implies the relations

$$\int_0^\pi \int_0^{2\pi} P_n(\cos \gamma) \, Y_m(\theta', \psi') \sin \theta' \, d\theta' \, d\psi' = 0, \qquad \text{if } m \neq n,$$

$$\int_0^\pi \int_0^{2\pi} P_m(\cos \gamma) \, Y_m(\theta', \psi') \sin \theta' \, d\theta' \, d\psi' = \frac{4\pi}{2m + 1} \, Y_m(\theta, \psi).$$

Comparing these formulas to formula (24), which gives the expansion of $1/r$, we have the conclusion, assuming $\rho < 1$,

$$(31) \qquad \int_0^\pi \int_0^{2\pi} \frac{1}{r} \, Y_m(\theta', \psi') \sin \theta' \, d\theta' \, d\psi' = \frac{4\pi\rho^m}{2m + 1} \, Y_m(\theta, \psi);$$

this equation holds for $\rho = 1$, for the first member, which is a potential of single layer, is a continuous function on the sphere itself. We therefore also have

$$(32) \quad \int_0^\pi \int_0^{2\pi} Y_m(\theta' \, \psi') \, \frac{\sin \theta'}{\sqrt{2 - 2 \cos \gamma}} d\theta' \, d\psi' = \frac{4\pi}{2m + 1} \, Y_m(\theta, \psi),$$

where $\cos \gamma$ is given by formula (23). The potential of single layer due to a layer of density $V_m(\theta', \psi')$, taken over the sphere, is therefore equal in the interior and on the surface of the sphere to $[(4\pi\rho^m)/(2m + 1)] \, Y_m(\theta, \psi)$. (See Exercise 7, Chap. V.)

Conversely, every function $f(\theta, \psi)$, satisfying a relation of the form

$$(33) \qquad \int_0^\pi \int_0^{2\pi} f(\theta', \psi') \, \frac{\sin \theta'}{\sqrt{2 - 2 \cos \gamma}} \, d\theta' \, d\psi' = 4\pi K f(\theta, \psi),$$

where K is a constant factor, is one of the functions $Y_m(\theta, \psi)$. Let us consider, indeed, the potential of single layer

$$V(\rho, \theta, \psi) = \int_0^\pi \int_0^{2\pi} \frac{f(\theta', \psi') \sin \theta'}{r} \, d\theta' \, d\psi',$$

where r stands for the distance of the point with polar coordinates

(ρ, θ, ψ) from the point $(1, \theta', \psi')$ of the sphere. This is a harmonic function in the interior of the sphere which reduces to $4\pi K f(\theta, \psi)$ for $\rho = 1$, from relation (33). Calculating the derivative $\partial V/\partial \rho$ by the usual rule for differentiation, we find, after several easy transformations

$$\rho \frac{\partial V}{\partial \rho} = \int_0^\pi \int_0^{2\pi} f(\theta', \psi') \left(\frac{\cos \phi}{r^2} - \frac{1}{r} \right) \sin \theta' \, d\theta' \, d\psi';$$

the second member is a harmonic function, since it is the difference of two potentials. On the sphere, this function is equal, from the properties of potentials and relation (33), to $2\pi(1 - K) f(\theta, \psi)$. It follows that the difference $\rho(\partial V/\partial \rho) - [(1 - K)/2K]V$ is a harmonic function zero on the surface of the sphere. It is therefore zero at every interior point, and the function V is a homogeneous function of degree $(1 - K)/2K$, which requires that $(1 - K)/2K$ be an integer m, and the function V is a function of the form $C\rho^m Y_m(\theta, \psi)$. The function $f(\theta, \psi)$ is itself identical with $Y_m(\theta, \psi)$, aside from a constant factor.

Remark I. When ρ is greater than one, the second member of (31) must be replaced by $\{4\pi/[(2m + 1) \rho^{m+1}]\} Y_m(\theta, \psi)$, for it is a harmonic function on the exterior of the sphere, according to Lord Kelvin's theorem, is zero at infinity, and assumes the same values as the first member for $\rho = 1$. It is therefore identical with the potential of single layer represented by the first member on the exterior of the sphere.

Remark II. We can also derive from the preceding formulas the value of the potential of double layer

$$W = \int_0^\pi \int_0^{2\pi} \frac{\cos \phi}{r^2} Y_m'(\theta', \psi') \sin \theta' \, d\theta' \, d\psi'$$

for an interior point or for a point exterior to the sphere. In the interior, W is a harmonic function which reduces to

$$2\pi Y_m(\theta, \psi) + \frac{2\pi}{2m + 1} Y_m(\theta, \psi),$$

according to relations (31) and (7), on the sphere itself; it is therefore equal to

$$2\pi \frac{2m + 2}{2m + 1} \rho^m Y_m(\theta, \psi).$$

We should see in the same way that this potential is equal to $-(4\pi m)/(2m + 1) \cdot [Y_m(\theta, \psi)]/\rho^{m+1}$ on the exterior of the sphere. Assuming $m = 0$, we have again the properties of Gauss's integral (III, 71).

77. C. Neumann's method. Neumann's method, which has been set forth in detail for convex contours (III, 57), can be extended without essential modification to convex surfaces.

Given a closed surface S, the principle of Neumann's method for solving the interior problem consists again of representing the harmonic function sought by a potential of double layer

$$\int \int_{(S)} \mu \, \frac{\cos \phi}{r^2} \, d\sigma.$$

The properties of this potential lead for the determination of the unknown function μ to the following functional equation (where we are assuming $\lambda = 1$),

$$(34) \quad \mu(M) = \int \int_{(S)} [\mu(M) - \mu(P)] \, \frac{\cos \phi}{r^2} \, d\sigma + \frac{1}{4\pi} \, U(M);$$

here $F(M)$ represents in general the value of the function F at a point M of the surface; U is the given continuous function on S; r is the distance between the two points M and P of this surface; ϕ is the angle made by the interior normal at P with PM; and the double integral is taken considering the point P as variable and the point M as fixed.

This functional equation is *formally* satisfied if we set

$$(35) \quad \mu(M) = \frac{1}{4\pi} [U_0(M) + \lambda U_1(M) + \ldots + \lambda^n U_n(M) + \ldots],$$

where $U_0(M)$ is equal to the given function $U(M)$, and the succeeding terms are derived from the first recurrently by means of the formula

$$(36) \quad U_m(M) = \frac{1}{4\pi} \int \int_{(S)} [U_{n-1}(M) - U_{n-1}(P)] \, \frac{\cos \phi}{r^2} \, d\sigma,$$

where the double integral is always taken by having the point P describe the surface S. We could prove absolutely as in III, **57** that all these functions U_n are continuous on S. To establish the

convergence of series (35) when the surface is *convex*, we appeal to
two lemmas analogous to those which have been established for a
convex contour.

Lemma I. Given on the convex surface S any two points M_1
and M_2 and a portion S' of this surface, possibly composed of several
separate pieces, the difference between the solid angles which the
various parts of S' subtend when viewed from the points M_1 and
M_2 is less than $2\pi h$, where h is a positive number less than unity
which depends only upon the convex surface.[6] Indeed, for this
difference to be equal to 2π, it would be necessary for S' to subtend
at M_1 a solid angle equal to 2π, that is to say, that S' comprise the
entire surface S, or else be composed of a surface bounded by a
plane face, on which M_1 would be situated. In both cases, the solid
angle which S' subtends from the point M_2 could not be zero unless
S reduced to a pyramid.

Lemma II. Let $F(M)$ be a positive or zero function on S, and J
the double integral

$$J = \int\int_{(S)} F(P) \left[\left(\frac{\cos \phi}{r^2} \right)_1 - \left(\frac{\cos \phi}{r^2} \right)_2 \right] d\sigma,$$

where $[(\cos \phi)/r^2]_1$ designates the cosine of the angle made by the
interior normal at P with the direction PM_1, divided by the square
of PM_1, and $[(\cos \phi)/r^2]_2$ has an analogous meaning.

Let us divide S into two parts S_1, S_2 such that we have

$$\left(\frac{\cos \phi}{r^2} \right)_1 \geqslant \left(\frac{\cos \phi}{r^2} \right)_2$$

[6] Neumann's proof is based on a slightly different lemma. Supposing the
surface S decomposed into two parts S', S'', and α and β any two points on S,
if we represent by $I_{\Sigma}\gamma$ the polyhedral angle which is subtended by the surface Σ
when viewed from the point γ, we have for a non-bi-star-shaped convex surface
the fundamental inequality

$$I_{S'}{}^{\alpha} + I_{S''}{}^{\beta} > 4\lambda\pi,$$

where λ is a *positive* number less than *one* which depends only on S. It is easy
to derive from this the lemma of the text. Let us assume $I_{S''}{}^{\alpha} \geq I_{S''}{}^{\beta}$; since the
sum $I_{S'}{}^{\alpha} + I_{S''}{}^{\alpha}$ is at most equal to 2π, Neumann's inequality gives *a fortiori*

$$2\pi - I_{S''}{}^{\alpha} + I_{S''}{}^{\beta} > 4\lambda\pi \text{ or } I_{S''}{}^{\alpha} - I_{S''}{}^{\beta} < 2\pi (1 - 2\lambda).$$

The factor $1 - 2\lambda$ is certainly less than *one*, and we can also conclude from
this that Neumann's factor λ is less than $\frac{1}{2}$. But the second inequality is applicable also to bi-star-shaped convex surfaces.

on S_1, and $[(\cos \phi)/r^2]_1 < [(\cos \phi)/r^2]_2$ on S_2, and let J_1 and J_2 be the double integrals taken over S_1 and S_2, respectively. We have $J = J_1 + J_2$, and consequently $|J|$ is less than the greater of the two numbers J_1 and $|J_2|$. Let L be an upper limit of $F(M)$; from the preceding lemma, each of these numbers is less than $2h\pi L$. We therefore also have $|J| < 2h\pi L$, whatever the points M_1 and M_2.

This being the case, let L and l be the maximum and the minimum of U on S; since M_1 and M_2 are any two points of S, we can write

$$U_1(M_1) - U_1(M_2) = \frac{1}{4\pi} \left[\quad U(M_1) \int\int_{(S)} \left(\frac{\cos \phi}{r^2}\right)_1 d\sigma \right.$$

$$\left. - U(M_2) \int\int_{(S)} \left(\frac{\cos \phi}{r^2}\right)_2 d\sigma \right]$$

$$+ \frac{1}{4\pi} \int\int_{(S)} [U(P) - l] \left[\left(\frac{\cos \phi}{r^2}\right)_2 - \left(\frac{\cos \phi}{r^2}\right)_1\right] d\sigma$$

$$+ \frac{l}{4\pi} \int\int_{(S)} \left[\left(\frac{\cos \phi}{r^2}\right)_2 - \left(\frac{\cos \phi}{r^2}\right)_1\right] d\sigma.$$

If the points M_1 and M_2 are ordinary points of S, the last integral is zero, and the absolute value of the first term

$$\tfrac{1}{2}[U(M_1) - U(M_2)]$$

is less than $\tfrac{1}{2}(L - l)$. Besides, $U(P) - l$ remains between 0 and $L - l$, and therefore, from the second lemma, the absolute value of the terms of the third line is less than

$$\frac{L - l}{4\pi} 2\pi h = \frac{L - l}{2} h.$$

The absolute value of $U_1(M_1) - U_1(M_2)$ is therefore itself less than $(L - l) \cdot \tfrac{1}{2}(1 + h) = (L - l)\rho$, *where ρ is a positive number less than one.* Since the function $U_1(M)$ is continuous, this inequality holds for all positions of the points M_1 and M_2; therefore, representing by L_1 and l_1 the maximum and the minimum of U_1, we have again $L_1 - l_1 < (L - l)\rho$, and we derive from this step by step that $L_i - l_i < (L - l)\rho_i$, L_i and l_i being the maximum and the minimum of U_i. The argument is completed as in III, **57**.

Remark. C. Neumann's method, applied to the sphere, does not seem to lead at once to formula (19), as in the case of the circle

(III, **57**). However, it is possible to connect the solution obtained directly to this method. The integral equation with whose solution we are concerned can indeed be written

(E) $$\mu(M) + \frac{1}{4\pi R} \int\int_{(S)} \frac{\mu(P)}{r} \, d\sigma = \frac{U(M)}{2\pi},$$

by noticing that we have $2R \cos \phi = r$, where r is the distance between the two points M and P of the surface. Setting

$$\mu(M) = \frac{U(M)}{2\pi} - V(M),$$

this equation becomes

(E') $$2\pi V(M) + \int\int_{(S)} V(P) \frac{d\sigma}{2Rr} = \frac{1}{4\pi R} \int\int_{(S)} U(P) \frac{d\sigma}{r};$$

this is an equation of the same form as the first, where the unknown function is $V(M)$. Now, to have the solution of the Dirichlet problem, it is not necessary to know $V(M)$, but only the potential of double layer

$$\int\int_{(S)} V(P) \frac{\cos \phi}{r^2} \, d\sigma,$$

for any interior point of the sphere. Relation (E') expresses precisely the fact that the value toward which this potential approaches when this interior point approaches a point M of the sphere is equal to the value of the potential of single layer

$$\frac{1}{4\pi R} \int\int_{(S)} U(P) \frac{d\sigma}{r}$$

at this same point. These two harmonic functions, assuming the same values at all points of the sphere, are identical in the interior, and the solution of the Dirichlet problem is represented by the difference between a potential of double layer and a potential of single layer. We have indeed returned to formula (20).

78. Green's function. Given a finite domain D bounded by a surface Σ, composed of one or several distinct closed surfaces, the corresponding Green's function is a function $G(x, y, z; a, b, c)$, zero on Σ, and harmonic in the neighborhood of every point of D, except in the neighborhood of the interior point $P(a, b, c)$, where it is of the form $(1/r) + g(x, y, z; a, b, c)$, the function g being harmonic. Knowledge of this Green's function allows us to solve the interior Dirichlet problem; it is sufficient for this purpose to compare the two formulas

$$U(a, b, c) = \frac{1}{4\pi} \int \int_{(\Sigma)} \left[U \frac{d(1/r)}{dn} - \frac{1}{r} \frac{dU}{dn} \right] d\sigma,$$

$$0 = \frac{1}{4\pi} \int \int_{(\Sigma)} \left[U \frac{d[G - (1/r)]}{dn} - [G - (1/r)] \frac{dU}{dn} \right] d\sigma,$$

from which we derive by combining them, and observing that G is zero on Σ,

$$(37) \qquad U(a, b, c) = \frac{1}{4\pi} \int \int_{(\Sigma)} U \frac{dG}{dn} d\sigma.$$

The proof assumes that the desired harmonic function has continuous partial derivatives on the surface Σ.

In the same way we call a function which is harmonic in the neighborhood of every point exterior to Σ (except in the neighborhood of a point (a, b, c) where it is infinite like $1/r$), is regular and zero at infinity, and zero on Σ, a Green's function for the exterior problem. Formulas (11) and (14) extend to functions harmonic on the exterior of Σ, and zero at infinity—there is nothing to change in the preceding calculations, and formula (37) again furnishes the solution of the exterior problem, with the derivative dG/dn taken along the *exterior* normal.

In the case of a sphere of radius R, let P be a point at a distance d from the center, P_1 be the harmonic conjugate point to P with respect to the extremities of the diameter passing through P, and r and r_1 the distances of a point M from the points P and P_1, respectively. For the interior problem, the Green's function is

$$\frac{1}{r} - \frac{R}{d} \frac{1}{r_1}, \text{ and } \frac{1}{r} - \frac{R}{d} \frac{1}{r_1}$$

for the exterior problem. In the first case, we have $d < R$, and $d > R$ in the second case.

Applying the general formula (37) to this particular case, we find again the results established directly in III , **74**.

We can also extend the definition of Green's function to linear equations in three variables, more general than Laplace's equation, as has been done in the case of two variables (III, **67**). The two equations[7]

$$(38) \qquad \mathscr{F}(u) = \Delta u + a\frac{\partial u}{\partial x} + b\frac{\partial u}{\partial y} + c\frac{\partial u}{\partial z} + gu = 0,$$

$$(39) \qquad \mathscr{G}(v) = \Delta v - \frac{\partial(av)}{\partial x} - \frac{\partial(bv)}{\partial y} - \frac{\partial(cv)}{\partial z} + gv = 0,$$

are adjoints of one another and give rise to the identity

$$(40) \qquad v\mathscr{F}(u) - u\mathscr{G}(v) = \frac{\partial}{\partial x}\left(v\frac{\partial u}{\partial x} - u\frac{\partial v}{\partial x} + auv\right)$$

$$+ \frac{\partial}{\partial y}\left(v\frac{\partial u}{\partial y} - u\frac{\partial v}{\partial y} + buv\right)$$

$$+ \frac{\partial}{\partial z}\left(v\frac{\partial u}{\partial z} - u\frac{\partial v}{\partial z} + cuv\right).$$

Let us assume the two functions u and v are regular in a finite domain D and continuous, with continuous first order partial derivatives, on the surface Σ which bounds this domain. We infer from identity (40) the new relation

$$\int\int\int_{(D)} [v\mathscr{F}(u) - u\mathscr{G}(v)]\, dx\, dy\, dz$$

$$+ \int\int_{(\Sigma)} \left(v\frac{\partial u}{\partial x} - u\frac{\partial v}{\partial x} + auv\right) dy\, dz + \ldots = 0,$$

where the double integral is taken over the *interior* side of the surface Σ. Let α, β, γ be the angles made by the interior normal with

[7] The equation $\mathscr{F}(u) = 0$ does not represent the general form of a linear equation of elliptic type in three variables. Given an equation of this type, there does not exist in general any choice of independent variables permitting the reduction of the equation to form (38). The condition for the possibility of this reduction resulted from the investigations of Cotton (Thesis, 15–17).

the axes; the preceding formula takes the simpler form

$$(41) \quad \int \int \int_{(D)} [v \mathscr{F}(u) - u \mathscr{G}(v)] \, dx \, dy \, dz$$

$$+ \int \int_{(\Sigma)} \left(v \frac{du}{dn} - u \frac{dv}{dn} \right) d\sigma$$

$$+ \int \int_{(\Sigma)} (a \cos \alpha + b \cos \beta + c \cos \gamma) \, uv \, d\sigma = 0.$$

This being the case, let $u(x, y)$ be an integral of the equation

$$\mathscr{F}(u) = f(x, y, z),$$

regular in the domain D, and let v be an integral of the adjoint equation

$$\mathscr{G}(v) = 0,$$

regular in the domain D, except in the neighborhood of a point (a, b, c) of this domain where it has the form $(1/r) + V$, U and V being regular functions and $U(a, b, c)$ being equal to one;[8] r always represents the distance of a point (x, y, z) from the point (a, b, c). We can apply the general formula (41) to the domain D', bounded by Σ and by a sphere S of center (a, b, c) and very small radius ρ. Making the radius ρ approach zero, the surface integral taken over S has again as its limit

$$4\pi u(a, b, c)$$

(III, **72**) and, passing to the limit, formula (41) gives us

(42)

$$\left\{ \begin{array}{l} u(a, b, c) = \\[2mm] -\dfrac{1}{4\pi} \displaystyle\int \int_{(\Sigma)} \left[v \dfrac{bu}{dn} - u \dfrac{dv}{dn} + (a \cos \alpha + b \cos \beta + c \cos \gamma) \, uv \right] d\sigma \\[4mm] -\dfrac{1}{4\pi} \displaystyle\int \int \int_{(D)} vf(x, y, z) \, dx \, dy \, dz. \end{array} \right.$$

[8] Solutions of this form have been obtained by Holmgren (*Arkiv. för Matematik*, Vol. 1, 1903). See also the paper by Hadamard referred to above.

This formula will permit us to solve the Dirichlet problem if the integral $v(x, y, z; a, b, c)$ is zero on Σ. We could similarly extend to mixed problems related to this equation the general considerations which have been set forth above for an equation in two variables (III, **68**).

II. NEWTONIAN POTENTIAL

We have already made use several times of potentials of single layer or of double layer. We are going to summarize quickly the principal properties of the Newtonian potential, which will be utilized in the sequel; the extension of these properties to the logarithmic potential does not present any difficulty.

79. Potential of volume. Let D be a finite domain in three dimensions, bounded by one or several closed surfaces S, $\mu(x, y, z)$ be a continuous function in this domain, and r be the distance of a variable point $M(x, y, z)$ from a fixed point $P(a, b, c)$. The function represented by the triple integral

$$(43) \quad V(a, b, c) = \int\int\int_{(D)} \frac{\mu(x, y, z)}{r}\, dx\, dy\, dz = \int\int\int_{(D)} \frac{\mu}{r}\, dv$$

is a continuous function, as are all its partial derivatives of any order, of the coordinates (a, b, c) of the point P in every region of space having no point in common with D; besides, it is a harmonic function, like the function $1/r$ itself (III, **27**). The partial derivatives of this function

$$(44) \quad \begin{cases} \dfrac{\partial V}{\partial a} = \int\int\int_{(D)} \mu\, \dfrac{x - a}{r^3}\, dv, \qquad \dfrac{\partial V}{\partial b} = \int\int\int_{(D)} \mu\, \dfrac{y - b}{r^3}\, dv, \\[4mm] \qquad\quad \dfrac{\partial V}{\partial c} = \int\int\int_{(D)} \mu\, \dfrac{z - c}{r^3}\, dv \end{cases}$$

are equal, aside from a constant factor, to the components of the attraction which is exerted on a material point of mass one located at P by a mass of variable density $\mu(x, y, z)$ distributed in the domain D, where it is assumed that the attraction occurs according to Newton's law; this explains the name of Newtonian potential given to the function $V(a, b, c)$.[9]

Integrals (43) and (44) still have meaning when the point P is in the domain D; it is sufficient to verify that these integrals, taken over the interior of a sphere with center at P, have a finite value.

Indeed, if we replace the rectangular coordinates by the spherical coordinates r, θ, ψ, where the point P is taken as the origin, integral (43) taken over the sphere becomes

$$(43') \qquad \int_0^\rho dr \int_0^\pi d\theta \int_0^{2\pi} \mu(a + r \sin\theta \cos\psi, \ldots) \, r \sin\theta \, d\psi,$$

where ρ is the radius of the sphere; the first of integrals (44) is similarly written

$$(44') \qquad \int_0^\rho dr \int_0^\pi d\theta \int_0^{2\pi} \mu(a + r \sin\theta \cos\psi, \ldots) \cos\psi \sin^2\theta \, d\psi.$$

---

[9] For an attraction properly so called, μ is essentially positive; if it is a matter of electrical action, μ can be positive or negative.

Let us consider an indefinite homogeneous line and let μ be the mass of a unit length. A portion AB of this line exerts on a point P outside the line an attraction which is in the plane PAB, and whose components are easy to calculate. When the two points A and B move apart indefinitely in opposite directions, the component parallel to the line becomes zero, while the normal component approaches a limit, independent of the manner in which A and B recede indefinitely, and this limit is in inverse ratio to the distance of the point from the line. In a general way, we can say that the components of the attraction exerted by an indefinite homogeneous line on a point P with coordinates (a, b, c) are equal, aside from a constant factor, to the partial derivatives with respect to a, b, c of the function $\mu \log (1/r)$, where r is the distance of the point P from the line. Similarly, the attraction of an indefinite solid cylinder on a point has a fixed value if we assume the density μ constant all along a parallel to the generatrices. Let us suppose that we have taken the Oz axis parallel to the generatrices, while the xy-plane is the perpendicular plane passing through the attracted point. The section of the cylinder by the xy-plane is a closed curve C, bounding a domain D. Decomposing this domain into elements of surface, and the cylinder itself into infinitely small cylinders having these surface elements as bases, we see that the components of the attraction exerted on the point P with coordinates (a, b) are equal, aside from a constant factor, to the partial derivatives with respect to a and b of the double integral $\iint_{(D)} \mu \log (1/r) \, dx \, dy$. This is a logarithmic potential of surface, which is thus found to be related to the Newtonian volume potential. Logarithmic potentials of single layer or of double layer can, in an analogous manner, be associated with Newtonian potentials of the same type.

We see that these integrals do not have any infinite element. If H is an upper bound of $|\mu|$ in the domain D, the absolute value of integral (43') is clearly less than $2\pi H\rho^2$.

Generally, the triple integral $\iiint (\mu/r)\, dv$, taken over a domain D' containing the point P and whose longest diameter is less than l, is itself less in absolute value than $2\pi Hl^2$, for this domain D' is interior to a sphere of radius l with the point P as center. We deduce from this that the triple integral (43) is uniformly convergent in the neighborhood of every point P_0 interior to the domain D, or on its boundary. Indeed, if with point P_0 as center we describe a sphere Σ of radius ρ, the triple integral $\iiint (\mu/r)\, dv$, taken over the volume bounded by this sphere, is less in absolute value than $8\pi H\rho^2$, for any interior point P of Σ. We conclude from this that the potential $V(a, b, c)$ is a continuous function everywhere in space (III, **48**). We see in the same way that the integral (44') is less in absolute value than $4\pi H\rho$, and consequently the integral $\iiint \mu [(x-a)/r^2]\, dv$, taken over a domain D' enclosing the point P and whose longest diameter is less than l, is itself less in absolute value than $4\pi Hl$. It is again a consequence that the integrals (44) are uniformly convergent in the neighborhood of every point P_0 interior to D, or on the boundary of D, and consequently these integrals are continuous functions of the coordinates (a, b, c) in the entire space.

Formulas (44) are still true in the domain D. We shall establish this for the first one, returning once more to classical reasoning. Given a point P of the domain D, with coordinates (a, b, c), let us draw about this point as center a sphere Σ of radius ρ, which decomposes D into two domains, D_1, D_2, one interior to the sphere, the other exterior. Let P_1 be a point with coordinates $(a + \Delta a, b, c)$ taken in D_1; calling r_1 the distance of this point P_1 from a variable point M, we can write

(45)

$$\begin{cases} V(a + \Delta a, b, c) - V(a, b, c) - \int\int\int_{(D)} \mu\, \frac{x-a}{r^3}\, dv \\ = \frac{\Delta V_1}{\Delta a} - \int\int\int_{(D_1)} \mu\, \frac{x-a}{r^3}\, dv + \left[\frac{\Delta V_2}{\Delta a} - \int\int\int_{(D_2)} \mu\, \frac{x-a}{r^3}\, dv \right], \end{cases}$$

where V_1 and V_2 represent the potentials relative to the domains

D_1 and D_2, respectively. Let us develop $(\Delta V_1)/\Delta a$:

$$\frac{\Delta V_1}{\Delta a} = \frac{1}{\Delta a} \int \int \int_{(D_1)} \mu(x, y, z)\left(\frac{1}{r_1} - \frac{1}{r}\right) dv$$

$$= \frac{1}{\Delta a} \int \int \int_{(D_1)} \mu(x, y, z)\frac{r - r_1}{r r_1} dv.$$

Observing that we have

$$|r - r_1| \leq |\Delta a|, \qquad \frac{1}{r r_1} < \tfrac{1}{2}\left(\frac{1}{r^2} + \frac{1}{r_1{}^2}\right),$$

we see that the absolute value of $\Delta V_1/\Delta a$ is less than

$$\delta = \frac{H}{2} \int \int \int_{(D_1)} \left(\frac{1}{r^2} + \frac{1}{r_1{}^2}\right) dv;$$

now it is easy to verify by using spherical coordinates that the integral $\int\int\int(dv/r^2)$, taken over a domain lying entirely in the interior of a sphere of radius l having P as its center, is less in absolute value than $4\pi l$. The number δ is therefore smaller than

$$\frac{H}{2}(4\pi\rho + 8\pi\rho) = 6\pi H\rho.$$

The sum of the first two terms of the second member of formula (45) is therefore less in absolute value than

$$4\pi H\rho + 6\pi H\rho = 10\pi H\rho.$$

This granted, let us choose first of all the number ρ in such a way that $10\pi H\rho$ will be smaller than $\tfrac{1}{2}\epsilon$, ϵ being an arbitrary positive number. The integral V_2 is thus a continuous function of the coordinates of the point P in the domain D_1, whose derivative is equal to

$$\int \int \int_{(D_2)} \mu\frac{x - a}{r} dv.$$

The last term of the second member of formula (45) therefore approaches zero with Δa, and, completing the argument as usual, we conclude from this that the first member also has zero for its limit. Formulas (44) which give *the first derivatives* of the potential therefore apply throughout three-dimensional space.

80. Poisson's formula. Differentiating formulas (44) again, we obtain triple integrals without meaning when the point P is in the domain D. To establish the existence of second derivatives, we first of all transform the integrals which represent the first derivatives by means of Green's formula. Let $P_0(a_0, b_0, c_0)$ be an interior point of D, and Σ a sphere with P_0 as center and having a radius ρ small enough to be entirely within the domain D; we shall again call the two portions of D separated by Σ D_1 and D_2, and the corresponding potentials V_1 and V_2. The potential $V_2(a, b, c)$ is a harmonic function in the interior of Σ. As to the potential $V_1(a, b, c)$, we have just seen that it has continuous first derivatives in this domain. Observing that we have

$$\mu \, \frac{x - a}{r^3} = - \frac{\partial}{\partial x} \left(\frac{\mu}{r} \right) + \frac{\partial \mu}{\partial x} \frac{1}{r},$$

we can write $\partial V_1/\partial a$, for example,

$$\frac{\partial V_1}{\partial a} = \int \int \int_{(D_1)} \frac{\partial \mu}{\partial x} \frac{dv}{r} - \int \int_{(\Sigma)} \frac{\mu}{r} \, dy \, dz,$$

applying the first Green's formula for triple integrals (I, **149**), where the double integral is taken over the exterior side of Σ. The triple integral of the second member represents a potential and, consequently, has continuous first derivatives everywhere in space. The same is true of the function represented by the surface integral when the point (a, b, c) is in the interior of Σ. The potential $V(a, b, c)$ therefore has continuous second derivatives in the entire domain D, boundaries excluded, since P_0 is any interior point whatever of D. Let us calculate ΔV for the point P_0; at this point $\Delta V_2 = 0$ and, consequently, $\Delta V = \Delta V_1$. The customary formulas for differentiation give us

$$(\Delta V_1)_0 = \int \int \int_{(D_1)} \left(\frac{\partial \mu}{\partial x} \frac{x - a_0}{r_0^3} + \frac{\partial \mu}{\partial y} \frac{y - b_0}{r_0^3} + \frac{\partial \mu}{\partial z} \frac{z - c_0}{r_0^3} \right) dv$$

$$- \int \int_{(\Sigma)} \mu \left(\frac{x - a_0}{r_0^3} \, dy \, dz + \frac{y - b_0}{r_0^3} \, dz \, dx + \frac{z - c_0}{r_0^3} \, dx \, dy \right),$$

where r_0 is the distance of the point P_0 from a variable point M. The first member is independent of the radius ρ; it is therefore sufficient to seek the limit of the second member when ρ approaches zero. Now, if we designate by K an upper bound of the absolute value of the partial derivatives of μ, the absolute value of the triple integral is, from an earlier remark, less than $12K\pi\rho$, and, therefore approaches zero with ρ. As to the surface integral, we have $r_0 = \rho$ on Σ, and $(x - a_0)/\rho$, $(y - b_0)/\rho$, $(z - c_0)/\rho$ represent precisely the direction cosines of the exterior normal. This integral reduces to

$$- \frac{1}{\rho^2} \int \int_{(\Sigma)} \mu(x, y, z) \, d\sigma$$

$$= - \int_0^\pi \int_0^{2\pi} \mu(a_0 + \rho \sin \theta \cos \psi, \ldots) \sin \theta \, d\theta \, d\psi,$$

and it is clear that it has for its limit

$$- \mu(a_0, b_0, c_0) \int_0^\pi \int_0^{2\pi} \sin \theta \, d\theta \, d\psi,$$

or $- 4\pi\mu_0$. For every point (a, b, c), *in the interior of the domain* D, we therefore have the relation among the second derivatives of the potential

$$(46) \qquad \Delta V = \frac{\partial^2 V}{\partial a^2} + \frac{\partial^2 V}{\partial b^2} + \frac{\partial^2 V}{\partial c^2} = - 4\pi\mu(a, b, c);$$

this is *Poisson's formula* which includes, if we wish, Laplace's formula as a special case. Indeed, it is sufficient to take $\mu(a, b, c) = 0$ at an exterior point to have once again the relation $\Delta V = 0$, which is applicable at all exterior points of the domain D. It is a consequence of comparing these two formulas that the second derivatives, or at least some of them, must become discontinuous when we cross the boundary S of the domain D. It is also important to observe that the preceding proof assumes that the density $\mu(x, y, z)$ has derivatives which are continuous, or at least bounded and integrable.[10]

All the preceding properties can be extended without difficulty to the logarithmic potential which we shall write, replacing $1/r$ by $\log 1/r$, as

$$V(a, b) = \int \int_{(D)} \mu(x, y) \log \frac{1}{r} \, dx \, dy,$$

[10] Poisson's formula has been extended by various geometers to more general cases. See, for example, two papers by Petrini [*Acta mathematica*, Vol. XXXI, 1908, p. 127; *Journal de Liouville*, 6th series, Vol. V, 1909, p. 117].

where the double integral is taken over a domain D in two dimensions of the plane, in which $\mu(x, y)$ is a continuous function; $V(a, b)$ is a continuous function, as are its first partial derivatives, in the entire plane, and its derivatives are obtained by applying the ordinary formula for differentiation under the integral sign. On the exterior of D, V is harmonic; in the interior of D, it has continuous second derivatives which satisfy the relation

(47) $$\Delta V = \frac{\partial^2 V}{\partial a^2} + \frac{\partial^2 V}{\partial b^2} = -2\pi\mu(a, b).$$

Summing up, the potential $V(a, b, c)$ is a function of the three variables (a, b, c) possessing the following properties:

1. It is continuous and has continuous first partial derivatives throughout space, and it vanishes at infinity (this point is established as in III, 70):

2. It is harmonic on the exterior of a finite domain D, bounded by one or several closed surfaces;

3. In the interior of D, it possesses continuous second derivatives which satisfy Poisson's relation $\Delta V = -4\pi\mu$.

These properties completely characterize the function $V(a, b, c)$. Indeed, let $V_1(a, b, c)$ be the potential due to the action of masses of density $\mu(x, y, z)$, distributed over the domain D. The difference $V - V_1$ is continuous everywhere in space, as are its first partial derivatives, and it is harmonic at every point of space, except perhaps on the surfaces S. But we have proven above (III, 72) that the second derivatives remain continuous on these surfaces, so that $V - V_1$ is harmonic in the entire space and, since this difference is zero at infinity, it is identically zero.

We can, in certain cases, make use of these properties to facilitate the calculation of the potential. For example, let us suppose that we wished to calculate the potential of a homogeneous sphere of density μ and of radius R. The function V, defined by the equations

$$V = 2\pi\mu \left(R^2 - \frac{d^2}{3} \right)$$

in the interior of the sphere,

$$V = \frac{4}{3}\pi\mu \frac{R^2}{d}$$

on the exterior, where d is the distance of the point P from the center, satisfies the same conditions as the potential we are seeking. It is continuous, as are its first derivatives, and zero at infinity; on the exterior of the sphere, we have $\Delta V = 0$ and $\Delta V = 4\pi\mu$ in the interior. It is therefore identical with this potential. Lejeune-Dirichlet has given a less elementary example by calculating synthetically the potential due to the attraction of a homogeneous ellipsoid (*Journal de Crelle*, Vol. 32).

81. Gauss's formula. From Poisson's formula we easily derive the value of the integral

$$\int\int_{(\Sigma)} \frac{dV}{dn}\, d\sigma,$$

taken over any closed surface Σ, the derivative dV/dn being taken along the *exterior* normal. Let us assume, for the sake of definiteness, that the domain in the interior of Σ is decomposed into only two parts, a domain D_1 which is part of D and a domain D_2 exterior to D. The domain D_1 is bounded by a part Σ_1 of Σ and by a part S' of the surfaces S which bound D. The domain D_2 is itself bounded by S' and by a portion Σ_2 of Σ. Green's formula (10), applied to the domain D_1, taking account of Poisson's formula and making $\phi = 1, \psi = V$, gives us

$$\int\int_{(\Sigma_1)} \frac{dV}{dn_1}\, d\sigma + \int\int_{(S')} \frac{dV}{dn_1}\, d\sigma = -4\pi \int\int\int_{(D_1)} \mu\, dv,$$

where dV/dn_1 represents the derivative along the exterior direction of the normal; since V is harmonic in D_2, we have besides

$$\int\int_{(\Sigma_2)} \frac{dV}{dn_2}\, d\sigma + \int\int_{(S')} \frac{dV}{dn_2}\, d\sigma = 0,$$

where dV/dn_2 has an analogous meaning. But on account of the continuity of the first derivatives of V, we have all along S'

$$\frac{dV}{dn_1} + \frac{dV}{dn_2} = 0;$$

adding the preceding formulas, we have

$$(48) \qquad \int\int_{(\Sigma)} \frac{dV}{dn}\, d\sigma = -4\pi M,$$

where M is equal to the triple integral

$$\int \int \int_{D_1} \mu \, dv,$$

that is, equal to the sum of the attracting masses contained in the interior of Σ.

82. Normal derivatives of a potential of single layer. The potential of single layer can be regarded as a limiting case of the volume potential. Let us consider the volume contained between a surface Σ and an infinitely close parallel surface at a distance ϵ from the first, and let us assume this volume to be filled with matter whose density ρ is the same all along a common normal. An element of this volume formed by the portions of the normals drawn at all points of an element $d\sigma$ of Σ can be expressed as $\epsilon d\sigma$. If we now allow ϵ to decrease indefinitely at the same time that δ increases in such a way that the product $\delta\epsilon$ approaches a limit μ at each point, the potential due to the action of the preceding volume becomes in the limit a surface integral

$$\int \int_{(\Sigma)} \frac{\mu}{r} d\sigma;$$

this is what justifies the name of *potential of single layer* given to this integral. The number μ is the surface density of this layer. The general properties of this potential have been established above; it only remains for us to study the discontinuity of the derivatives when we cross Σ.

Let us assume that the surface Σ is closed, and let M_0 be an ordinary point of this surface. On the normal at M_0 let us take two infinitely close points P_i, P_e on both sides of M_0. The derivatives of the potential at these two points, taken in the interior direction of the normal at M_0, respectively approach limits, which we shall represent by dV_i/dn_i and dV_e/dn_i, when the points P_i and P_e approach M_0 indefinitely.[11] Let us take the point M_0 as the origin of

[11] From the mean value formula, dV_i/dn_i is the limit of the ratio $[V(P_i) - V(M_0)]/M_0P_i$ when the point P_i approaches the point M_0 along the interior normal, while dV_e/dn_i is the limit of the ratio $[V(M_0) - V(P_e)]/M_0P_e$ when P_e approaches M_0 along the exterior normal. Generally, when a point P with coordinates a, b, c approaches M_0, the derivatives $\partial V/\partial a$, $\partial V/\partial b$ approach limits which are the same, whether the point P is interior or exterior to Σ; only the derivative $\partial V/\partial c$ has two different limits, if we have taken the z-axis parallel to the normal at M_0 (see Poincaré, *Le potentiel newtonien*).

coordinates, the direction of the interior normal for the positive direction of the z-axis, and two perpendicular lines of the tangent plane for the x- and y-axis; we shall suppose that the portion of Σ nearby to M_0 is representable in cylindrical coordinates by an equation of the form $z = \rho^{i+\alpha} f(\rho, \omega)$, where α is positive and the function f is continuous with continuous partial derivatives $\partial f/\partial \rho$, $\partial f/\partial \omega$ in the neighborhood of the origin. These conditions are certainly satisfied when z has continuous second derivatives in the neighborhood of the origin. The formulas for change of variable show at once that the derivatives p and q are of the form $\rho^{\alpha} f_1(\rho, \omega)$, where f_1 is continuous for $\rho = 0$.

The derivative dV/dz at any point P of the z-axis, interior or exterior to Σ, has the expression

$$(49) \qquad \frac{dV}{dz} = \int \int_{(\Sigma)} \mu \, \frac{\cos \psi_1}{r^2} \, d\sigma,$$

where ψ_1 is the angle made by the direction Pz with the direction PM, going from P to any point whatever M of Σ. If the point P coincides with the point M_0 itself, this integral becomes

$$(50) \qquad V'_0 = \int \int_{(\Sigma)} \mu \, \frac{\cos \psi}{r_0^2} \, d\sigma,$$

where r_0 is the distance of M_0 from any point M of Σ, and ψ is the angle made by the interior normal at M_0 with the direction M_0M. To make certain that this integral has a finite value, it is sufficient to consider a small portion Σ' of Σ surrounding the origin and projecting onto the xy-plane into the interior of a closed curve γ. An element of the integral (50) taken over Σ' can be written, using polar coordinates, as $[\pi(\rho, \omega) \, d\rho \, d\omega]/\rho^{1-\alpha}$, the function $\pi(\rho, \omega)$ being bounded in the neighborhood of the origin. It does not follow that dV/dz has V'_0 as a limit when the point P approaches the point M_0, for nothing substantiates the continuity of this integral in the neighborhood of the point M_0. We are going to show, on the contrary, that it has a discontinuity at this point similar to that of a potential of double layer. To this end, let us consider the auxiliary integral

$$(51) \qquad I = \int \int_{(\Sigma)} \left(\mu \, \frac{\cos \psi_1}{r^2} + \mu_0 \, \frac{\cos \phi}{r^2} \right) d\sigma,$$

where ϕ is the angle made by the interior direction of the normal at M with MP; using reasoning exactly similar to that in III, 49 and

71, we are going to prove first of all that this integral is continuous for the point M_0. To do this, let us consider the trihedron having any point M of Σ as its vertex, and the direction MP, the interior direction MN of the normal at M, and the parallel Mz' to the z-axis for its edges. The angle of MP with Mz' is $\pi - \psi_1$, the angle of MP and of MN is ϕ; let us call the angle of MN and of Mz', θ, and Ω the plane angle of the dihedral angle which has MN as an edge; we have, from the fundamental formula of spherical trigonometry,

$$\cos (\pi - \psi_1) = \cos \theta \cos \phi + \sin \theta \sin \phi \cos \Omega,$$

and the integral I can be written

$$(52) \qquad I = - \int \int_{(\Sigma)} (\mu \cos \theta - \mu_0) \frac{\cos \phi}{r^2} d\sigma$$

$$- \int \int_{(\Sigma)} \mu \sin \phi \cos \Omega \frac{\sin \theta \, d\sigma}{r^2}.$$

The first double integral of the second member is continuous at the point M_0; if, indeed, we consider the potential of double layer

$$\int \int \frac{\nu \cos \phi}{r^2} d\sigma,$$

where $\nu = \mu \cos \theta$, this double integral is nothing but

$$- \int \int_{(\Sigma)} (\nu - \nu_0) \frac{\cos \phi}{r^2} d\sigma,$$

and we have proven above that this integral is continuous at the point M_0 (III, **49**, **71**). To prove that the same is true of the second integral, it is sufficient to prove that this integral is uniformly convergent in the neighborhood of the point M_0 (III, **48**), or that the integral

$$\int \int \frac{\sin \theta}{r^2} d\sigma,$$

taken over an infinitely small portion Σ' of Σ, surrounding the origin, is itself infinitely small. Now, if we go over to polar coordinates, an element of this integral is of the form $\rho^{\alpha-1} \pi(\rho, \omega) \, d\rho \, d\omega$, the function $\pi(\rho, \omega)$ being bounded. The integral taken over an infinitely small domain is therefore itself infinitely small.

This point being won, let us assume first of all that the point

P of the z-axis is an interior point P_i; the limit of the integral I when this point P_i approaches the origin is clearly $(dV_i/dn_i) + 4\pi\mu_0$; on the contrary, if the point P is an exterior point P_e, the limit will be dV_e/dn_i. Finally, if the point P is the point M_0 itself, I is equal to $V'_0 + 2\pi\mu_0$. Equating these three numbers, we obtain the desired values

(53)
$$\begin{cases} \dfrac{dV_i}{dn_i} = -2\pi\mu_0 + \int\int_{(\Sigma)} \mu\,\dfrac{\cos\psi}{r_0^2}\,d\sigma, \\[4mm] \dfrac{dV_e}{dn_i} = 2\pi\mu_0 + \int\int_{(\Sigma)} \mu\,\dfrac{\cos\psi}{r_0^2}\,d\sigma; \end{cases}$$

these relations[12] can also be written (suppressing the subscript on r_0) as

(54)
$$\begin{cases} \dfrac{dV_e}{dn_i} - \dfrac{dV_i}{dn_i} = 4\pi\mu_0, \\[4mm] \dfrac{dV_e}{dn_i} + \dfrac{dV_i}{dn_i} = 2\int\int_{(\Sigma)} \mu\,\dfrac{\cos\psi}{r^2}\,d\sigma. \end{cases}$$

We have for the normal derivatives of a logarithmic potential of single layer $V = \int_C \mu \log(1/r)\,ds$ at a point M_0 of the curve C (III, **49**) entirely similar formulas which are established in the same way:

(55)
$$\begin{cases} \dfrac{dV_i}{dn_i} = -\pi\mu_0 + \int_{(C)} \mu\,\dfrac{\cos\psi}{r}\,ds, \\[4mm] \dfrac{dV_e}{dn_i} = \pi\mu_0 + \int_{(C)} \mu\,\dfrac{\cos\psi}{r}\,ds, \end{cases}$$

where r is the distance of M_0 from a variable point M of C, and ψ is the angle made by M_0M with the interior direction of the normal at M_0.

83. Newtonian potential of double layer. We shall show again how the theory of magnetism leads to surface integrals which are called *potentials of double layer* (III, **71**). Let us imagine a layer of

---

[12] The second of these relations (54) was reestablished by Plemelj in 1904 *Monatshefte für Mathematik und Physik*).

positive density μ distributed over a surface Σ and a layer of negative density $-\mu'$ distributed over a parallel surface Σ', at an infinitely small distance ϵ from the first. The normals to Σ drawn around the contour of an element $d\sigma$ of Σ cut out on the surface Σ' a surface element $d\sigma'$; we shall assume that μ' has been chosen in such a way that we have constantly $\mu\, d\sigma = \mu'\, d\sigma'$. The sum of the potentials of these two layers at an exterior point P is equal to the surface integral

$$\int\int_{(\Sigma)} \mu d\sigma \left(\frac{1}{r} - \frac{1}{r'}\right),$$

where r and r' are the distances of the point P from the elements $d\sigma$ and $d\sigma'$. If the distance ϵ approaches zero, and if at the same time the density μ increases in such a way that the product $\mu\epsilon$ remains equal to μ_1, this integral has as limit the double integral

$$\int\int_{(\Sigma)} \mu_1 \frac{d(1/r)}{dn}\, d\sigma,$$

where the derivative d/dn is taken in the direction of the normal which goes from Σ to Σ'. We have once again the expression which we have taken as the definition of a potential of double layer.

The normal derivative of this potential behaves in quite a different manner from that of a potential of single layer, when we cross the surface Σ. Let M_0 be a point of Σ; P, P' two nearby points on the normal at M_0, on different sides of this point and at the same distance h from this point. The derivatives

$$\left(\frac{dW}{dn}\right)_P, \quad \left(\frac{dW}{dn}\right)_{P'},$$

taken in a fixed direction chosen on the normal at M_0 do not necessarily approach a limit when h approaches zero, but we have shown that *their difference approaches zero with* h.

Comments and Exercises

1. Derive from the formula which gives the solution of the Dirichlet problem for the sphere the value of the surface integral

$$\int\int_S \frac{d\sigma}{r^3},$$

where r represents the distance from a fixed point P, interior or exterior to the sphere S, to a variable point M of the sphere.

2. Prove by an inversion that formula (19) can be written

$$U(a, b, c) = \frac{1}{4\pi} \int \int_{(S)} U' \frac{d\sigma}{Rr},$$

where U' is the given value of U at the point M' of the sphere where the line MP again intersects the sphere (cf. Exercise 4, Chap. V).

3. Given a homogenous cylinder of density μ, of radius R, and of altitude h, calculate the potential of volume for a point of the axis, and the derivative of this potential in the direction of this axis. Derive from this the discontinuity of the derivative of a potential of single layer due to a homogeneous circular layer, by making h approach zero and μ increase in such a way that μh has a limit μ'.

4. *Poincaré's lemma.* Let S be a sphere of radius R and center at O, A be an exterior point, and P an interior point. Assuming the point A to be fixed, $1/AP$ is a harmonic function of the coordinates of the point P interior to S, and consequently we have, from formula (19), this chapter,

$$(1) \qquad \Delta = \frac{1}{AP} - \int \int_S \frac{1}{AM} \frac{R_2 - \overline{OP}^2}{4\pi R.\overline{PM}^3} d\sigma = 0.$$

The same formula (10), where we have assumed $U = 1$, gives us the relation

$$(2) \qquad \int \int_S \frac{R^2 - \overline{OP}^2}{4\pi R.\overline{PM}^3} d\sigma = 1.$$

Finally, let us consider the point P as fixed and the point A as variable; the difference Δ becomes zero at every point of S, from the continuity of the potential of single layer. This difference Δ is harmonic in the interior of S, except at the point P where it is equal to $+\infty$. Being zero on the sphere, it is therefore positive at every interior point. Combining all these results, we obtain the following proposition on which Poincaré's method of "balayage" is based:

Given a unit mass located at a point P *in the interior of a sphere, if we distribute this mass over the entire surface of the sphere in such a way that the density at any point* M *of it is inversely proportional to the cube of* MP, *the spherical layer thus obtained will have the same potential as the original mass at every exterior point and a smaller potential at every interior point.*

CHAPTER VII

THE HEAT EQUATION

Linear equations of parabolic type partake at one and the same time of the properties of equations of elliptic type and those of hyperbolic type. I shall restrict myself in this chapter to explaining the principal properties of the equation of heat propagation, in which we have already been interested several times[1] (III, **30, 31, 32**).

84. General remarks. Particular integrals. The partial differential equation

$$(1) \qquad \qquad \mathscr{F}(u) = \frac{\partial^2 u}{\partial x^2} - \frac{\partial u}{\partial y} = 0$$

is, among equations of two variables of parabolic type, the analogue of Laplace's equation among equations of elliptic type. In this chapter, we shall represent by $u(x, y)$ any integral of this equation; similarly $v(x, y)$ will represent an integral of the adjoint equation

---

[1] Since Fourier, this equation has been the subject of a large enough number of papers:

Poisson, *Théorie mathématique de la chaleur*, Chap. VI, Paris, 1835.

Schläfli, *Journal de Crelle*, Vol. 72.

Betti, *Memorie delle Soc. italiana delle Scienze*, 3rd series, Vol. I.

Appell, *Journal de Liouville*, 4th series, Vol. VIII.

Volterra, *Leçons professées à Stockholm* (Upsala, 1906).

The principal problems with boundary conditions have been solved in various works, due principally to Holmgren and E.-E. Levi. The last sections of this chapter (**88, 90, 91**) are essentially taken almost completely from the works of M. Holmgren.

General equations of parabolic type have been studied in important papers by E. Levi (*Annali di Matematica*, 1908), H. Block (*Arkiv. de Stockholm*, Vol. V), M. Gevrey (*Journal de Mathématiques*, 6th series, Vol. IX, 1913; Vol. X, 1914; *Ann. de l'École Normale supérieure*, 3rd series, Vol. XXXV, 1918).

(III, **41**) which here is

$$(2) \qquad \mathscr{G}(v) = \frac{\partial^2 v}{\partial x^2} + \frac{\partial v}{\partial y} = 0.$$

These two equations have a single family of characteristics, which consists of parallels to the x-axis. We shall say that one of these functions, $u(x, y)$ or $v(x, y)$, is *regular* in a domain D if it is continuous and has continuous first partial derivatives in this domain. It will even be sufficient to say that the derivative with respect to y is continuous; for if $\partial u/\partial y$, for example, is a continuous function, equation (1) proves that the same is true of $\partial^2 u/\partial x^2$ and, consequently, of $\partial u/\partial x$.

Since equation (1) has constant coefficients, it possesses particular integrals of the form $e^{ax + by}$, (III, **27**); the relation between a and b is, in this case, $b = a^2$.[2] From the integral $e^{ax + a^2 y}$ thus obtained we can derive any infinity of others by taking its successive derivatives with respect to the parameter a, or, what amounts to the same thing, by taking the successive coefficients of the expansion of this integral, in powers of a. Let us write this expansion in the form

$$(3) \qquad e^{ax+a^2 y} = 1 + \sum_{n=1}^{+\infty} \frac{n^n}{n!} V_n(x, y);$$

$V_n(x, y)$ is a polynomial of degree n in x, y, homogeneous in x and $\sqrt{y}$,

$$(4) \qquad \begin{cases} V_n(x, y) = x^n + n(n-1)\, x^{n-2} y + \cdots \\[2mm] \qquad + \dfrac{n(n-1)\ldots(n-2p+1)}{p!}\, x^{n-2p} y^p + \cdots \end{cases}$$

which is terminated by a term in $y^{\frac{1}{2}n}$ if n is even and by a term in $xy^{\frac{1}{2}(n-1)}$, if n is odd. These polynomials V_n are integrals of equation (1), from their very definition. We can easily verify this by observing that equation (3), differentiated with respect to x and to y, gives the relations

$$(5) \qquad \frac{\partial V_n}{\partial x} = n V_{n-1}, \qquad \frac{\partial V_n}{\partial y} = n(n-1)\, V_{n-2},$$

---

[2] Replacing a by αi, we again find the integrals $e^{-\alpha^2 y} \cos \alpha x$, $e^{-\alpha^2 y} \sin \alpha x$ (III, **31**).

from which we deduce immediately that V_n satisfies equation (1). Every polynomial U_n of degree n in x, y, satisfying this equation (1), *is a linear combination with constant coefficients of the polynomials $V_0 = 1, V_1, \ldots, V_n$.* Indeed, every polynomial which satisfies (1) is completely determined if the coefficients of the terms free of y are known, since by means of equation (1) and those which are derived from it by differentiation, we can express all the derivatives of an integral in terms of only derivatives taken with respect to x. If then we choose the coefficients $C_0, C_1, \ldots, C_n$ in such a way that the polynomial

$$C_0 V_0 + C_1 V_1 + \ldots + C_n V_n$$

has the same terms free of y as U_n has, these polynomials are necessarily identical.

The polynomials $V_n(x, y)$ are readily expressed in terms of the Hermite polynomials $P_n(z)$, defined by the equality

$$\frac{d^n}{dz^n} \left(e^{-z^2} \right) = e^{-z^2} P_n(z).$$

Indeed, let us write the formula which gives the development of $e^{-(z + h)^2}$, dividing both members by e^{-z^2}.

$$e^{-2hz - h^2} = 1 + \sum_{n=1}^{+\infty} \frac{h^n}{n!} P_n(z);$$

in order to identify the first member with the first member of formula (3), it is sufficient to replace h by $a\sqrt{-y}$ and z by $-x/(2\sqrt{-y})$. Writing that the second members of the two formulas are identical after this transformation, we obtain the following expression for $V_n(x, y)$:

$$V_n(x, y) = (-y)^{\frac{1}{2}n} P_n \left(\frac{-x}{2\sqrt{-y}} \right).$$

Rolle's theorem proves easily that the equation $P_n(z) = 0$ has its n roots real and distinct, equal two by two in absolute value. It follows that the equation $V_n(x, y) = 0$ represents $n/2$ parabolas if n is even, $(n - 1)/2$ parabolas and the y-axis if n is odd.

It is evident that equation (1) is not changed in form by the change of variables $x' = kx + \alpha$, $y' = k^2 y + \beta$, whatever the constants k, α, β. If $u(x, y)$ is an integral, the same is therefore true of

$u(kx + \alpha, k^2 y + \beta)$. There also exists for equation (1) a transformation analogous to an inversion, which is defined by the formulas

$$x' = \frac{x}{y}, \qquad y' = \frac{1}{y}, \qquad u = \frac{u'}{\sqrt{y}} \, e^{-x^2/4y} \, ;$$

making the calculation, we find that equation (1) is replaced by an equation of the same form[3] $\partial^2 u'/\partial x'^2 = \partial u'/\partial y'$. Therefore, if $u(x, y)$ is an integral of equation (1), the same is true of the function

$$\frac{1}{\sqrt{y}} \, e^{-x^2/4y} \, u\left(\frac{x}{y}, -\frac{1}{y}\right).$$

85. Analytic integrals. We are first of all going to complete what has already been said (III, **15**) about analytic integrals of equation (1), while restricting ourselves at the same time to the real domain. Let $u(x, y)$ be an analytic integral holomorphic in the neighborhood of a point (x_0, y_0), which reduces for $x = x_0$ to a holomorphic function $\phi(y)$, and whose derivative $\partial u/\partial x$ is equal to $\psi(y)$ for the same value of x. The expansion of $u(x, y)$ in powers of $x - x_0$ is, as we have already seen,

$$(6) \quad u(x, y) = \phi(y) + \frac{(x - x_0)}{1} \psi(y) + \frac{(x - x_0)^2}{1 \cdot 2} \phi'(y)$$

$$+ \frac{(x - x_0)^3}{1 \cdot 2 \cdot 3} \psi'(y) + \ldots + \frac{(x - x_0)^{2n}}{(2n)!} \phi^{(n)}(y)$$

$$+ \frac{(x - x_0)^{2n+1}}{(2n + 1)!} \psi^{(n)}(y) + \ldots .$$

In order to transform this series (6) into a double power series T, it will be sufficient to replace $\phi(y)$ and $\psi(y)$ and their derivatives by their expansions in powers of $y - y_0$. Let R be the radius of the smaller circle of convergence of the two power series in $y - y_0$; since r is any positive number whatever less than R, the series

---

[3] Appell has proven that all transformations of the form

$$x' = \phi(x, y), \qquad y' = \psi(x, y), \qquad u = \lambda(x, y)u',$$

by which equation (1) is changed into itself, reduce to combinations of simple transformations (*Journal de Mathématiques,* 4th series, Vol. VIII, 1892, p. 187).

$\phi(y)$ and $\psi(y)$ have as a dominant function an expression

$$\frac{M}{1 - \dfrac{y - y_0}{r}}.$$

If therefore we replace in series (6) $\phi(y)$ and $\psi(y)$ by this function the double series T' thus obtained will certainly dominate the double series T derived from (6) without any modification.

The auxiliary array T' is absolutely convergent provided the absolute value of $y - y_0$ is less than r. Indeed, let us replace $x - x_0$ and $y - y_0$ by their absolute values, and let us group together the terms of same degree in $|x - x_0|$; it is clear that the coefficients of $|x - x_0|^{2n}$ and of $|x - x_0|^{2n+1}$ will be, respectively,

$$\frac{Mn!}{(2n)! \left[1 - \dfrac{|y - y_0|}{r}\right]^{n+1} r^n}, \qquad \frac{Mn!}{(2n + 1)! \left[1 - \dfrac{|y - y_0|}{r}\right]^{n+1} r^n}$$

and therefore this array is absolutely convergent for any x if we have $|y - y_0| < r$. Since the number r can be taken as close to R as we like, we conclude from this that the double series

$$(7) \qquad u(x, y) = \sum a_{ik} (x - x_0)^i (y - y_0)^k,$$

which represents the function $u(x, y)$ in the neighborhood of the point (x_0, y_0), is absolutely convergent in the strip B of the xy-plane bounded by the two characteristics $y = y_0 + R$, $y = y_0 - R$. It cannot be convergent in a wider strip since at least one of the power series which represent $\phi(y)$ and $\psi(y)$ is divergent outside of the interval $(y_0 - R, y_0 + R)$. Let x_1 be any value of x; the functions $u(x_1, y)$, $[\partial u(x_1, y)]/\partial x_1$ can be expanded in power series in $y - y_0$, which are certainly convergent in the interval $(y_0 - R, y_0 + R)$; we obtain them in fact by replacing x by x_1 in $u(x, y)$ and $\partial u/\partial x$. They cannot both be convergent in a larger interval, for, reasoning in reverse order, we would derive from this that the series $\phi(y)$ and $\psi(y)$ were themselves convergent in a wider interval. As a result of this remark, in the study of the analytic extension of the function $u(x, y)$ defined by series (7), we can give to the variable x any constant value whatever and consider u as a function of the single variable y. Let us assume that the two functions $\phi(y)$ and $\psi(y)$ can be extended analytically in an interval (α, β) containing the first

$(y_0 - R, y_0 + R)$, by giving *real* values to y: then the integral $u(x, y)$ is analytic and regular in the strip bounded by the characteristics $y = \alpha$, $y = \beta$, but it cannot be extended analytically outside this strip, at least if we exclude complex values for the variable y. Moreover, it may happen that one of the numbers α, β or both at once, is infinite; in this latter case, the integral is holomorphic in the entire plane. This would occur, for example, if we took

$$\phi(y) = \frac{1}{1 + y^2}, \qquad \psi(y) = 0.$$

The study of analytic integrals raises another question. An integral of this nature is determined if we are given the function $F(x)$ to which it reduces for a given value of y, for $y = 0$, say. This function $F(x)$ is necessarily an entire function of x, but it is not any entire function. To find a characteristic property, let us write its development in powers of x:

$$(8) \quad F(x) = \phi(0) + x\psi(0) + \frac{x^2}{1 \cdot 2} \phi'(0) + \frac{x^3}{1 \cdot 2 \cdot 3} \psi'(0) + \cdots$$

$$+ \frac{x^{2n}}{(2n)!} \phi^{(n)}(0) + \frac{x^{2n+1}}{(2n + 1)!} \psi^{(n)}(0) + \cdots,$$

where $\phi(y)$ and $\psi(y)$ always represent the functions to which u and $\partial u / \partial x$ reduce for $x = 0$. The letters M and r have the same meaning as just above; hence $F(x)$ has as a dominant function the series

$$F_1(x) = M[1 + x + \frac{x^2}{1 \cdot 2 \cdot r} + \frac{x^3}{1 \cdot 2 \cdot 3 \cdot r} + \cdots$$

$$+ \frac{n!}{(2n)!} \frac{x^{2n}}{r^n} + \frac{n!}{(2n + 1)!} \frac{x^{2n+1}}{r^n} + \cdots].$$

This new series has its terms respectively less than those of the series $L(1 + x) e^{Kx^2}$, provided that the two numbers L and K satisfy the inequalities

$$L > \frac{M(n!)^2}{(2n)! \, (Kr)^n},$$

whose second member is the general term of a convergent series if K has been so chosen that $4Kr$ is less than 1. The function $F(x)$ itself therefore has as a dominant function an expression of the form $L(1 + x) e^{Kx^2}$, where L and K are two positive numbers.

Conversely, if a power series $F(x)$ satisfies this condition, equation (1) possesses a holomorphic integral in the neighborhood of the origin which reduces to $F(x)$ for $y = 0$. If this solution exists, we have for $u(0, y)$, $(\partial u/\partial x)_0$ the developments in powers of y (III, **15**)

$$\phi(y) = F(0) + \frac{F''(0)}{1 \cdot 2} y + \ldots + \frac{F^{(2n)}(0)}{n!} y^n + \ldots,$$

$$\psi(y) = F'(0) + F'''(0) y + \ldots + \frac{F^{(2n+1)}(0)}{n!} y^n + \ldots,$$

and it is sufficient to prove that these two power series have a radius of convergence different from zero. Now the first, for example, has as dominant function the series

$$L \sum \frac{(2n)!}{(n!)^2} K^n y^n,$$

which is convergent if we have $|4Ky| < 1$, and the same is true of the second. To sum up, *in order for equation* (1) *to have a holomorphic integral in the neighborhood of the origin reducing, for* y = 0, *to an entire function* F(x), *it is necessary and sufficient that* F(x) *have a dominant function of the form*

$$L(1 + x) e^{Kx^2},$$

where L *and* K *are two positive numbers.*

This condition can be replaced by another where only the order of the size of the coefficients of the series $F(x)$ is involved (see Exercise 1).

Let us also note that if the two functions $\phi(y)$, $\psi(y)$ are holomorphic in the real interval (α, β), series (6) represents the integral in every strip bounded by the lines $y = \alpha$, $y = \beta$. On the contrary, series (7) is in general convergent only in a narrower strip contained in the first one.

86. Fundamental solution. The transformations defined at the end of III, **84** make possible the derivation from the integral

$u(x, y) = 1$ of an integral depending upon the two arbitrary parameters ξ, η,

$$u(x, y) = \frac{1}{\sqrt{y - \eta}}\, e^{-[(x-\xi)^2/4(y-\eta)]}$$

which plays relative to equation (1) a role analogous to that of log r in the theory of harmonic functions. We can also derive it from the particular integral $e^{-\alpha^2(y-\eta)}\cos \alpha\,(x - \xi)$, which depends upon the three parameters α, ξ, η, by a quadrature (cf. III, 30). This function has a real value only if $y > \eta$; but it is convenient for what follows to make the following convention. We shall represent by $U(x, y; \xi, \eta)$ the function defined by the equalities

$$(9) \quad \begin{cases} U(x, y; \xi, \eta) = \dfrac{1}{\sqrt{y - \eta}}\, e^{-[(x-\xi)^2/4(y-\eta)]} & \text{for } y > \eta, \\[2mm] U(x, y; \xi, \eta) = 0 & \text{for } y \leqq \eta. \end{cases}$$

The function thus defined is an integral of equation (1) which is regular for all systems of real values of x and y, except at the point $(x = \xi,\ y = \eta)$; indeed, every partial derivative of the function $u(x, y)$ is a sum of terms of the form

$$\frac{P(x)}{(y - \eta)^{n+\frac{1}{2}}}\, e^{-[(x-\xi)^2/4(y-\eta)]},$$

where $P(x)$ is a polynomial, and this expression approaches zero at the same time as $y - \eta$, provided that $x - \xi$ does not also approach zero.

Considered as a function of (ξ, η), $U(x, y; \xi, \eta)$ is similarly an integral of the adjoint equation, regular in the entire plane except at the point $\xi = x, \eta = y$, and identically zero for $\eta \geqslant y$. Differentiating U any number of times with respect to x, y, ξ, η, we obtain new functions $U^{(i)}\,(x, y; \xi, \eta)$ which have the same properties as the function U. Each of these functions, considered as a function of the pair of variables (x, y), is a solution of equation (1), regular in the entire plane except at the point $x = \xi, y = \eta$; considered as a function of (ξ, η), it is a solution of the adjoint equation

$$\frac{\partial^2 v}{\partial \xi^2} + \frac{\partial v}{\partial \eta} = 0,$$

having in the entire plane the sole singular point $\xi = x, \eta = y$. All these functions are identically zero if $\eta \geqslant y$.

From the fundamental solution $U(x, y; \xi, \eta)$ we can also derive by quadratures new integrals analogous to the logarithmic potential of single layer. Let $P(\xi, \eta)$, $Q(\xi, \eta)$ be any two continuous functions of the coordinates (ξ, η) of a point M along an arc of the curve C, and lying in the finite part of the plane. The line integral

$$(10) \qquad u(x, y) = \int_C U(x, y; \xi, \eta) [P(\xi, \eta)\, d\xi + Q(\xi, \eta)\, d\eta]$$

represents an integral of equation (1) which is regular, as are all its partial derivatives, in every domain D having no point in common with the curve C; we can, in fact, apply the customary formulas of differentiation any number of times if the point (x, y) remains in the domain D. Let us remark that from the definition of $U(x, y; \xi, \eta)$ we must take for the calculation of $u(x, y)$ only that portion of the arc C lying below the characteristic passing through the point (x, y). It follows that below the characteristic passing through the point of C of minimum ordinate, $u(x, y)$ is zero; the same is true for all points of this characteristic which do not belong to C. Above a characteristic $y = y_0$, having the arc C entirely below, $u(x, y)$ is a holomorphic analytic function of the two variables x, y. Indeed, let us regard for a moment x and y as complex variables; if ξ, η represent the coordinates of any point of the arc C, $U(x, y; \xi, \eta)$ is a holomorphic function of the variables x and y whatever the domain is in which the complex variable x ranges, provided that the real part of y is greater than y_0 (we take for $\sqrt{y - \eta}$ the positive determination when y is real). It follows that $u(x, y)$ represents a holomorphic function of the two variables x, y above the characteristic $y = y_0$.[4]

In order to study what $u(x, y)$ becomes when the point (x, y) approaches a point M of the contour C, it is necessary to make hypotheses on the form of this contour.

87. Poisson's formula. We shall first study the case where the curve C is a segment of the characteristic. The definite integral

$$(11) \qquad u(x, y) = \int_a^b \frac{\phi(\xi)}{\sqrt{y - h}}\, e^{-[(x-\xi)^2/4(y-h)]}\, d\xi,$$

where $\phi(\xi)$ is a continuous function in the interval (a, b), represents,

---

[4] It is sufficient to return to the reasoning of II, 1, Chap. V, observing that the hypothesis that F is analytic with respect to the variable of integration plays no part in the proof.

from the properties already established, an integral of equation (1), which is regular at every point of the plane not lying on the segment *AB* of the characteristic $y = h$, bounded by the two points *A* and *B*, with abscissas a and b. We assume, for the sake of definiteness, that $a < b$. This function $u(x, y)$ is zero at every point below the characteristic $y = h$, and at every point of this characteristic outside of the segment *AB*. In the portion of the plane lying above, it is a holomorphic function of the variables x, y. It remains for us to investigate what the limit of $u(x, y)$ is when the point (x, y), assumed above *AB*, approaches a point of this segment. We shall rely for this purpose on several lemmas of frequent use in this theory.

Let $F(u)$ be a continuous function, or at least bounded and integrable, and having only discontinuities of the first kind in an interval (a, b). Let us propose finding the limit of the integral

$$(12) \qquad I = \int_a^b \frac{F(u)}{\sqrt{y}}\, e^{-(u^2/4y)}\, du$$

when the *positive* number y approaches zero.

First case. Let us suppose first of all that a and b are both positive or both negative, for example $0 < a < b$. If M is an upper limit of $|F(u)|$ in the interval (a, b), we clearly have

$$|I| < \frac{M}{\sqrt{y}}\, (b - a)\, e^{-(a^2/4y)},$$

and this expression approaches zero with y. We therefore have $\lim I = 0$.

Second case. Let us assume that one of the limits is zero, for example $a = 0$, $b > 0$. Let β be a positive number less than b such that $|F(u) - F(+ 0)|$ is less than a given number η in the interval $(0, \beta)$; we can choose β small enough that the number η itself is smaller than any preassigned number. We can write

$$I = F(+ 0) \int_0^\beta e^{-(u^2/4y)}\, \frac{du}{\sqrt{y}}$$

$$+ \int_0^\beta [F(u) - F(+ 0)]\, e^{-(u^2/4y)}\, \frac{du}{\sqrt{y}} + \int_0^\beta \frac{F(u)}{\sqrt{y}}\, e^{-(u^2/4y)}\, du,$$

or again, setting $u = 2t\sqrt{y}$ in the first two integrals,

$$I = F(+\,0) \int_0^{\beta/2\sqrt{y}} 2e^{-t^2}\,dt$$

$$+\,2 \int_0^{\beta/2\sqrt{y}} [F(2\sqrt{y}t) - F(+\,0)]\,e^{-t^2}\,dt$$

$$+ \int_\beta^b \frac{F(u)}{\sqrt{y}}\,e^{-(u^2/4y)}\,du.$$

From the way in which we have chosen the number β, the absolute value of the second integral is less than

$$2\eta \int_0^{+\infty} e^{-t^2}\,dt = \eta\,\sqrt{\pi}.$$

Let us suppose β taken in such a way that $\eta\,\sqrt{\pi} < \epsilon$, where ϵ is a preassigned positive number; this number β being thus fixed, let us make y decrease indefinitely: the first integral has $\sqrt{\pi}\,F(+\,0)$ as its limit, and the second has zero as its limit. It is therefore possible to find a positive number h such that we have

$$|I - \sqrt{\pi}\,F(+\,0)| < \epsilon,$$

when $y < h$ and, consequently, I has the limit $\sqrt{\pi}\,F(+\,0)$. We should see similarly that when a is zero and $b < 0$, the limit of I is $-\sqrt{\pi}\,F(-\,0)$.

Third case. Let us suppose that a and b have different signs, for example, $a < 0$, $b > 0$. We have

$$I = \int_0^b \frac{F(u)}{\sqrt{y}}\,e^{-(u^2/4y)}\,du - \int_0^a \frac{F(u)}{\sqrt{y}}\,e^{-(u^2/4y)}\,du;$$

the two integrals of the second member have the limits $\sqrt{\pi}\,F(+\,0)$, $-\sqrt{\pi}\,F(-\,0)$, respectively. The limit of I is therefore

$$\sqrt{\pi}\,[F(+\,0) + F(-\,0)].$$

In particular, if the function $F(u)$ is continuous for $u = 0$, the limit of I is $2\sqrt{\pi}\,F(0)$.

That granted, let us seek the limit of integral (11) when the point (x, y), above AB, is approached by a point with coordinates (x_0, h) of this segment $(a < x_0 < b)$. We shall first suppose that the point (x, y) moves on a parallel to Oy. We have to find the limit of the integral

$$\int_a^b \frac{\phi(\xi)}{\sqrt{y-h}} e^{-[(x_0-\xi)^2/4(y-h)]} \, d\xi = \int_{a-x_0}^{b-x_0} \frac{\phi(x_0 + u)}{\sqrt{y-h}} e^{-[u^2/4(y-h)]} \, du$$

when $y - h$ approaches zero. The limit $a - x_0$ is negative, the other one, $b - x_0$ is positive; if $\phi(\xi)$ is continuous at the point x_0, the limit is, we have just seen, $2\sqrt{\pi} \, \phi(x_0)$. At the extremities A and B of the segment, the limit will be $\sqrt{\pi} \, \phi(a)$ or $\sqrt{\pi} \, \phi(b)$.

Let us now suppose that the point (x, y) approaches an interior point (x_0, h) of the segment AB in *any* manner. The integral whose limit we must find can be written

$$\int_{a-x}^{b-x} \frac{\phi(x + u)}{\sqrt{y-h}} e^{-[u^2/4(y-h)]} \, du$$

$$= \int_{a-x}^{b-x} \frac{\phi(x_0)}{\sqrt{y-h}} e^{-[u^2/4(y-h)]} \, du$$

$$+ \int_{a-x}^{b-x} \frac{\phi(x + u) - \phi(x_0)}{\sqrt{y-h}} e^{-[u^2/4(y-h)]} \, du;$$

the first integral of the second member can be put in the form

$$(13) \qquad 2 \int_{(a-x)/(2\sqrt{y-h})}^{(b-x)/(2\sqrt{y-h})} \phi(x_0) \, e^{-t^2} \, dt$$

and has the limit $2\sqrt{\pi} \, \phi(x_0)$ when x approaches the number x_0 *contained between* a *and* b and when y approaches h.

As to the second integral, it is easy to prove that it approaches zero by decomposing it as follows:

$$\int_{a-x}^{-\epsilon} + \int_{-\epsilon}^{\epsilon} + \int_{\epsilon}^{b-x},$$

where ϵ is a very small positive number. Let η be an upper limit of $|\phi(x + u) - \phi(x_0)|$, when x varies from $x_0 - \epsilon$ to $x_0 + \epsilon$ and u from $-\epsilon$ to $+\epsilon$; the absolute value of the second integral is less than $2\eta \sqrt{\pi}$ and, consequently, can be made smaller than any given positive number by taking ϵ small enough. This number ϵ having been chosen in this manner, we prove as above that the first and the third integrals approach zero when $y - h$ approaches zero and x approaches x_0.

It is to be noted that the proof no longer applies when the point (x, y) approaches one of the extremities of the segment AB, for integral (13) is indeterminate when x approaches a and y approaches h; the limit of this integral depends upon the manner in which the point (x, y) approaches the point A (see Exercise 2).

To sum up, the value of the definite integral

$$(14) \qquad u(x, y) = \frac{1}{2\sqrt{\pi}} \int_a^b \frac{\phi(\xi)}{\sqrt{y - h}} e^{-[(x-\xi)^2/4(y-h)]} \, d\xi$$

approaches $\phi(x_0)$ when the point (x, y) approaches in any manner the point (x_0, h) of the interior of the segment AB of the characteristic, while staying above this segment.

Integral (14) retains a meaning when one of its limits becomes infinite, provided that the function $\phi(\xi)$ satisfies certain conditions. If there exists a positive number K such that the product

$$\phi(\xi) \, e^{-K\xi^2}$$

is bounded for all values of ξ from a to $+ \infty$, the definite integral

$$(15) \qquad \frac{1}{2\sqrt{\pi}} \int_a^{+\infty} \frac{\phi(\xi)}{\sqrt{y - h}} e^{-[(x-\xi)^2/4(y-h)]} \, d\xi$$

has a meaning when the point (x, y) remains in a bounded domain D lying between the two characteristics $y = h + \epsilon$, $y = h + (1 - H)/4K$, where H is a positive number less than 1.

Any element whatever of the integral is, in fact, less in absolute value than the corresponding element of the integral

$$(16) \qquad \frac{1}{2\sqrt{\pi}} \int_a^{+\infty} \frac{M}{\sqrt{y - h}} e^{-[(H\xi^2+2x\xi-x^2)/4(y-h)]} \, d\xi,$$

where M is an upper limit of $|\phi(\xi)\,e^{-K\xi^2}|$. Now the auxiliary integral (16) is uniformly convergent in the domain D; the same is therefore true of the integral (15), which consequently represents a solution of equation (1) regular below the line $y = h + (1 - H)/4K$, except on the part of the line $y = h$ which extends from the point (a, h) to infinity in the positive direction. This function is zero below this characteristic and on the part to the left of the point (a, h). Above the characteristic it is holomorphic in x and y. When the point (x, y) approaches a point with the coordinates (x_0, h), where $x_0 > a$, the limit of integral (15) is equal to $\phi(x_0)$, for we can divide the integral in two, one taken from a up to a number $b < x_0$, the other taken from b to $+\infty$. The first, we have just seen, has the limit $\phi(x_0)$, while the second approaches zero. Retaining the same hypotheses on the function $\phi(\xi)$, the conclusions clearly can be extended to the integral $\int_{-\infty}^{a}$ and consequently to the integral[5]

$$(17) \qquad u(x, y) = \frac{1}{2\sqrt{\pi}} \int_{-\infty}^{+\infty} \frac{\phi(\xi)}{\sqrt{y - h}} e^{-[(x-\xi)^2/4(y-h)]} \, d\xi;$$

where $\phi(\xi)$ is a continuous function such that $\phi(\xi) \, e^{-K\xi^2}$ remains bounded; the definite integral (17) represents a solution of equation (1) which is holomorphic in the strip bounded by the characteristics

$$y = h, \qquad y = h + \frac{1}{4K},$$

and which approaches $\phi(x_0)$ when the point (x, y) of this strip approaches the point (x_0, h) of the characteristic; the number H can, in fact, be assumed as small as we wish.

If the product $\phi(\xi) \, e^{-K\xi^2}$ is bounded for any positive constant K, the function $u(x, y)$ is holomorphic in every region lying above the characteristic $y = h$. This is so in particular if the function $\phi(\xi)$ is itself bounded. We could extend these properties to the case where $\phi(\xi)$ has discontinuities of the first kind, but, at a point of discontinuity x_0 $u(x, y)$ does not necessarily approach $\phi(x_0)$ when the point (x, y) approaches the point (x_0, h); it always approaches this limit when the point (x, y) approaches the point of discontinuity along a parallel to Oy.

Formula (17) gives the general solution of a problem in the theory of heat, a special case of which we have already treated (III, **31**). Given a homogeneous filament, indefinite in both directions, of very slender section, let us suppose that the temperature $\phi(x)$ of a cross section with abscissa x, at time h, is known, and that we ask for the temperature of any cross section at a later time. Representing the time by the letter y, the required temperature is a function $u(x, y)$ of the variables x and y which, by a suitable choice of units, satisfies equation (1); this function must be regular in the entire part of the xy-plane lying above the line $y = h$, and must reduce to $\phi(x)$ for $y = h$. From its physical significance, the function $\phi(x)$ is clearly bounded, and consequently the function $u(x, y)$ represented by formula (17) satisfies all the stated conditions. We shall see later

---

[5] One proceeds in the same manner to prove rigorously that formula (28) of III, **30** represents the desired integral when the function $f(x, y, z)$ remains bounded.

(III, **89**) that it is the only one. This permits us to generalize the remark made above (III, **31**) in the particular case when the function ϕ is periodic; the function $u(x, y)$ which expresses the temperature of the cross section with abscissa x at a time y_1 subsequent to the time h is an entire function of x which cannot be taken arbitrarily.

Remark. We established above (III, **15**) by means of certain hypotheses on the function $F(x)$ a formula which represents an integral of equation (1) reducing for $y - h$ to the function $F(x)$. Poisson has shown that this formula and formula (17) can be derived one from the other. Let us assume, for simplification, that $h = 0$; formula (17) becomes, setting $\xi = x + 2\sqrt{y}\, t$,

$$u(x, y) = \frac{1}{\sqrt{\pi}} \int_{-\infty}^{+\infty} \phi(x + 2\sqrt{y}\, t)\, e^{-t^2}\, dt.$$

Let us replace $\phi(x + 2\sqrt{y}\, t)$ by its expansion in powers of $2\sqrt{y}\, t$; the general term of the integral has the expression

$$\frac{2^n y^{\frac{1}{2}n} \phi^{(n)}(x)}{n!\sqrt{\pi}} \int_{-\infty}^{+\infty} t^n\, e^{-t^2} dt.$$

If n is odd, this term is zero; supposing n even, let us replace n by $2n$. Taking account of an earlier formula, this term reduces to $[y^n \phi^{(2n)}(x)]/n!$, and we have the formula of III, **15**, in which we have replaced F by ϕ, and y_0 by zero.

Despite all the interest of this transformation, the argument is clearly lacking in rigor. Moreover, the two formulas are very far from being equivalent. The first assumes that $F(x)$ is an entire function of a certain kind and gives us the value of u on both sides of the characteristic $y = y_0$. On the contrary, formula (17) by no means assumes the function $\phi(x)$ to be analytic, but it is applicable only above the line $y = h$.

88. Integrals analogous to the potential. Let us now take for the path of integration an arc AB represented by the equation

$$x = \chi(y),$$

the function $\chi(y)$ being continuous in the interval (a, b), with $a < b$. The function $\phi(y)$ being continuous in the same interval, we have seen that the definite integral

$$(18) \qquad \Phi(x, y) = \int_a^y \frac{\phi(\eta)}{\sqrt{y - \eta}} \, e^{-\frac{[x-\chi(\eta)]^2}{4(y-\eta)}} \, d\eta$$

represents a solution of equation (1) which is regular, as are all its partial derivatives of any order whatever, in every region of the plane having no point in common with the arc AB. This function is still continuous when the point (x, y) falls on the arc AB, for integral (18) remains uniformly convergent in the neighborhood of any point whatever of this arc (III, **48**).

Indeed, this integral taken along an infinitely small arc CD is itself infinitely small, whatever the position of the neighboring point (x, y); representing by H an upper bound of $|\phi(\eta)|$, we clearly have as an upper bound of the absolute value of the integral along this arc an expression of the form

$$H \int_\alpha^y \frac{d\eta}{\sqrt{y - \eta}}$$

which is infinitely small with the difference $y - \alpha$. We shall see a little later that $\partial\Phi/\partial x$ is discontinuous when the point (x, y) crosses the arc AB.

The characteristics $y = a$, $y = b$, passing through the lowest and the highest point of the arc AB, divide the plane into several regions. Below the line $A'A$ and on this line itself (Fig. 14), we

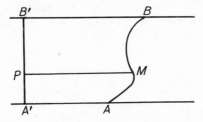

FIG. 14.

have $\Phi(x, y) = 0$; above $B'B$, $\Phi(x, y)$ is a holomorphic analytic function of the two variables x and y (III, **86**). It remains for us to study the nature of this function in the strip contained between these two characteristics, to the right or to the left of arc AB. Let us assume that the point (x, y) moves on the parallel $A'B'$ to the

Oy-axis, taken between the two characteristics, and having no point in common[6] with AB. Let x_0 be the abscissa of A'; $\Phi(x_0, y)$ is a continuous function of y, along with all its partial derivatives, in the interval (a, b), but *this is not in general an analytic function of* y, if $\phi(\eta)$ is any continuous function whatever. Indeed, the value of this function at a point P of $A'B'$ depends only upon the values of $\phi(\eta)$ along the arc AM. If therefore we replace $\phi(\eta)$ by another continuous function $\phi_1(\eta)$ which coincides with $\phi(\eta)$ along AM, but which differs from it along MB, the new integral $\Phi(x, y)$ will coincide with $\Phi(x_0, y)$ along $A'P$, but will be different from $\Phi(x_0, y)$ along PB'. Since the point P is any point of $A'B'$, it follows that $\Phi(x_0, y)$ cannot be a holomorphic function of y along $A'B'$, nor even along any portion whatever of $A'B'$, if the function $\phi(\eta)$ is any continuous function. However, the derivatives of this function $\Phi(x_0, y)$ satisfy certain inequalities analogous to those which characterize analytic functions[7] (I, **191**; II, 1, **84**, notes).

We are first going to prove that when we give a fixed value to y, between a and b, $\Phi(x, y)$ is a holomorphic function of the complex variable $x = x' + ix''$ in the neighborhood of the value $x = x_0$. We have

$$[x' + ix'' - \chi(\eta)]^2 = [x' - \chi(\eta)]^2 - x''^2 + 2ix''[x' - \chi(\eta)];$$

let 2ρ be the minimum of $|\chi(\eta) - x_0|$ when x varies from a to b. If we have $|x' - x_0| < \rho$, $|x''| < \rho$, the real part of $[x - \chi(\eta)]^2$ is positive and consequently the modulus of the exponential factor in integral (18) is less than unity. The modulus of any element whatever of this integral is therefore less than the corresponding element of the integral

$$\int_a^y \frac{H}{\sqrt{y - \eta}} \, d\eta,$$

[6] This hypothesis does not reduce generality. Indeed, let A_1B_1 be a segment parallel to Oy, lying between the characteristics

$$y = \alpha, \qquad y = \beta, \qquad (u < \alpha < \beta < b),$$

and having no point in common with the arc AB. The integral (18) along AB decomposes into three parts: the integral from a to α, which represents a holomorphic function of y along A_1B_1, the integral from β to b which is zero for every point of this segment, and finally the integral from α to β, studied in the text.

[7] E. Holmgren, *Comptes rendus*, December 30, 1907 and January 9, 1908; *Arkiv. för Matematik*, Vol. IV, 14 and 18.

where H is an upper bound of $|\phi(\eta)|$. It follows that if we have given to x complex values such that $|x - x_0|$ does not exceed the number ρ, integral (18) is uniformly convergent and therefore represents a holomorphic function of x in this region. The modulus of this function is less than $2H\sqrt{y - a}$ and hence less than $2H\sqrt{b - a}$. To sum up, when we assign any value whatever between a and b to y, $\Phi(x, y)$ is a holomorphic function of x in a circle of radius ρ drawn about the point x_0 as center, whose modulus remains less than a positive number M, when we have $|x - x_0| \leqslant \rho$, *where the two numbers* M *and* ρ *are independent of the value assigned to* y.

At any point of $A'B'$, with coordinates (x_0, y), we therefore have

$$(19) \qquad \left| \frac{\partial^n \Phi}{\partial x^n} \right| < \frac{Mn!}{\rho^n};$$

but, from equation (1) and those derived from it by successive differentiation, any integral whatever of this equation will also satisfy the relation $\partial^n u / \partial y^n = \partial^{2n} u / \partial x^{2n}$. Therefore, setting $f(y) = \Phi(x_0, y)$ for brevity, and $r = \rho^2$, the function $f(y)$ satisfies the following conditions:

1. It is continuous, as are all its partial derivatives, in the interval (a, b);

2. At any point of this interval, the successive derivatives satisfy the conditions

$$(19') \qquad f^{(n)}(y) < \frac{M(2n)!}{r^n},$$

where M and r are two positive numbers *independent* of y.

We shall say for brevity that a function $f(y)$ satisfying these conditions is of class 2 in the interval (a, b), class 1 consisting of holomorphic functions. It is clear moreover that these latter are contained among the functions of class 2. We see readily that the sum of any number of functions of class 2 is again a function of that class; in particular, the sum of a function of class 2 and of a holomorphic function is a function of the same kind.

Setting

$$(20) \quad \Psi(x, y) = \int_a^y \phi(\eta) \frac{x - \chi(\eta)}{(y - \eta)^{3/2}} e^{-\{[x - \chi(\eta)]^2 / 4(y - \eta)\}} \, d\eta$$

$$= -2 \int_a^y \phi(\eta) \frac{\partial U}{\partial x} \, d\eta,$$

the derivative with respect to x of integral (18) has the expression $-\frac{1}{2}\Psi(x, y)$.

The function $\Psi(x, y)$ is again an integral of equation (1), regular in the entire strip included between the lines $y = a$, $y = b$, except on the path of integration Γ. We can extend the definition to the entire plane by conveniently taking $\phi(\eta) = 0$ for $\eta > b$. This function is also an analytic function of x, when we give y a constant value; from the way in which we have derived the function $\Phi(x, y)$, it satisfies inequalities of the same form as inequalities (19), at every point of a segment $A'B'$, and, consequently, is a function of y of class 2 along this segment.

The integral (20) is the analogue of the potential of double layer[8] and has along Γ a discontinuity of which a study has been made by Holmgren. We shall assume that the function $\chi(y)$ has a continuous derivative $\chi'(y)$ in the interval (a, b).

Following the same procedure as in III, **49**, we shall study first of all the simple case where $\phi(\eta) = 1$. The integral

$$(21) \qquad F(x, y) = \int_a^y \frac{x - \chi(\eta)}{(y - \eta)^{3/2}} e^{-\{[x-\chi(\eta)]^2/4(y-\eta)\}} \, d\eta$$

no longer has, as in the case of Gauss's integral, a simple geometric interpretation which makes the discontinuity intuitive; a direct study is therefore necessary. Integral (21) retains a meaning when the point $M(x, y)$ coincides with a point P with coordinates (X, Y) of arc Γ:

$$(22) \qquad F(X, Y) = \int_a^y \frac{X - \chi(\eta)}{(Y - \eta)^{3/2}} e^{-\{[X-\chi(\eta)]^2/4(Y-\eta)\}} \, d\eta;$$

but $F(x, y)$ approaches different limits when the point (x, y) approaches the point (X, Y), depending upon whether the point (x, y) is to the right or to the left of arc Γ. To prove this, let us consider the auxiliary integral

$$(23) \qquad F_1(x, y) = \int_a^y \frac{-2\chi'(\eta)}{\sqrt{y - \eta}} e^{-\{[x-\chi(\eta)]^2/4(y-\eta)\}} \, d\eta,$$

which is continuous on arc Γ, for it is of the form of those which have been studied at the beginning of this section. We have, as an

---

[8] When the characteristic directions are the same, the characteristic coming from any point of Γ can be considered as the conjugate of the tangent with respect to the set of these two directions.

elementary calculation proves,

$$(24) \qquad F(x, y) + F_1(x, y) = 4 \int_\alpha^\beta e^{-u^2}\, du,$$

where $u = [x - \chi(\eta)]/2\sqrt{y - \eta}$ and the limits α and β are determined according to the position of the point (x, y). Let us first suppose that this point is on the right of Γ, or that $x > \chi(y)$; when η varies from a to y, u varies from $[x - \chi(a)]/2\sqrt{y - a}$ to $+ \infty$. If the point (x, y) were on the left of Γ, the limit β would be $- \infty$. We therefore have, when the point (x, y) is not on Γ,

$$F(x, y) + F_1(x, y) = 4 \int_{[x-\chi(a)/2\sqrt{y-a}]}^{\pm\infty} e^{-u^2}\, du,$$

a relation which, letting the point (x, y) approach the point (X, Y), becomes

$$(25) \qquad \lim F(x, y) + \lim F_1(x, y) = 4 \int_{[x-\chi(a)/2\sqrt{y-a}]}^{\pm\infty} e^{-u^2}\, du,$$

the $+$ sign corresponding to the case when the point (x, y) is on the right of Γ, and the $-$ sign to the contrary case.

If we have $x = X$, $y = Y$, the limits for u are $[X - \chi(a)]/2\sqrt{Y - a}$ and zero; formula (24) gives

$$(26) \qquad F(X, Y) + F_1(X, Y) = 4 \int_{[X-\chi(a)/2\sqrt{Y-a}]}^{0} e^{-u^2}\, du.$$

Subtracting the relations (25) and (26) member by member, and noting that $F_1(x, y)$ is continuous at the point (X, Y), we get

$$(27) \quad \lim F(x, y) = F(X, Y) + 4 \int_0^{\pm\infty} e^{-u^2}\, du = F(X, Y) \pm 2\sqrt{\pi}.$$

In this formula we must take the $+$ or $-$ sign according as the point (x, y) is to the right or to the left of Γ.

Let us now consider any integral of the form (20), which we can write as

$$(20') \quad \Psi(x, y) = \int_a^y [\phi(\eta) - \phi(y)] \frac{x - \chi(\eta)}{(y - \eta)^{3/2}} e^{-\{[x-\chi(\eta)]^2/4(y-\eta)\}}\, d\eta$$

$$+ \phi(y) \int_a^y \frac{x - \chi(\eta)}{(y - \eta)^{3/2}} e^{-\{[x-\chi(\eta)]^2/4(y-\eta)\}}\, d\eta.$$

If the function $\phi(y)$ satisfies the Lipschitz condition in the interval (a, b), the absolute value of any element of the first integral is less than the corresponding element of an integral

$$\int_a^y \frac{H \, d\eta}{\sqrt{y - \eta}}.$$

Consequently, this integral is uniformly convergent in the neighborhood of any point (X, Y) of Γ and represents a continuous function in the neighborhood of Γ. The discontinuity of $\Psi'(x, y)$ when the point (x, y) approaches a point (X, Y) is inferred immediately from the discontinuity of the second integral which we have just studied and we have, finally, the general formula

$$(28) \quad \lim \Psi'(x, y) = \pm \, 2\sqrt{\pi}\phi(Y)$$

$$+ \int_a^Y (\phi\eta) \, \frac{X - \chi(\eta)}{(Y - \eta)^{3/2}} \, e^{-\{[X-\chi(\eta)]^2/4(Y-\eta)\}} \, d\eta,$$

where the sign must be taken as above.

In the particular case where the arc Γ is a segment of the line $x = x_0$, the integral which occurs in the second member is identically zero. We infer from this that *the limit of the integral*

$$u(x, y) = \frac{1}{2\sqrt{\pi}} \int_a^y \phi(\eta) \, \frac{x - x_0}{(y - \eta)^{3/2}} \, e^{-\{(x-x_0)^2/4(y-\eta)\}} \, d\eta$$

is equal to $\pm \, \phi(Y)$ when the point approaches a point (x_0, Y) of this line.

89. Extension of Green's formula. Applications.

Let us consider any two functions $\phi(x, y)$, $\Psi'(x, y)$ of the variables (x, y), possessing derivatives up to the second order; we have identically, $\mathscr{F}(\quad)$ and $\mathscr{G}(\quad)$ having the same meaning as above (III, **84**),

$$(29) \quad \psi\mathscr{F}(\phi) - \phi\,\mathscr{G}(\psi) = \frac{\partial}{\partial x}\left[\psi\,\frac{\partial\phi}{\partial x} - \phi\,\frac{\partial\psi}{\partial x}\right] - \frac{\partial}{\partial y}\,(\phi\psi).$$

If the functions ϕ and ψ are continuous, as well as the partial derivatives of these functions which occur in the preceding formula, in the interior of a finite domain D bounded by a contour C, we derive from this formula (29) the following relation, which is the equivalent of Green's formula (III, **50**):

$$(30) \qquad \int\!\!\int_{(D)} [\psi \mathscr{F}(\phi) - \phi\, \mathscr{G}(\psi)]\, dx\, dy$$

$$= \int_C \phi\psi\, dx + \left(\psi\, \frac{\partial\phi}{\partial x} - \phi\, \frac{\partial\psi}{\partial x}\right) dy,$$

where the line integral is taken in the positive direction. We readily infer from it a series of consequences entirely like those which have been developed for Laplace's equation. Replacing ψ by unity and ϕ by an integral u of equation (1), regular in D, we obtain the new relation

$$(31) \qquad \int_C u\, dx + \frac{\partial u}{\partial x}\, dy = 0,$$

which is evidently equivalent to equation (1) itself, from Green's first formula. Similarly, replacing ψ by unity and ϕ by the square, u^2, of a regular integral in D, we get

$$(32) \qquad 2\int\!\!\int_{(D)} \left(\frac{\partial u}{\partial x}\right)^2 dx\, dy = \int_C u^2\, dx + 2u\, \frac{\partial u}{\partial x}\, dy.$$

From this formula, analogous to formula (12a) of III, **50**, we derive an important consequence. Let $u(x, y)$ be a regular integral in the interior of a contour $ABFE$ like that of Figure 15, formed of two segments AB, EF of characteristics, and of two arcs AE, BF, each of which can be intersected in only one point by a characteristic; the segment EF is above AB, and one or the other, or even both, of these segments can reduce to a point. *If this integral is zero along the two arcs* AE, BF *and the segment* AB, *it is zero in the entire domain.*

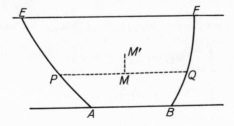

Fig. 15.

Indeed, let M be any point of this domain and PQ the segment of the characteristic passing through M and included between the arcs AE and BF. Relation (32) applied to the domain D bounded by the contour $ABQPA$ gives

$$2 \int \int_{(D')} \left(\frac{\partial u}{\partial x}\right)^2 dx \, dy + \int_{PQ} u^2 \, dx = 0,$$

since u is zero by hypothesis along $PABQ$. Since all the elements of these two integrals are positive or zero, we must therefore have $u = 0$ all along PQ, and consequently u is zero in the entire domain D, since M is any point of this domain. We conclude from this that there cannot exist two regular integrals in the domain D, assuming given values along AB, AE, and BE. The problem of determining this integral is analogous to the Dirichlet problem for the Laplace equation. The reasoning which precedes proves that it cannot have more than one solution, but it does not prove that the one solution exists.

To obtain a relation analogous to the fundamental formula (13) of III, **51**, it is sufficient to apply the same method, replacing the function log r by the fundamental solution $U(x, y; \xi, \eta)$. Let M be a point with coordinates (x_0, y_0) in the preceding domain, M' be a neighboring point in the same domain, with coordinates $(x_0, y_0 + h)$, where h is a positive number. Let us apply the general formula (30), replacing the letters x and y by the letters ξ, η, respectively, and taking for ϕ an integral $u(\xi, \eta)$ of equation (1), regular in D, and for ψ the function

$$U_0 = U(x_0, y_0 + h; \xi, \eta),$$

which is a solution of the adjoint equation regular in the same domain. This formula now gives us the relation

$$\int_C u(\xi, \eta) \, U(x_0, y_0 + h; \xi, \eta) \, d\xi + \left(U_0 \frac{\partial u}{\partial \xi} - u \frac{\partial U_0}{\partial \xi}\right) d\eta = 0,$$

where C represents the contour $ABQPA$; this can be rewritten as

$$(33) \qquad \int_{PQ} u(\xi, y_0) \; e^{-(x_0-\xi)^2/4h} \, \frac{\partial \xi}{\sqrt{h}}$$

$$= \int_{(PABQ)} u(\xi, \eta) U(x_0, y_0 + h; \xi, \eta) \, d\xi$$

$$+ \left(U_0 \frac{\partial u}{\partial \xi} - u \frac{\partial U_0}{\partial \xi}\right) d\eta.$$

We have seen above (III, **87**) that the first member of this equality has $2\sqrt{\pi}\, u(x_0, y_0)$ as a limit when the positive number h approaches zero, since x_0 is included between the abscissas of the points P and Q. The limit of the second member is obtained immediately, since $U(x_0, y_0 + h; \xi, \eta)$ and $\partial U_0/\partial\xi$ are continuous functions of h along the contour $PABQ$. Suppressing the indices of the letters x_0, y_0, we therefore obtain the relation

$$
(34) \qquad u(x, y) = \frac{1}{2\sqrt{\pi}} \int_{(PABQ)} u(\xi, \eta)\, U(x, y; \xi, \eta)\, d\xi
$$

$$
+ \left(U\, \frac{\partial u}{\partial \xi} - u\, \frac{\partial U}{\partial \xi} \right) d\eta,
$$

which is the analogue of relation (13) of III, **51**. Replacing U by its expression, it can be written again as

$$
(35) \qquad u(x, y) = \frac{1}{2\sqrt{\pi}} \int_{(PABQ)} \frac{e^{-(\eta-\xi)^2/4(y-\eta)}}{\sqrt{y-\eta}} \left[u(\xi, \eta)\, d\xi + \frac{du}{\partial \xi}\, d\eta \right.
$$

$$
\left. - u(\xi, \eta)\, \frac{x-\xi}{2(y-\eta)}\, d\eta \right]^9.
$$

Formula (35) does not give the solution of the problem with boundary conditions which was under consideration just now, for the second member can be calculated only if the values of $\partial u/\partial\xi$ along the arcs AE and BF are known. We can however eliminate the value of $\partial u/\partial\xi$ on every part of the contour composed of a line segment (see Exercise 3).

Poisson's formula of III, **87** can be derived as a limiting case of the general formula (35). Let us assume that in the portion of the strip bounded by the two characteristics with ordinates h and $h + \delta$ passing through A and E, lying to the right of the arc AE, the integral $u(x, y)$ is regular and moreover that there exists a positive number K such that the products

$$
u(x, y)\, e^{-Kx^2}, \qquad \frac{\partial u}{\partial x}\, e^{-Kx}
$$

---

[9] Every integral of the equation $\mathscr{F}(u) = f(x, y)$, regular in D, satisfies a relation which differs from relation (35) only by the addition to the second member of the term

$$
\frac{1}{2\sqrt{\pi}} \int\int_{(D')} f(\xi, \eta) e^{-[(x-\xi)^2/(4(y-\eta))]}\, \frac{d\xi\, d\eta}{\sqrt{y-\eta}}.
$$

are bounded in this domain. We are going to look for what formula (35) gives when we take for BF a segment of the line $x = R$, where R is a positive number which we shall make increase indefinitely. The portion of the line integral arising from BQ is equal to

$$(36) \quad \frac{1}{2\sqrt{\pi}} \int_h^y \frac{e^{-(x-R)^2/4(y-\eta)}}{\sqrt{y-\eta}} \left[\left(\frac{\partial u}{\partial \xi}\right)_R - u(R, \eta)\, \frac{x-R}{2(y-\eta)} \right] d\eta.$$

We are going to prove that this integral approaches zero when R increases indefinitely, provided that the numbers K and δ satisfy a certain condition. Let us take the first part; by hypothesis the product $(\partial u/\partial \xi)\, e^{-KR^2}$ is bounded, and consequently the absolute value of this integral is less than

$$\frac{M}{2\sqrt{\pi}}\, e^{-\epsilon R^2} \int_h^y \frac{e^{(K+\epsilon)R^2 - \frac{(x+R)^2}{4(y-\eta)}}}{\sqrt{y-\eta}}\, d\eta,$$

where M is a fixed number and ϵ an arbitrary positive number. The factor $e^{-\epsilon R^2}$ approaches zero when R increases indefinitely, so that it is sufficient to show that the absolute value of the integral

$$(37) \qquad \int_h^y \frac{e^{\frac{4(K+\epsilon)(y-\eta)R^2 - (x-R)^2}{4(y-\eta)}}}{\sqrt{y-\eta}}\, d\eta$$

maintains a finite value. Now, the numerator of the exponent is smaller than $4(K + \epsilon)\, \delta R^2 - (x - R)^2$, and this numerator will be negative for very large values of R if the coefficient of R^2, that is $4(K + \epsilon)\, \delta - 1$, is negative; the absolute value of integral (37) is therefore less than

$$\int_h^y \frac{d\eta}{\sqrt{y-\eta}},$$

which has a finite value. The first part of integral (36) therefore approaches zero when R increases indefinitely, provided that δ is less than $1/[4(K + \epsilon)]$; and, since ϵ is an arbitrary positive number, this condition will be satisfied if the numbers K and δ satisfy the relation $4K\delta < 1$. We should prove in the same manner that the second part of integral (36) also approaches zero when R increases indefinitely and, in formula (35), the path of integration $PABQ$ must be replaced by the segment PA and the segment of the characteristic extending from point A to infinity towards the right.

If the integral $u(x, y)$ is regular in every strip bounded by the two characteristics $y = h$, $y = h + \delta$, and if in this strip the products $u\ e^{-Kx^2}$, $\partial u/\partial x\ e^{-Kx^2}$ remain bounded, the two positive numbers K and δ satisfying the relation $4K\delta < 1$, we can likewise take for the curve AE a segment of the line $x = -R$, where R is a positive number which we shall make increase indefinitely. We verify as just now that the portion of the line integral (35) arising from PA approaches zero, and formula (35) becomes in the limit

$$(38) \qquad u(x, y) = \frac{1}{2\sqrt{\pi}} \int_{-\infty}^{+\infty} \frac{e^{-(x-\xi)^2/4(y-\eta)}}{\sqrt{y - \eta}}\ \phi(\xi)\ d\xi,$$

where $\phi(x)$ is the value of the integral $u(x, h)$ along the characteristic $y = h$; we have again Poisson's formula (17) of III, **87**. If the products $u(x, y)\ e^{-Kx^2}$, $\partial u/\partial x\ e^{-Kx^2}$ remain bounded in the part of the plane lying above the characteristic $y = h$, however small the positive number K, the number δ can be taken as large as we wish, and therefore formula (38) is applicable in all this part of the plane.

90. Properties of integrals. Formula (35) permits us to prove several important properties of integrals of equation (1). Let $u(x, y)$ be a regular integral in a domain D. Let us take in the interior of D a partial domain bounded like the one in the preceding paragraph, for example a rectangle R bounded by two segments AB, EF of characteristics and two parallels AE, BF to the Oy axis. Applying formula (35) to any point M of this rectangle, with coordinates x, y, the function $u(x, y)$ is expressed as a sum of line integrals taken along AB, AP, BO, respectively. The integral along AB is an analytic function of the two variables x, y in the rectangle R (III, **87**); each of the integrals taken along the segments AP, BQ is the sum of a function $\Phi(x, y)$ and of a function $\Psi(x, y)$ (III, **88**). The integral $u(x, y)$ therefore has the same properties in the rectangle R as these functions themselves: all its partial derivatives are regular in this rectangle; if we give a constant value y_0 to y, $u(x, y_0)$ is a holomorphic function of x, while if x is given a constant value x_0, $u(x_0, y)$ is a function of y of class 2.

Since every line segment parallel to one of the axes and lying entirely in the domain D, can be enclosed in the interior of a rectangle just as the preceding one was itself contained in D, we can therefore state the following theorems: *If an integral* u(x, y) *is regular in a domain* D, 1. *all its partial derivatives are regular in the same domain;* 2. *along a segment of a characteristic interior to*

D, u(x, y) *is a holomorphic function of* x; 3. *along a line segment
parallel to* Oy *interior to* D, u(x, y) *is a function of* y *of class* 2.

These properties belong also to the partial derivatives of $u(x, y)$,
since they are themselves integrals of equation (1). In particular,
$\partial u/\partial x$ is a function of y of class 2 along every segment parallel to Oy
lying in the interior of a domain where $u(x, y)$ is regular. Conversely,
given two functions of class 2 in an interval (a, b), $\phi(y)$, $\psi(y)$, there
exists an integral satisfying the Cauchy conditions for $x = x_0$:

$$u(x_0, y) = \phi(y), \qquad \left(\frac{\partial u}{\partial x}\right)_{x_0} = \psi(y),$$

and regular in the rectangle bounded by the lines $y = a$, $y = b$,
$x = x_0 \pm r$, where r is a suitable positive number. Indeed, the
partial derivatives of the functions $\phi(y)$, $\Psi(y)$ satisfy by hypothesis
the inequalities

$$(39) \qquad |\phi^{(n)}(y)| < \frac{M(2n)}{\rho^n}, \qquad |\psi^{(n)}(y)| < \frac{M(2n)!}{\rho^n},$$

for every value of y in the interval (a, b); M and ρ are two positive
numbers which we can evidently take the same for the two functions.
Series (6), considered in III, **85**, as well as those derived from it by
differentiating twice with respect to x or once with respect to y,
are uniformly convergent, from relations (39), whatever the value of
y in the interval (a, b), provided that we have $(x - x_0) < \rho^{\frac{1}{2}}$. The
sum of this series represents, therefore, an integral of equation (1)
satisfying the Cauchy conditions. It is moreover the only integral
satisfying these conditions which is regular in the domain D enclosing in its interior the line segment considered. Indeed, if there
did exist two of them, their difference would be a regular integral
in D, and zero, as well as its derivative with respect to x, all along
this line segment. All the partial derivatives of this integral would
therefore be zero along the same segment and, since this integral is
an analytic function of x, it would follow that it is identically zero.[10]

The preceding properties have been generalized by considering
instead of a line segment parallel to Oy an arc of the curve AB,
represented by an equation $x = \chi(y)$, where $\chi(y)$ is a holomorphic

---

[10] If the functions $\phi(y)$ and $\psi(y)$ satisfy the inequalities

$$(39') \qquad |\phi^{(n)}(y)| < \frac{M\Gamma[n(1 + \alpha)]}{\rho^n}, \qquad |\psi^{(n)}(y)| < \frac{M\Gamma[n(1 + \alpha)]}{\rho^n},$$

where α is a positive number *less than* 1, for every value of y in the interval
(a, b), formula (6) represents an integral satisfying the Cauchy conditions which
is regular in the strip included between the characteristics $y = a$, $y = b$.

function of y in the interval (a, b). If an integral $u(x, y)$ is regular in a domain D enclosing the arc AB in its interior, the function $u[\chi(y), y]$, to which it is equal along this arc is of class 2. Conversely, given two functions $\phi(y)$, $\psi(y)$, of class 2 in an interval (a, b), there exists one and only one integral of equation (1), regular in a domain enclosing the arc AB, and bounded by the lines $y = a$, $y = b$, and the two curves $x = \chi(y) \pm r$ (where r is a positive number) satisfying the Cauchy conditions along arc AB

$$(40) \qquad u(x, y) = \phi(y), \qquad \frac{\partial u}{\partial x} = \psi(y), \qquad \text{for } x = \chi(y).$$

We shall refer to the works of Holmgren for the proofs. Schwarz's theorem on the analytic extension of a harmonic function has likewise been extended by Holmgren to integrals of equation (1). Let $u(x, y)$ be a regular integral in a domain D; we say that it can be extended into a domain D' contiguous to the first if there exists an integral $U(x, y)$, regular in the domain $D + D'$, which coincides with $u(x, y)$ in D. If the domain D is bounded in part by an arc AB, which is intersected in only one point by a characteristic, the extension of $u(x, y)$ across this arc AB can be possible in only one way, since along a characteristic, $u(x, y)$ is a holomorphic function of x. We have noted above that this was no longer true of it across a segment of a characteristic (III, **88**). This granted, let us assume that the arc AB is represented by the equation $x = \chi(y)$, where the function $\chi(y)$ is holomorphic for every value of y between a and b, and that $u(x, y)$ is a regular integral on one side of this arc, to the right, for example, and assumes on AB a set of given values $f(y)$. In order to be able to extend this integral $u(x, y)$ across the arc AB, *it is necessary and sufficient that the function* f(y) *be of class 2* [11] *in any interval* (α, β) *included in the interval* (a, b).

[11] We deduce from this proposition a result analogous to that which has been indicated (footnote 7, Chap. V) relative to the *generalized* Cauchy problem. Let it be required to determine an integral $u(x, y)$, satisfying the Cauchy conditions (40) and defined on one side only of the arc AB on which the values are given. This problem is in general impossible if the functions $\phi(y)$ and $\psi(y)$ are any continuous functions. Indeed, let $u_1(x, y)$ be a regular integral on the same side of the arc AB and satisfying the first Cauchy condition (see section **91**); the difference $u(x, y) - u_1(x, y)$, being zero along the arc AB, can be extended to the other side and consequently

$$\frac{\partial u}{\partial x} - \frac{\partial u_1}{\partial x} = \psi(y)\frac{\partial u_1}{\partial x}$$

must be a function of y of class 2 along the entire segment AB not including the extremities.

91. Problems with boundary conditions. Let D be a domain bounded as in III, **89** by two segments AB, EF of characteristics with ordinates h and l ($l > h$), and two arcs of the curve AE, BF, included between these characteristics, defined respectively by the two equations $x = \chi_1(y)$, $x = \chi_2(y)$; the functions χ_1, χ_2, χ'_1, χ'_2, are assumed continuous in the interval (h, l) and $\chi_1 > \chi_2$. We propose to prove that there exists one and only one integral, regular in the domain D, which reduces on each of the arcs AE, BF to a given continuous function $f_1(y)$ or $f_2(y)$, and on AB to another continuous function $g(x)$ which agrees with the first ones at the points A and B. We can assume, without loss of generality, that $g(x) = 0$; indeed, we have seen (III, **87**) how we can form in an infinite number of ways, a regular integral above the arc AB and assuming the given values on AB. Let $u_1(x, y)$ be one of these integrals; setting $u - u_1 = z$, the new unknown function $z(x, y)$ must reduce to zero along arc AB and to given continuous functions of y along arcs AE, BF. We shall therefore assume that we have made this transformation first of all, and that consequently we have $g(x) = 0$.

From what has been said in III, **89**, this problem does not have more than one solution. To prove that this solution exists, it is sufficient to employ a method analogous to Neumann's (III, **57**) of trying to represent the desired integral as a sum of functions $\Psi(x, y)$ (III, **88**). For this purpose, let us set

$$(41) \qquad u(x, y) = \int_h^y \mu_1(\eta) \, \frac{x - \chi_1(\eta)}{(y - \eta)^{3/2}} \, e^{-[x-\chi_1(\eta)]^2/4(y-\eta)} \, d\eta$$
$$+ \int_h^y \mu_2(\eta) \, \frac{x - \chi_2(\eta)}{(y - \eta)^{3/2}} \, e^{-[x-\chi_2(\eta)]^2/4(y-\eta)} \, d\eta,$$

where μ_1 and μ_2 are continuous functions to be determined in the interval (h, l). From what we have proven above, $u(x, y)$ is a regular integral in D, zero along AB. When the point (x, y) approaches a point (X, Y) of the arc AE, while remaining to the right of this arc, $u(x, y)$ must approach $f_1(Y)$, which requires that we have [formula (28)]

(42)

$$2\sqrt{\pi}\,\mu_1(Y) + \int_h^Y \mu_1(\eta) \, \frac{\chi_1(Y) - \chi_1(\eta)}{(Y - \eta)^{3/2}} \, e^{-\{[\chi_1(Y)-\chi_1(\eta)]^2/4(Y-\eta)\}} \, d\eta$$
$$+ \int_h^Y \mu_2(\eta) \, \frac{\chi_1(Y) - \chi_2(\eta)}{(Y - \eta)^{3/2}} \, e^{-\{[\chi_1(Y)-\chi_2(\eta)]^2/4(Y-\eta)\}} \, d\eta = f_1(Y).$$

Similarly, by observing that $u(x, y)$ approaches $f_2(Y)$ when the point (x, y) approaches a point with ordinate Y of the arc BF, while remaining to the left of this arc, we obtain an entirely similar relation

(43)

$$- 2\sqrt{\pi}\,\mu_2(Y) + \int_h^Y \mu_1(\eta)\,\frac{\chi_2(Y) - \chi_1(\eta)}{(Y - \eta)^{3/2}}\,e^{-\{[\chi_2(Y)-\chi_1(\eta)]^2/4(Y-\eta)\}}\,d\eta$$

$$+ \int_h^Y \mu_2(\eta)\,\frac{\chi_2(Y) - \chi_2(\eta)}{(Y - \eta)^{3/2}}\,e^{-\{[\chi_2(Y)-\chi_2(\eta)]^2/4(Y-\eta)\}}\,d\eta = f_2(Y).$$

The two relations (42) and (43) form a system of integral equations of the form

(44)
$$\begin{cases} \mu_1(Y) + \displaystyle\int_h^Y \mu_1(\eta)K_1(Y, \eta)\,d\eta + \int_h^Y \mu_2(\eta)K_2(Y, \eta)\,d\eta = F_1(Y), \\[2mm] \mu_2(Y) + \displaystyle\int_h^Y \mu_1(\eta)H_1(Y, \eta)\,d\eta + \int_h^Y \mu_2(\eta)H_2(Y, \eta)\,d\eta = F_2(Y), \end{cases}$$

$K_1, K_2, H_1, H_2, F_1, F_2$ being given functions, and μ_1, μ_2 the unknown functions. We shall prove in the following chapter that this system has one and only one solution, under certain conditions which are satisfied here.

Instead of being given the value of the unknown function at each point of the arcs AE, BF, we can be given the value of $\partial u/\partial x$, or, more generally, assume that on each of these arcs we know the value of $u(x, y)$, where this function satisfies a relation of the form

(45)
$$\frac{\partial u}{\partial x} + \lambda(y)\,u = f(y),$$

where $\lambda(y)$ and $f(y)$ are known functions of y. We come again to a system of two integral equations of the form (44) in seeking to represent the unknown function by the sum of a function $\Phi(x, y)$ and of a function $\Psi(x, y)$, or by the sum of two functions $\Phi(x, y)$ (III, **88**). It is sufficient to replace a function $\Psi(x, y)$ in formula (41) by a function $\Phi(x, y)$, defined by an integral taken along that one of the arcs for which the unknown function satisfies a relation of the form (45), and to observe that $\partial\Phi/\partial x$ is a function $\Psi(x, y)$. The application of relation (28) leads again to a system of two integral equations. We have directly solved a problem of this sort in III, **32**, for equation (35) in that section differs only in notation from equation (1) in this chapter. Since the solution obtained is an odd function of r, the given data of the problem make known the value of the unknown function v in the interval $(-R, +R)$ for $t = 0$, and we have, besides, a linear relation between $\partial v/\partial r$ and v for $r = \pm R$.

Let us consider the domain $\mathscr{D}$ formed by the portion of the strip between two characteristics, lying to the right or to the left of an arc Γ, defined by an equation $x = \chi(y)$. Assuming that one of the arcs AE, BF of Figure 15 recedes indefinitely, we are led as a limiting case to the following problem: *To determine a regular integral in $\mathscr{D}$, zero along the part of the characteristic which bounds this domain from below, knowing the value of this integral at each point of Γ, or knowing that along Γ, u and $\partial u/\partial x$ satisfy a relation of the form* (45).

We shall again seek to represent, according to the case, the unknown function $u(x, y)$ by a function $\Phi(x, y)$ or by a function $\Psi(x, y)$, which will lead to *one* integral equation for the determination of the auxiliary unknown which occurs under the sign $\int$. Let us take, for example, the first case, and let us set

$$u(x, y) = \int_{h}^{y} \mu(\eta) \frac{x - \chi(\eta)}{(y - \eta)^{3/2}} e^{-\{[x-\chi(\eta)]^2/4(y-\eta)\}} \, d\eta;$$

the function $\mu(\eta)$ is determined by the integral equation

$$(46) \quad \pm 2\sqrt{\pi} \, \mu(y)$$
$$+ \int_{h}^{y} \mu(\eta) \frac{\chi(y) - \chi(\eta)}{(y - \eta)^{3/2}} e^{-\{[\chi(y)-\chi(\eta)]^2/4(y-\eta)\}} \, d\eta = f(y).$$

This equation is solved immediately if the curve Γ reduces to a segment of the line $x = x_0$, for then we have $\chi(y) = \chi(\eta)$ and we infer from that $\pm 2\sqrt{\pi} \, \mu(y) = f(y)$. This result has already been pointed out at the close of III, **88**.

The solution of these different problems also reduces to the determination of an integral of the adjoint equation playing the same role as Green's function. We shall restrict ourselves, for the sake of definiteness, to the first of these problems, the one in which we are given the values of u along the contour $EABF$ (Fig. 15), this integral being zero along AB. If we also knew the values of $\partial u/\partial x$ along the arcs AE, BF, the value of u at a point (x, y) of the domain D would be given by formula (35), which here becomes

$$(47) \quad u(x, y)$$
$$= \frac{1}{2\sqrt{\pi}} \int_{(PA+BQ)} \frac{e^{-(x-\xi)^2/4(y-\eta)}}{\sqrt{y - \eta}} \left\{ \left[\frac{\partial u}{\partial \xi} - u(\xi, \eta) \frac{x - \xi}{2(y - \eta)} \right] d\eta + u \, d\xi \right\}.$$

Let $g(x, y; \xi, \eta)$ be an integral of the adjoint equation

$$\frac{\partial^2 g}{\partial \xi^2} + \frac{\partial g}{\partial \eta} = 0$$

depending upon the two parameters (x, y), regular in the interior of the contour $PABQ$, and assuming the value zero at each point of the segment PQ and the same values as

$$\frac{1}{\sqrt{y - \eta}} \, e^{-(x-\xi)^2/4(y-\eta)}$$

along PA and BQ. Since the two functions $u(\xi, \eta)$, $g(x, y; \xi, \eta)$ are regular in the interior of the contour $ABQPA$, the general formula (30) gives, since $u = 0$ along AB and $g = 0$ along PQ,

$$(48) \quad 0 = \frac{1}{2\sqrt{\pi}} \int_{(PA+BQ)} \left[g(x, y; \xi, \eta) \frac{\partial u}{\partial \xi} - u(\xi, \eta) \frac{\partial g}{\partial \xi} \right] d\eta + ug \, d\xi.$$

Subtracting the two preceding equalities (47) and (48) member by member, $\partial u/\partial \xi$ disappears, from the hypothesis concerning the values of g along the arcs AP, BQ, and there remains

$(49) \quad u(x, y)$

$$= \frac{1}{2\sqrt{\pi}} \int_{(PA+BQ)} u(\xi, \eta) \left[\frac{\partial g}{\partial \xi} - \frac{x - \xi}{2(y - \eta)^{3/2}} \, e^{-(x-\xi)^2/4(y-\eta)} \right] d\eta$$

$$= \frac{1}{2\sqrt{\pi}} \int_{(PA+BQ)} u(\xi, \eta) \frac{\partial G}{\partial \xi} \, d\eta,$$

where we have set

$$(50) \quad G(x, y; \xi, \eta) = g(x, y; \xi, \eta) - \frac{1}{\sqrt{y - \eta}} \, e^{-[(x-\xi)^2/4(y-\eta)]} \, d\eta.$$

We notice the analogy of formula (49) with formula (37) (III, **62**), which gives the solution of the Dirichlet problem.

Comments and Exercises

1. The conditions obtained in section **85** for the coefficients of $F(x)$

$$|a_{2n}| < \frac{M}{r^n} \frac{n!}{(2n)!}, \qquad |a_{2n+1}| < \frac{M}{r^n} \frac{n!}{(2n + 1)!}$$

can be transformed as follows. The first, for example, can be written

$$\sqrt[2n]{|a_{2n}|} < \frac{\sqrt[2n]{M}}{\sqrt{r}} \; \sqrt[2n]{\frac{n!}{(2n)!}},$$

and, upon replacing $n!$ and $(2n)!$ by their asymptotic expressions, (I, **141**), we arrive at an inequality of the form

$$\sqrt[2n]{|a_{2n}|} < \frac{L}{\sqrt{2n}},$$

where L is independent of n. We have an entirely similar inequality for the radical $\sqrt[2n+1]{|a_{2n+1}|}$ and, consequently, the product $\sqrt{n}\ \sqrt[n]{|a_n|}$ remains bounded. (Le Roux, *Bulletin des Sciences mathématiques*, Vol. XIX, 2nd series, 1895, p. 127).

2. To find the limit of the integral (III, **87**)

$$I = \int_0^a \frac{1}{\sqrt{y}}\, e^{-(x-\xi)^2/4y}\, d\xi, \qquad (a > 0),$$

when x and y approach zero, let us write, setting $\xi = x + 2\sqrt{y}\,t$,

$$I = 2\int_{-(x/2\sqrt{y})}^{(a-x)/2\sqrt{y}} e^{-t^2}\, dt = 2\int_{-(x/2\sqrt{y})}^{0} e^{-t^2}\, dt + 2\int_0^{(a-x)/\sqrt{2y}} e^{-t^2}\, dt.$$

When x and y approach zero, the second integral approaches $\sqrt{\pi}$, but the first has a limit only if $x/\sqrt{y}$ approaches a limit 2λ, and this limit is

$$2\int_{-\lambda}^0 e^{-t^2}\, dt.$$

We easily pass from this particular case to the general case in which we should have under the sign $\int$ a function $\phi(\xi)$ as a factor.

3. When, in Figure 15, the curve AE is a part of a line, we can make the portion of the line integral along AP, which depends upon $\partial u/\partial \xi$, vanish in formula (35).

Let (x_1, y) be the coordinates of a point M_1 *exterior* to the domain D, having the same ordinate as the point $M(x, y)$; since the function $U(x_1, y; \xi, \eta)$ is regular in this domain, we have, from the general formula (30),

(35′)

$$\int_{PAQB} \frac{e^{-(x_1-\xi)^2/4(y-\eta)}}{\sqrt{y-\eta}} \left[u(\xi, \eta)\, d\xi + \frac{\partial u}{\partial \xi}\, d\eta - u(\xi, \eta) \frac{x_1 - \xi}{2(y-\eta)}\, d\eta \right] = 0.$$

To be able to combine the two relations (35) and (35′) in such a way as to eliminate the values of $\partial u / \partial \xi$ along AE, it is sufficient to be able to choose the two numbers x_1 and K in such a way that we have, all along AE, the relation

$$(x - \xi)^2 - (x_1 - \xi)^2 = 4K(y - \eta).$$

Now, if we consider (ξ, η) as the running coordinates, this equation represents a straight line. In order that segment AE be a part of this line, it will be sufficient to choose on the prolongation of PQ the point $M_1(x_1, y)$ symmetric to M with respect to the point P and then to determine the constant K by equating, for example, the coefficients which give the slopes.

4. If $u(x, y)$ is an integral of equation (1), the same is true of the function

$$u_1(x, y) = \int u \, dx + \frac{\partial u}{\partial x} \, dy.$$

The values of $\partial u / \partial x$ on the arcs AE, BF (Fig. 15) are equal to the values of u on these arcs.

5. When, in Figure 15, arc AE is a segment of the line $x = x_0$, and the arc BF is taken off to infinity toward the right, the Green's function $g(x, y; \xi, \eta)$ for a point (x, y) lying to the right of AE, in the strip included between the two characteristics passing through the points A and E, has the expression

$$\frac{1}{\sqrt{y - \eta}} \, e^{-(2x_0 - x - \xi)\,/4(y-\eta)}.$$

Derive from this the result established at the end of section **88**.

INDEX

A CATALOGUE OF SELECTED
DOVER SCIENCE BOOKS

A CATALOGUE OF SELECTED
DOVER SCIENCE BOOKS

Physics: The Pioneer Science, Lloyd W. Taylor. Very thorough non-mathematical survey of physics in a historical framework which shows development of ideas. Easily followed by laymen; used in dozens of schools and colleges for survey courses. Richly illustrated. Volume 1: Heat, sound, mechanics. Volume 2: Light, electricity. Total of 763 illustrations. Total of cvi + 847pp.

60565-5, 60566-3 Two volumes, Paperbound 5.50

THE RISE OF THE NEW PHYSICS, A. d'Abro. Most thorough explanation in print of central core of mathematical physics, both classical and modern, from Newton to Dirac and Heisenberg. Both history and exposition: philosophy of science, causality, explanations of higher mathematics, analytical mechanics, electromagnetism, thermodynamics, phase rule, special and general relativity, matrices. No higher mathematics needed to follow exposition, though treatment is elementary to intermediate in level. Recommended to serious student who wishes verbal understanding. 97 illustrations. Total of ix + 982pp.

20003-5, 20004-3 Two volumes, Paperbound $5.50

INTRODUCTION TO CHEMICAL PHYSICS, John C. Slater. A work intended to bridge the gap between chemistry and physics. Text divided into three parts: Thermodynamics, Statistical Mechanics, and Kinetic Theory; Gases, Liquids and Solids; and Atoms, Molecules and the Structure of Matter, which form the basis of the approach. Level is advanced undergraduate to graduate, but theoretical physics held to minimum. 40 tables, 118 figures. xiv + 522pp.

62562-1 Paperbound $4.00

BASIC THEORIES OF PHYSICS, Peter C. Bergmann. Critical examination of important topics in classical and modern physics. Exceptionally useful in examining conceptual framework and methodology used in construction of theory. Excellent supplement to any course, textbook. Relatively advanced.
Volume 1. Heat and Quanta. Kinetic hypothesis, physics and statistics, stationary ensembles, thermodynamics, early quantum theories, atomic spectra, probability waves, quantization in wave mechanics, approximation methods, abstract quantum theory. 8 figures. x + 300pp.   60968-5 Paperbound $2.00
Volume 2. Mechanics and Electrodynamics. Classical mechanics, electro- and magnetostatics, electromagnetic induction, field waves, special relativity, waves, etc. 16 figures. viii + 260pp.   60969-3 Paperbound $2.75

FOUNDATIONS OF PHYSICS, Robert Bruce Lindsay and Henry Margenau. Methods and concepts at the heart of physics (space and time, mechanics, probability, statistics, relativity, quantum theory) explained in a text that bridges gap between semi-popular and rigorous introductions. Elementary calculus assumed. "Thorough and yet not over-detailed," *Nature*. 35 figures. xviii + 537 pp.

60377-6 Paperbound $3.50

EINSTEIN'S THEORY OF RELATIVITY, Max Born. Relativity theory analyzed, explained for intelligent layman or student with some physical, mathematical background. Includes Lorentz, Minkowski, and others. Excellent verbal account for teachers. Generally considered the finest non-technical account. vii + 376pp.
60769-0 Paperbound $2.50

PHYSICAL PRINCIPLES OF THE QUANTUM THEORY, Werner Heisenberg. Nobel Laureate discusses quantum theory, uncertainty principle, wave mechanics, work of Dirac, Schroedinger, Compton, Wilson, Einstein, etc. Middle, non-mathematical level for physicist, chemist not specializing in quantum; mathematical appendix for specialists. Translated by C. Eckart and F. Hoyt. 19 figures. viii + 184pp.
60113-7 Paperbound $2.00

PRINCIPLES OF QUANTUM MECHANICS, William V. Houston. For student with working knowledge of elementary mathematical physics; uses Schroedinger's wave mechanics. Evidence for quantum theory, postulates of quantum mechanics, applications in spectroscopy, collision problems, electrons, similar topics. 21 figures. 288pp.
60524-8 Paperbound $3.00

ATOMIC SPECTRA AND ATOMIC STRUCTURE, Gerhard Herzberg. One of the best introductions to atomic spectra and their relationship to structure; especially suited to specialists in other fields who require a comprehensive basic knowledge. Treatment is physical rather than mathematical. 2nd edition. Translated by J. W. T. Spinks. 80 illustrations. xiv + 257pp.
60115-3 Paperbound $2.00

ATOMIC PHYSICS: AN ATOMIC DESCRIPTION OF PHYSICAL PHENOMENA, Gaylord P. Harnwell and William E. Stephens. One of the best introductions to modern quantum ideas. Emphasis on the extension of classical physics into the realms of atomic phenomena and the evolution of quantum concepts. 156 problems. 173 figures and tables. xi + 401pp.
61584-7 Paperbound $2.50

ATOMS, MOLECULES AND QUANTA, Arthur E. Ruark and Harold C. Urey. 1964 edition of work that has been a favorite of students and teachers for 30 years. Origins and major experimental data of quantum theory, development of concepts of atomic and molecular structure prior to new mechanics, laws and basic ideas of quantum mechanics, wave mechanics, matrix mechanics, general theory of quantum dynamics. Very thorough, lucid presentation for advanced students. 230 figures. Total of xxiii + 810pp.
61106-X, 61107-8 Two volumes, Paperbound $6.00

INVESTIGATIONS ON THE THEORY OF THE BROWNIAN MOVEMENT, Albert Einstein. Five papers (1905-1908) investigating the dynamics of Brownian motion and evolving an elementary theory of interest to mathematicians, chemists and physical scientists. Notes by R. Fürth, the editor, discuss the history of study of Brownian movement, elucidate the text and analyze the significance of the papers. Translated by A. D. Cowper. 3 figures. iv + 122pp.
60304-0 Paperbound $1.50

MICROSCOPY FOR CHEMISTS, Harold F. Schaeffer. Thorough text; operation of microscope, optics, photomicrographs, hot stage, polarized light, chemical procedures for organic and inorganic reactions. 32 specific experiments cover specific analyses: industrial, metals, other important subjects. 136 figures. 264pp.
61682-7 Paperbound $2.50

THE ELECTRONIC THEORY OF ACIDS AND BASES, by William F. Luder and Saverio Zuffanti. Full, newly revised (1961) presentation of a still controversial theory. Historical background, atomic orbitals and valence, electrophilic and electrodotic reagents, acidic and basic radicals, titrations, displacement, acid catalysis, etc., are discussed. xi + 165pp.
60201-X Paperbound $2.00

OPTICKS, Sir Isaac Newton. A survey of 18th-century knowledge on all aspects of light as well as a description of Newton's experiments with spectroscopy, colors, lenses, reflection, refraction, theory of waves, etc. in language the layman can follow. Foreword by Albert Einstein. Introduction by Sir Edmund Whittaker. Preface by I. Bernard Cohen. cxxvi + 406pp.
60205-2 Paperbound $3.50

LIGHT: PRINCIPLES AND EXPERIMENTS, George S. Monk. Thorough coverage, for student with background in physics and math, of physical and geometric optics. Also includes 23 experiments on optical systems, instruments, etc. "Probably the best intermediate text on optics in the English language," Physics Forum. 275 figures. xi + 489pp.
60341-5 Paperbound $3.50

PIEZOELECTRICITY: AN INTRODUCTION TO THE THEORY AND APPLICATIONS OF ELECTROMECHANICAL PHENOMENA IN CRYSTALS, Walter G. Cady. Revised 1963 edition of most complete, most systematic coverage of field. Fundamental theory of crystal electricity, concepts of piezoelectricity, including comparisons of various current theories; resonators; oscillators; properties, etc., of Rochelle salt; ferroelectric crystals; applications; pyroelectricity, similar topics. "A great work," Nature. Many illustrations. Total of xxx + 840pp.
61094-2, 61095-0 Two volumes, Paperbound $6.00

PHYSICAL OPTICS, Robert W. Wood. A classic in the field, this is a valuable source for students of physical optics and excellent background material for a study of electromagnetic theory. Partial contents: nature and rectilinear propagation of light, reflection from plane and curved surfaces, refraction, absorption and dispersion, origin of spectra, interference, diffraction, polarization, Raman effect, optical properties of metals, resonance radiation and fluorescence of atoms, magneto-optics, electro-optics, thermal radiation. 462 diagrams, 17 plates. xvi + 846pp.
61808-0 Paperbound $4.25

MIRRORS, PRISMS AND LENSES: A TEXTBOOK OF GEOMETRICAL OPTICS, James P. C. Southall. Introductory-level account of modern optical instrument theory, covering unusually wide range: lights and shadows, reflection of light and plane mirrors, refraction, astigmatic lenses, compound systems, aperture and field of optical system, the eye, dispersion and achromatism, rays of finite slope, the microscope, much more. Strong emphasis on earlier, elementary portions of field, utilizing simplest mathematics wherever possible. Problems. 329 figures. xxiv + 806pp.
61234-1 Paperbound $3.75

FUNDAMENTAL FORMULAS OF PHYSICS, edited by Donald H. Menzel. Most useful reference and study work, ranges from simplest to most highly sophisticated operations. Individual chapters, with full texts explaining formulae, prepared by leading authorities cover basic mathematical formulas, statistics, nomograms, physical constants, classical mechanics, special theory of relativity, general theory of relativity, hydrodynamics and aerodynamics, boundary value problems in mathematical physics, heat and thermodynamics, statistical mechanics, kinetic theory of gases, viscosity, thermal conduction, electromagnetism, electronics, acoustics, geometrical optics, physical optics, electron optics, molecular spectra, atomic spectra, quantum mechanics, nuclear theory, cosmic rays and high energy phenomena, particle accelerators, solid state, magnetism, etc. Special chapters also cover physical chemistry, astrophysics, celestian mechanics, meteorology, and biophysics. Indispensable part of library of every scientist. Total of xli + 787pp.
60595-7, 60596-5 Two volumes, Paperbound $5.00

INTRODUCTION TO EXPERIMENTAL PHYSICS, William B. Fretter. Detailed coverage of techniques and equipment: measurements, vacuum tubes, pulse circuits, rectifiers, oscillators, magnet design, particle counters, nuclear emulsions, cloud chambers, accelerators, spectroscopy, magnetic resonance, x-ray diffraction, low temperature, etc. One of few books to cover laboratory hazards, design of exploratory experiments, measurements. 298 figures. xii + 349pp.
(EUK) 61890-0 Paperbound $2.50

CONCEPTS AND METHODS OF THEORETICAL PHYSICS, Robert Bruce Lindsay. Introduction to methods of theoretical physics, emphasizing development of physical concepts and analysis of methods. Part I proceeds from single particle to collections of particles to statistical method. Part II covers application of field concept to material and non-material media. Numerous exercises and examples. 76 illustrations. x + 515pp.
62354-8 Paperbound $4.00

AN ELEMENTARY TREATISE ON THEORETICAL MECHANICS, Sir James Jeans. Great scientific expositor in remarkably clear presentation of basic classical material: rest, motion, forces acting on particle, statics, motion of particle under variable force, motion of rigid bodies, coordinates, etc. Emphasizes explanation of fundamental physical principles rather than mathematics or applications. Hundreds of problems worked in text. 156 figures. x + 364pp. 61839-0 Paperbound $2.50

THEORETICAL MECHANICS: AN INTRODUCTION TO MATHEMATICAL PHYSICS, Joseph S. Ames and Francis D. Murnaghan. Mathematically rigorous introduction to vector and tensor methods, dynamics, harmonic vibrations, gyroscopic theory, principle of least constraint, Lorentz-Einstein transformation. 159 problems; many fully-worked examples. 39 figures. ix + 462pp. 60461-6 Paperbound $3.00

THE PRINCIPLE OF RELATIVITY, Albert Einstein, Hendrick A. Lorentz, Hermann Minkowski and Hermann Weyl. Eleven original papers on the special and general theory of relativity, all unabridged. Seven papers by Einstein, two by Lorentz, one each by Minkowski and Weyl. "A thrill to read again the original papers by these giants," School Science and Mathematics. Translated by W. Perret and G. B. Jeffery. Notes by A. Sommerfeld. 7 diagrams. viii + 216pp.
60081-5 Paperbound $2.00

THE PSYCHOLOGY OF INVENTION IN THE MATHEMATICAL FIELD, Jacques Hadamard. Important French mathematician examines psychological origin of ideas, role of the unconscious, importance of visualization, etc. Based on own experiences and reports by Dalton, Pascal, Descartes, Einstein, Poincaré, Helmholtz, etc. xiii + 145pp.   20107-4 Paperbound $1.50

INTRODUCTION TO CHEMICAL PHYSICS, John C. Slater. A work intended to bridge the gap between chemistry and physics. Text divided into three parts: Thermodynamics, Statistical Mechanics, and Kinetic Theory; Gases, Liquids and Solids; and Atoms, Molecules and the Structure of Matter, which form the basis of the approach. Level is advanced undergraduate to graduate, but theoretical physics held to minimum. 40 tables, 118 figures. xiv + 522pp.
62562-1 Paperbound $4.00

POLAR MOLECULES, Pieter Debye. Explains some of the Nobel Laureate's most important theories on dielectrics, including fundamental electrostatic field relations, polarization and molecular structure, measurements of polarity, constitution of simple polar molecules, anomalous dispersion for radio frequencies, electrical saturation effects, connections with quantum theory, energy levels and wave mechanics, rotating molecules. 33 figures. 172pp.   60064-5 Paperbound $2.00

THE CONTINUUM AND OTHER TYPES OF SERIAL ORDER, Edward V. Huntington. Highly respected systematic account of modern theory of the continuum as a type of serial order. Based on the Dedekind-Cantor ordinal theory. Mathematics held to an elementary level. vii + 82pp.   60130-7 Paperbound $1.00

CONTRIBUTIONS TO THE FOUNDING OF THE THEORY OF TRANSFINITE NUMBERS, Georg Cantor. The famous articles of 1895-1897 which founded a new branch of mathematics, translated with 82-page introduction by P. Jourdain. Not only a great classic but still one of the best introductions for the student. ix + 211pp.
60045-9 Paperbound $2.00

ESSAYS ON THE THEORY OF NUMBERS, Richard Dedekind. Two classic essays, on the theory of irrationals, giving an arithmetic and rigorous foundation; and on transfinite numbers and properties of natural numbers. Translated by W. W. Beman. iii + 115pp.   21010-3 Paperbound $1.50

GEOMETRY OF FOUR DIMENSIONS, H. P. Manning. Part verbal, part mathematical development of fourth dimensional geometry. Historical introduction. Detailed treatment is by synthetic method, approaching subject through Euclidean geometry. No knowledge of higher mathematics necessary. 76 figures. ix + 348pp.
60182-X Paperbound $3.00

AN INTRODUCTION TO THE GEOMETRY OF N DIMENSIONS, Duncan M. Y. Sommerville. The only work in English devoted to higher-dimensional geometry. Both metric and projective properties of n-dimensional geometry are covered. Covers fundamental ideas of incidence, parallelism, perpendicularity, angles between linear space, enumerative geometry, analytical geometry, polytopes, analysis situs, hyperspacial figures. 60 diagrams. xvii + 196pp.   60494-2 Paperbound $1.50

THE THEORY OF SOUND, J. W. S. Rayleigh. Still valuable classic by the great Nobel Laureate. Standard compendium summing up previous research and Rayleigh's original contributions. Covers harmonic vibrations, vibrating systems, vibrations of strings, membranes, plates, curved shells, tubes, solid bodies, refraction of plane waves, general equations. New historical introduction and bibliography by R. B. Lindsay, Brown University. 97 figures. lviii + 984pp.
60292-3, 60293-1 Two volumes, Paperbound $6.00

ELECTROMAGNETIC THEORY: A CRITICAL EXAMINATION OF FUNDAMENTALS, Alfred O'Rahilly. Critical analysis and restructuring of the basic theories and ideas of classical electromagnetics. Analysis is carried out through study of the primary treatises of Maxwell, Lorentz, Einstein, Weyl, etc., which established the theory. Expansive reference to and direct quotation from these treatises. Formerly *Electromagnetics*. Total of xvii + 884pp.
60126-9, 60127-7 Two volumes, Paperbound $4.50

ELEMENTARY CONCEPTS OF TOPOLOGY, Paul Alexandroff. Elegent, intuitive approach to topology, from the basic concepts of set-theoretic topology to the concept of Betti groups. Stresses concepts of complex, cycle and homology. Shows how concepts of topology are useful in math and physics. Introduction by David Hilbert. Translated by Alan E. Farley. 25 figures. iv + 57pp.
60747-X Paperbound $1.25

THE ELEMENTS OF NON-EUCLIDEAN GEOMETRY, Duncan M. Y. Sommerville. Presentation of the development of non-Euclidean geometry in logical order, from a fundamental analysis of the concept of parallelism to such advanced topics as inversion, transformations, pseudosphere, geodesic representation, relation between parataxy and parallelism, etc. Knowledge of only high-school algebra and geometry is presupposed. 126 problems, 129 figures. xvi + 274pp.
60460-8 Paperbound $2.00

NON-EUCLIDEAN GEOMETRY: A CRITICAL AND HISTORICAL STUDY OF ITS DEVELOPMENT, Roberto Bonola. Standard survey, clear, penetrating, discussing many systems not usually represented in general studies. Easily followed by nonspecialist. Translated by H. Carslaw. Bound in are two most important texts: Bolyai's "The Science of Absolute Space" and Lobachevski's "The Theory of Parallels," translated by G. B. Halsted. Introduction by F. Enriques. 181 diagrams. Total of 431pp.
60027-0 Paperbound $2.75

ELEMENTS OF NUMBER THEORY, Ivan M. Vinogradov. By stressing demonstrations and problems, this modern text can be understood by students without advanced math backgrounds. "A very welcome addition," *Bulletin, American Mathematical Society*. Translated by Saul Kravetz. Over 200 fully-worked problems. 100 numerical exercises. viii + 227pp.
60259-1 Paperbound $2.50

THEORY OF SETS, E. Kamke. Lucid introduction to theory of sets, surveying discoveries of Cantor, Russell, Weierstrass, Zermelo, Bernstein, Dedekind, etc. Knowledge of college algebra is sufficient background. "Exceptionally well written," *School Science and Mathematics*. Translated by Frederick Bagemihl. vii + 144pp.
60141-2 Paperbound $1.75

MATHEMATICAL FOUNDATIONS OF STATISTICAL MECHANICS, A. I. Khinchin. Introduction to modern statistical mechanics: phase space, ergodic problems, theory of probability, central limit theorem, ideal monatomic gas, foundation of thermodynamics, dispersion and distribution of sum functions. Provides mathematically rigorous treatment and excellent analytical tools. Translated by George Gamow. viii + 179pp. 60147-1 Paperbound $2.00

INTRODUCTION TO PHYSICAL STATISTICS, Robert B. Lindsay. Elementary probability theory, laws of thermodynamics, classical Maxwell-Boltzmann statistics, classical statistical mechanics, quantum mechanics, other areas of physics that can be studied statistically. Full coverage of methods; basic background theory. ix + 306pp. 61882-X Paperbound $2.75

DIALOGUES CONCERNING TWO NEW SCIENCES, Galileo Galilei. Written near the end of Galileo's life and encompassing 30 years of experiment and thought, these dialogues deal with geometric demonstrations of fracture of solid bodies, cohesion, leverage, speed of light and sound, pendulums, falling bodies, accelerated motion, etc. Translated by Henry Crew and Alfonso de Salvio. Introduction by Antonio Favaro. xxiii + 300pp. 60099-8 Paperbound $2.25

FOUNDATIONS OF SCIENCE: THE PHILOSOPHY OF THEORY AND EXPERIMENT, Norman R. Campbell. Fundamental concepts of science examined on middle level: acceptance of propositions and axioms, presuppositions of scientific thought, scientific law, multiplication of probabilities, nature of experiment, application of mathematics, measurement, numerical laws and theories, error, etc. Stress on physics, but holds for other sciences. "Unreservedly recommended," *Nature* (England). Formerly *Physics: The Elements.* ix + 565pp. 60372-5 Paperbound $4.00

THE PHASE RULE AND ITS APPLICATIONS, Alexander Findlay, A. N. Campbell and N. O. Smith. Findlay's well-known classic, updated (1951). Full standard text and thorough reference, particularly useful for graduate students. Covers chemical phenomena of one, two, three, four and multiple component systems. "Should rank as the standard work in English on the subject," *Nature.* 236 figures. xii + 494pp. 60091-2 Paperbound $3.50

THERMODYNAMICS, Enrico Fermi. A classic of modern science. Clear, organized treatment of systems, first and second laws, entropy, thermodynamic potentials, gaseous reactions, dilute solutions, entropy constant. No math beyond calculus is needed, but readers are assumed to be familiar with fundamentals of thermometry, calorimetry. 22 illustrations. 25 problems. x + 160pp.
60361-X Paperbound $2.00

TREATISE ON THERMODYNAMICS, Max Planck. Classic, still recognized as one of the best introductions to thermodynamics. Based on Planck's original papers, it presents a concise and logical view of the entire field, building physical and chemical laws from basic empirical facts. Planck considers fundamental definitions, first and second principles of thermodynamics, and applications to special states of equilibrium. Numerous worked examples. Translated by Alexander Ogg. 5 figures. xiv + 297pp. 60219-2 Paperbound $2.50

INTRODUCTION TO ASTROPHYSICS: THE STARS, Jean Dufay. Best guide to observational astrophysics in English. Bridges the gap between elementary popularizations and advanced technical monographs. Covers stellar photometry, stellar spectra and classification, Hertzsprung-Russell diagrams, Yerkes 2-dimensional classification, temperatures, diameters, masses and densities, evolution of the stars. Translated by Owen Gingerich. 51 figures, 11 tables. xii + 164pp.

(USCO) 60771-2 Paperbound $2.00

INTRODUCTION TO BESSEL FUNCTIONS, Frank Bowman. Full, clear introduction to properties and applications of Bessel functions. Covers Bessel functions of zero order, of any order; definite integrals; asymptotic expansions; Bessel's solution to Kepler's problem; circular membranes; etc. Math above calculus and fundamentals of differential equations developed within text. 636 problems. 28 figures. x + 135pp.
60462-4 Paperbound $1.75

DIFFERENTIAL AND INTEGRAL CALCULUS, Philip Franklin. A full and basic introduction, textbook for a two- or three-semester course, or self-study. Covers parametric functions, force components in polar coordinates, Duhamel's theorem, methods and applications of integration, infinite series, Taylor's series, vectors and surfaces in space, etc. Exercises follow each chapter with full solutions at back of the book. Index. xi + 679pp.
62520-6 Paperbound $4.00

THE EXACT SCIENCES IN ANTIQUITY, O. Neugebauer. Modern overview chiefly of mathematics and astronomy as developed by the Egyptians and Babylonians. Reveals startling advancement of Babylonian mathematics (tables for numerical computations, quadratic equations with two unknowns, implications that Pythagorean theorem was known 1000 years before Pythagoras), and sophisticated astronomy based on competent mathematics. Also covers transmission of this knowledge to Hellenistic world. 14 plates, 52 figures. xvii + 240pp.

22332-9 Paperbound $2.50

THE THIRTEEN BOOKS OF EUCLID'S ELEMENTS, translated with introduction and commentary by Sir Thomas Heath. Unabridged republication of definitive edition based on the text of Heiberg. Translator's notes discuss textual and linguistic matters, mathematical analysis, 2500 years of critical commentary on the Elements. Do not confuse with abridged school editions. Total of xvii + 1414pp.

60088-2, 60089-0, 60090-4 Three volumes, Paperbound $8.50

AN INTRODUCTION TO SYMBOLIC LOGIC, Susanne K. Langer. Well-known introduction, popular among readers with elementary mathematical background. Starts with simple symbols and conventions and teaches Boole-Schroeder and Russell-Whitehead systems. 367pp.
60164-1 Paperbound $2.25

Prices subject to change without notice.

Available at your book dealer or write for free catalogue to Dept. Sci, Dover Publications, Inc., 180 Varick St., N.Y., N.Y. 10014. Dover publishes more than 150 books each year on science, elementary and advanced mathematics, biology, music, art, literary history, social sciences and other areas.